YO-ARS-429

POPULAR MECHANICS DO-IT-YOURSELF ENCYCLOPEDIA

POPULAR MECHANICS DO-IT-YOURSELF ENCYCLOPEDIA

FOR

HOME OWNER, CRAFTSMAN
AND HOBBYIST
IN TWELVE VOLUMES

Volume II

Complete Index in Volume XII

J. J. LITTLE & IVES Co., Inc. ● NEW YORK

COPYRIGHT 1955 BY POPULAR MECHANICS COMPANY

DESIGNED AND PRODUCED BY
BOOKSERVICE AMERICA, NEW YORK

5655

NO PART OF THE TEXT OR
ILLUSTRATIONS IN THIS BOOK
MAY BE USED WITHOUT
FORMAL PERMISSION FROM
POPULAR MECHANICS COMPANY

ALL RIGHTS RESERVED UNDER
PAN-AMERICAN COPYRIGHT CONVENTION.
AND THE INTERNATIONAL COPYRIGHT CONVENTION

FIRST PRINTING 1955
PRINTED IN THE UNITED STATES OF AMERICA

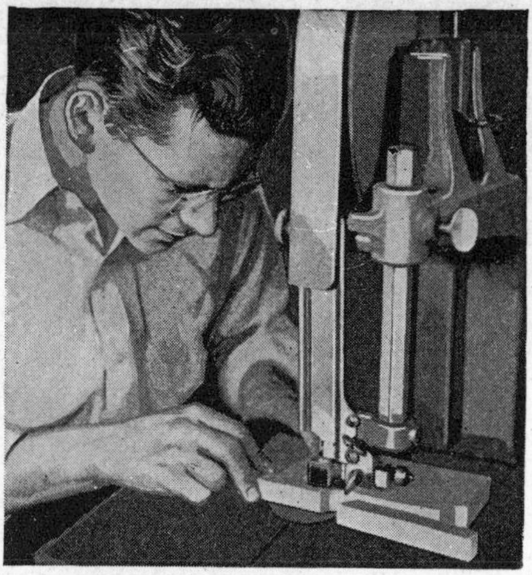

BOOK ENDS

ATTRACTIVE book ends like these make ideal gifts, as the design can be suited to the recipient's tastes—even to his initial. For instance, instead of the spaniel you can use a likeness of another dog—a bulldog is particularly effective. The horsehead book ends are made of three laminations, the long curve of neck and mane being cut first, after which the pieces are glued together and the head and inside of the neck cut as one piece. In the spaniel

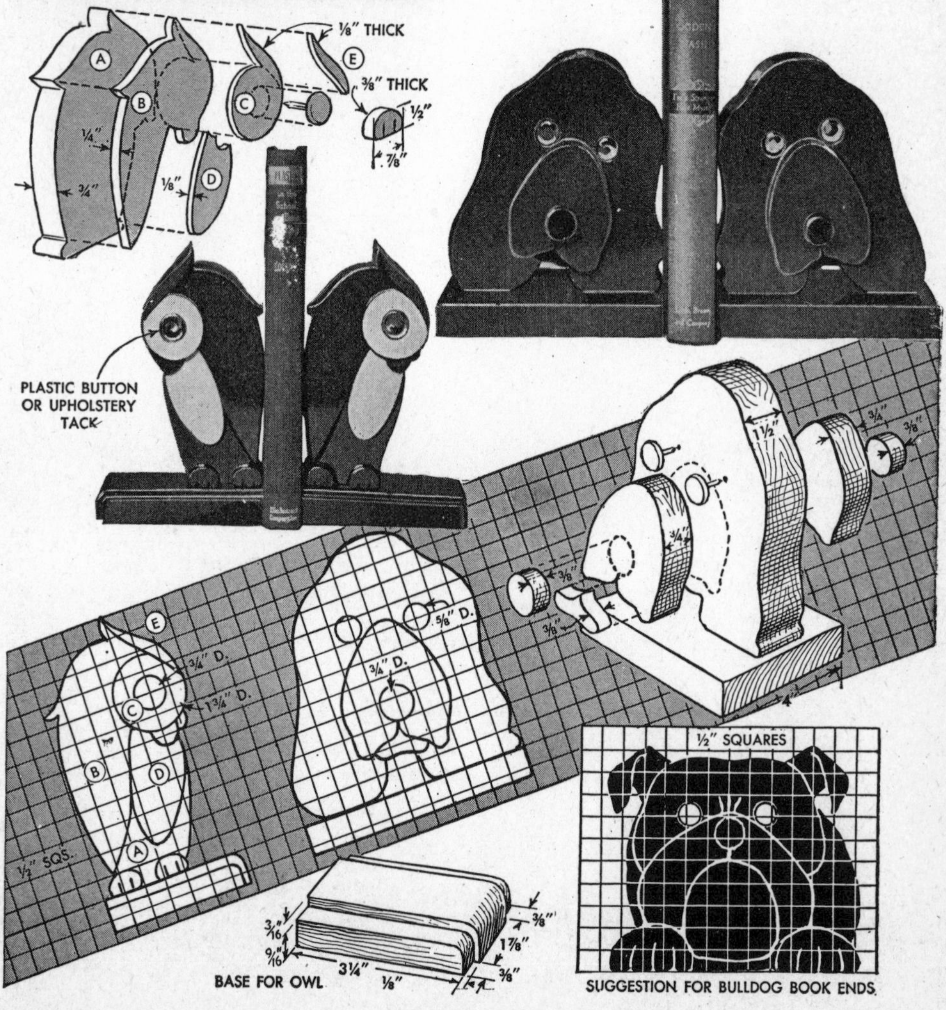

1/8" THICK
3/8" THICK
1/2"
7/8"
1/4"
3/4"
1/8"
PLASTIC BUTTON
OR UPHOLSTERY
TACK
1 1/2"
3/4"
3/8"
3/4" D.
1 3/4" D.
5/8" D.
3/4" D.
1/2" SQS.
4"
1/2" SQUARES
3/16"
9/16"
3 1/4"
1/8"
3/8"
1 7/8"

BASE FOR OWL

SUGGESTION FOR BULLDOG BOOK ENDS

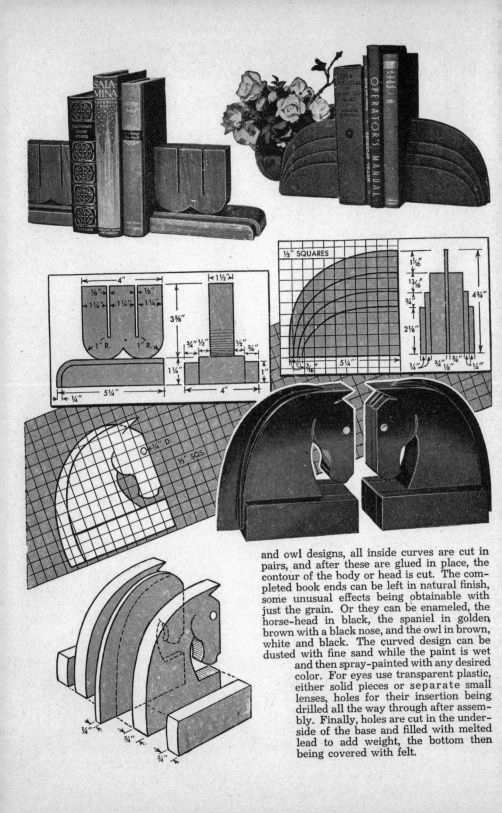

½" SQUARES

4"

1½"

3⅝"

¾" ½" ½" ¾"

1¼"

5¼"

4"

¼"

1½" R. 1" R.

⅛" ⅛"

1¼" 1¼" 1¼"

1" R. 1" R.

1¹⁄₁₆"

1³⁄₁₆"

¾"

4¾"

2⅛"

¼" ¾" 1¾" ¼"
    ⅛"

5¼"

³⁄₁₆"

¼" D.

½" SQS.

¼" ¾"

¾"

and owl designs, all inside curves are cut in pairs, and after these are glued in place, the contour of the body or head is cut. The completed book ends can be left in natural finish, some unusual effects being obtainable with just the grain. Or they can be enameled, the horse-head in black, the spaniel in golden brown with a black nose, and the owl in brown, white and black. The curved design can be dusted with fine sand while the paint is wet and then spray-painted with any desired color. For eyes use transparent plastic, either solid pieces or separate small lenses, holes for their insertion being drilled all the way through after assembly. Finally, holes are cut in the underside of the base and filled with melted lead to add weight, the bottom then being covered with felt.

BOOKCASE

TAKING little space in comparison to its large capacity, this rotating bookcase is made to order for the limited study quarters of a high school or college student. It features a novel "ball bearing" base on which the bookcase itself rotates on five wooden balls which roll in a track turned in the surface of the base. With the balls spaced to distribute the load uniformly, the upper part can be rotated very easily for quick selection of books from either side.

The book section is constructed first, preferably of hardwood, such as maple, birch, walnut or mahogany. Fig. 4 gives

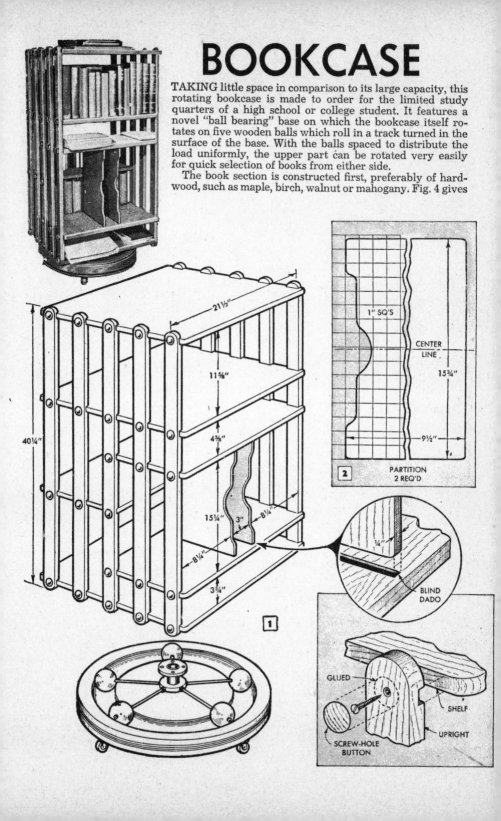

21½"

11⅝"

4⅝"

40¼"

15¼"   3"   8¼"

8¼"

3¾"

1

1" SQ'S

CENTER LINE

15¾"

9½"

2 PARTITION 2 REQ'D

¼"

BLIND DADO

GLUED

SHELF

UPRIGHT

SCREW-HOLE BUTTON

the size and shape of the 10 side members and indicates where each one is notched to receive the shelves. Each member is keyed with the assembly drawing in Fig. 3 to show just where it goes. The wide shelves can be made of plywood, or of solid stock by gluing edgewise several pieces of random widths. Note that between two of the shelves there are two scrolled partitions, Fig. 2, which form a compartment for magazines and newspapers. These are glued vertically in blind dadoes, 3 in. apart. Top surfaces of the shelves, and all other parts, should be sanded smooth before assembling. Holes for flathead screws are bored through each side member, at the notch, and then countersunk slightly so that the screwheads will be flush. Use glue in addition to screws in assembling the parts, and check the whole unit for squareness. Each screwhead is covered by a wood screw-hole button, made for the purpose. Wooden dress buttons will do also, as well as metal furniture glides. The wooden buttons are simply glued over the screwheads. In the case of the bottom shelf, it will be necessary to stain or paint it before it is screwed in place.

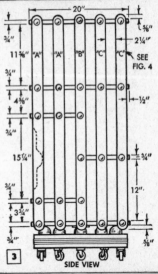

3 SIDE VIEW

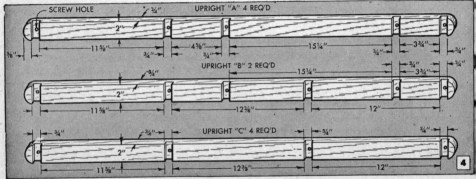

SCREW HOLE — UPRIGHT "A" 4 REQ'D

UPRIGHT "B" 2 REQ'D

UPRIGHT "C" 4 REQ'D

4

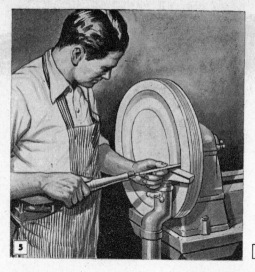

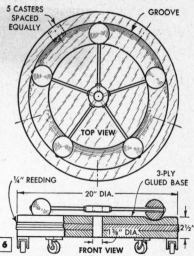

TOP VIEW

5 CASTERS SPACED EQUALLY — GROOVE — 3-PLY GLUED BASE

¼" REEDING — 20" DIA. — 1⅜" DIA. — 2½"

FRONT VIEW

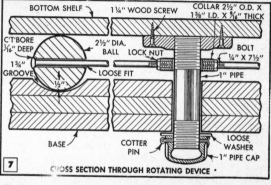

CROSS SECTION THROUGH ROTATING DEVICE

BOTTOM SHELF — 1¼" WOOD SCREW — COLLAR 2½" O.D. X 1⅜" I.D. X ⁵⁄₁₆" THICK — C'T'BORE ⅛₁₆" DEEP — 2½" DIA. BALL — LOCK NUT — BOLT ¼" X 7½" — 1¾" GROOVE — ½" — LOOSE FIT — 1" PIPE — BASE — COTTER PIN — LOOSE WASHER — 1" PIPE CAP

The base is built up of three wood disks totaling 2½ in. in thickness. Cut each slightly oversize and glue all three together with the grain at right angles, one to the other. To turn work of this size, it is necessary to mount it on the left-hand end of the lathe headstock as shown in Fig. 5. The ball track in the face of the base is made 1¾ in. wide and ½ in. deep and ¼-in. reeding is turned in the edge as shown in Fig. 6.

The rotating device is detailed in Fig. 7. It consists of a threaded length of 1-in. pipe, which turns freely in a hole bored through the base at the center, and has a floor flange at one end for fastening the pipe to the bottom of the bookcase. The axles or spokes on which the five wooden balls rotate, are ¼-in. bolts turned into tapped holes equidistantly spaced in the edge of a metal collar. This collar slips over the pipe kingpin like a wheel, after which the base is locked in place by a pipe cap as shown. Five swivel plate casters are screwed to the base. You can use balls from an indoor croquet set and turn the ball race in the base to suit.

Books Kept Upright in Case

SPRING INSIDE CURTAIN ROD

This handy little device is not conspicuous and will keep the books vertical and in neat order on shelves. It is made from a telescoping curtain rod and two slip-on erasers. The rod can be purchased for a nickel in most stores and after being cut to the proper length for the shelves it will be used on, it is assembled with a compression spring inside as indicated. When the erasers are slipped over the ends, the spring forces them against the two shelves so that they stay in a vertical position and hold the books in place.

FAN BOOKRACK

G OOD DESIGN, usefulness and ease of construction — these features are the measure of a wood novelty such as this fan bookrack. The fan design is relieved by means of wide V-cuts which expose a contrasting inlay simulating the fan lacings. Begin by making the piece shown in detail C at the right. This piece is ½ in. thick, 9 in. wide and 12 in. long and the ends are bandsawed on an 8-in. radius. Lathe-turn grooves in the piece and inlay with a contrasting wood as in Fig. 1. Then cut on the dotted lines, detail C, and make the fixture shown in detail B. Now, grind straight molding cutters to the wide V-shape required and set up to shape the endpieces on the circular saw as in Fig. 2. After running the shaping cuts, rabbet the straight edges of the endpieces to take the bottom and back of the rack. These parts are of ⅜-in. stock. Finish all parts in the natural color before assembling. Finally, fit the simulated fan loop at the lower corners of the endpieces. See detail A and also Fig. 3. These parts should be made from the same contrasting wood as the lacing inlays and are finished in the natural color.

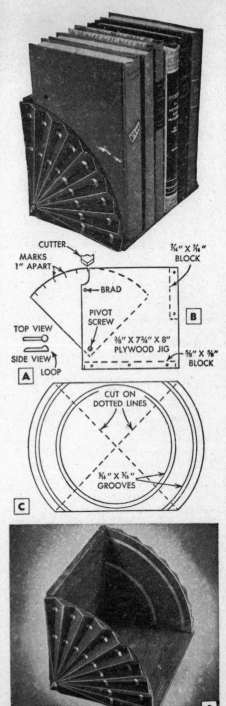

A — CUTTER / MARKS 1" APART / TOP VIEW / SIDE VIEW / LOOP

B — BRAD / PIVOT SCREW / ⅜" X 7¾" X 8" PLYWOOD JIG / ³⁄₁₆" X ⁷⁄₁₆" BLOCK / ⅝" X ⅝" BLOCK

C — CUT ON DOTTED LINES / ³⁄₁₆" X ³⁄₁₆" GROOVES

BOOKSHELF

A NOVEL hourglass design in open scroll-work distinguishes this wall bookshelf. Two drawers add to its usefulness and decorative value. If desired, the bookshelf can be built entirely of plywood, or solid stock can be used for the scrolled ends and drawer fronts with plywood for the shelves and back. The shelves are set in blind grooves, or dadoes, cut in the scrolled sides, and the exposed front edges are faced with a cloverleaf molding. The details below show how to lay out the scroll patterns directly on the wood, and also give the radii for cuts on the stepped edges of the side panels. Drawers are of conventional construction.

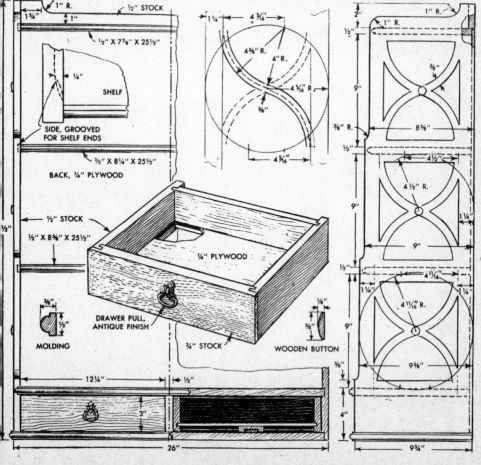

1" R.
1¾"
1"
½" STOCK
½" X 7⅞" X 25½"
¼"
SHELF
SIDE, GROOVED FOR SHELF ENDS
½" X 8¼" X 25½"
BACK, ¼" PLYWOOD

1¼"
4 ⁵⁄₁₆"
4⅜" R.
4" R.
4 ⁵⁄₁₆" R
⅝"
4 ⁵⁄₁₆"

2"
1" R.
½"
1" R.
⅝"
9"
8⅜"
⅜" R.
½"
4½"
4½" R.
9"
1¼"
9"
½"
1¼"
4 ¹¹⁄₁₆"
4 ¹¹⁄₁₆" R.
1¼"
9"
9⅜"
⅝"
4"
9¾"

½" STOCK
½" X 8⅜" X 25½"
½"
¼" PLYWOOD
¾" STOCK

⅜"
½"
MOLDING

DRAWER PULL, ANTIQUE FINISH

⅛"
⅝"
WOODEN BUTTON

12¼"
½"
3"
26"

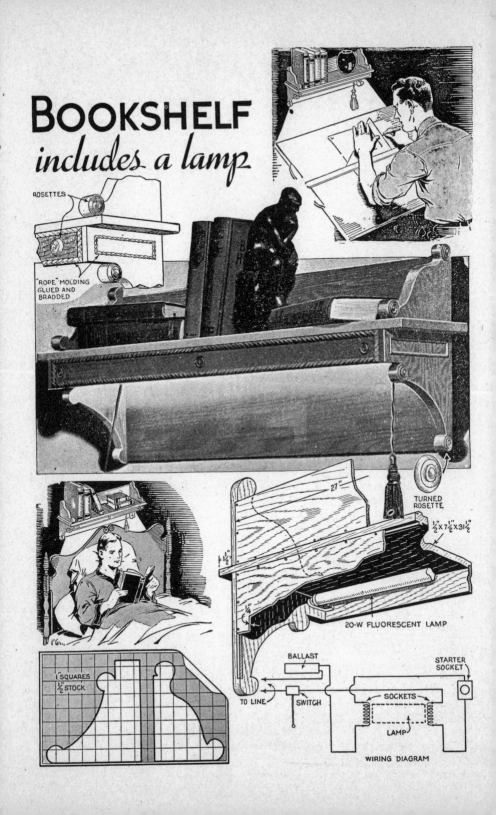

BOOKSHELF
includes a lamp

ROSETTES

"ROPE" MOLDING GLUED AND BRADDED

TURNED ROSETTE

27"

1½"

¼"

½" x 7½" x 3½"

20-W FLUORESCENT LAMP

1" SQUARES
½" STOCK

BALLAST

TO LINE

SWITCH

SOCKETS

LAMP

STARTER SOCKET

WIRING DIAGRAM

BOOMERANGS

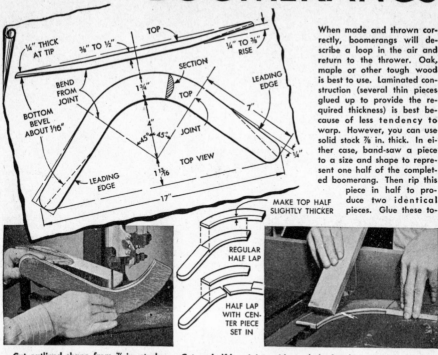

When made and thrown correctly, boomerangs will describe a loop in the air and return to the thrower. Oak, maple or other tough wood is best to use. Laminated construction (several thin pieces glued up to provide the required thickness) is best because of less tendency to warp. However, you can use solid stock ⅞ in. thick. In either case, band-saw a piece to a size and shape to represent one half of the completed boomerang. Then rip this piece in half to produce two identical pieces. Glue these to-

Cut outlined shape from ⅞-in. stock, then rip to get two identical pieces

Cut a half-lap joint with a dado head or straight molding cutter. Leave the top lap a little thicker than the bottom

Glue the joint. Spring the tips upward on blocks to get required rise

Sand or plane the bottom bevel—about 1/16 in. probably will be enough. You can increase it later if it is necessary

Plane the top surface from joint to tip

Round the top surface with a wood rasp and sand smooth

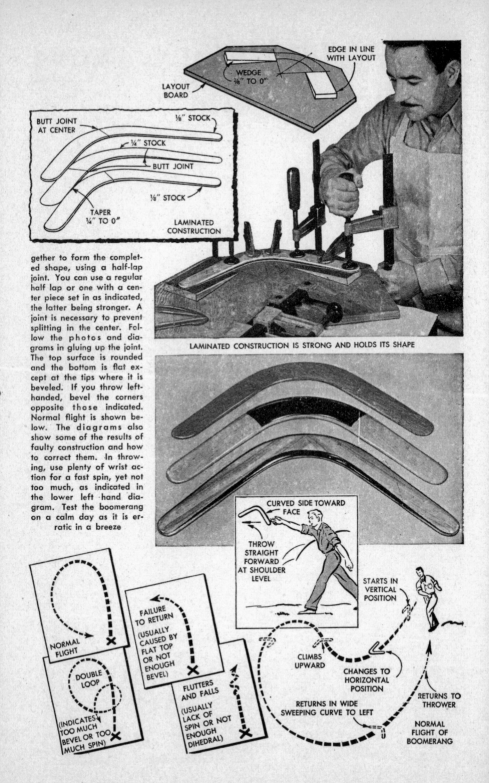

LAYOUT BOARD

EDGE IN LINE WITH LAYOUT

WEDGE ⅛" TO 0"

BUTT JOINT AT CENTER

⅛" STOCK

¼" STOCK

BUTT JOINT

⅛" STOCK

TAPER ¼" TO 0"

LAMINATED CONSTRUCTION

gether to form the completed shape, using a half-lap joint. You can use a regular half lap or one with a center piece set in as indicated, the latter being stronger. A joint is necessary to prevent splitting in the center. Follow the photos and diagrams in gluing up the joint. The top surface is rounded and the bottom is flat except at the tips where it is beveled. If you throw left-handed, bevel the corners opposite those indicated. Normal flight is shown below. The diagrams also show some of the results of faulty construction and how to correct them. In throwing, use plenty of wrist action for a fast spin, yet not too much, as indicated in the lower left hand diagram. Test the boomerang on a calm day as it is erratic in a breeze

LAMINATED CONSTRUCTION IS STRONG AND HOLDS ITS SHAPE

CURVED SIDE TOWARD FACE

THROW STRAIGHT FORWARD AT SHOULDER LEVEL

NORMAL FLIGHT

DOUBLE LOOP

(INDICATES TOO MUCH BEVEL OR TOO MUCH SPIN)

FAILURE TO RETURN

(USUALLY CAUSED BY FLAT TOP OR NOT ENOUGH BEVEL)

FLUTTERS AND FALLS

(USUALLY LACK OF SPIN OR NOT ENOUGH DIHEDRAL)

STARTS IN VERTICAL POSITION

CLIMBS UPWARD

CHANGES TO HORIZONTAL POSITION

RETURNS TO THROWER

RETURNS IN WIDE SWEEPING CURVE TO LEFT

NORMAL FLIGHT OF BOOMERANG

BOWLING IN MINIATURE

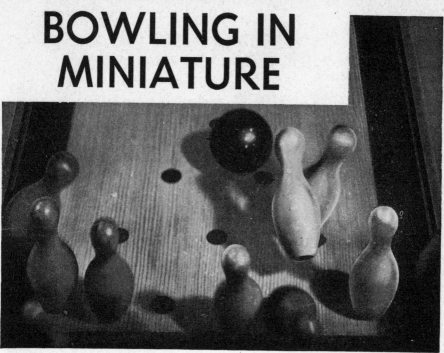

DETAIL OF PIN

1

HERE'S regulation bowling scaled down to pint size. All items of the equipment, except the length of the alleys, are reduced to approximately one-fifth size, making the unit ideal for use in home playrooms. This reduction scale makes a golf ball just about the right size and weight for the miniature bowling ball, Fig. 3, and brings the pins down to a height of 3 in. and a maximum diameter of 1⅛ in. To be in the same scale with the standard 80-ft. alley, the miniature alley would be 16 ft. long. However, the details in Fig. 4 dimension an 8-ft. alley which was found to be just as effective as the longer one in duplicating the conditions of play and is, of course, a more convenient length for the recreation room. Miniature bowling is scored in the same way as the regulation game, small score sheets being ruled on ordinary typewriter paper.

The alley bed is built up from two or more pieces of ¾-in. stock, edge-glued, doweled and cleated across the bottom. The gutters are formed by ½ x 1¾-in. strips assembled with an edging strip of ¾-in. stock as shown in section B-B, Fig. 4. Note that these edging strips are 8 ft. 7¼ in. long, the 7¼-in. extension on each side forming the frame for the pit. The sides of the pit are 5 in. wide and have both front and rear ends cut at angles as shown in

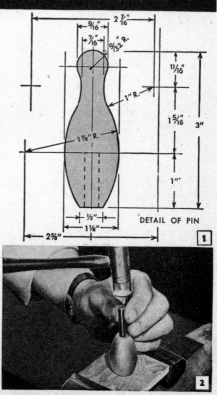

2

Fig. 4. Sides are doweled to the edge strips. Nail ¼-in. plywood in the open frame to form the bottom of the pit and then cover the bottom, sides and the back with felt, section C-C. Before sanding the surface of the alley, locate the pattern for spotting the pins. Drill ½-in. holes about halfway through the alley bed and drive ½-in. dowels into the holes, cutting each one off flush with the surface. When sanded flush, the short dowels will finish somewhat darker than the alley, making it easy to spot the pins quickly.

The legs are X-braced to give lateral rigidity and individual metal braces fold flush in stopped rabbets cut on the inside corner of each leg as in section A-A, Fig. 4. This arrangement allows the leg assemblies to fold flat against the bottom of the alley. Turn the pins from hardwood to the dimensions given in Fig. 1 and drill a ⅜-in. hole in the bottom of each pin. Bring the pins to a uniform weight of 1 oz. by driving short lengths of ⅜-in. brass rod into the holes as in Fig. 2. A few drops of glue will hold the weights in place. Varnish and wax the alley, and paint the gutters black.

Above, photo illustrates the relative size of the miniature bowling ball and pins, with a possible strike in the making. Below, use selected hardwood for the alley and sand the surface smooth and flat

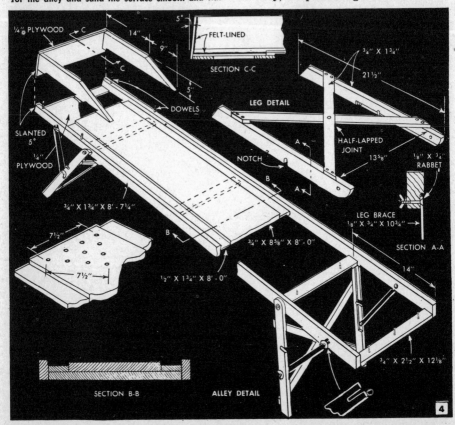

BOWLS

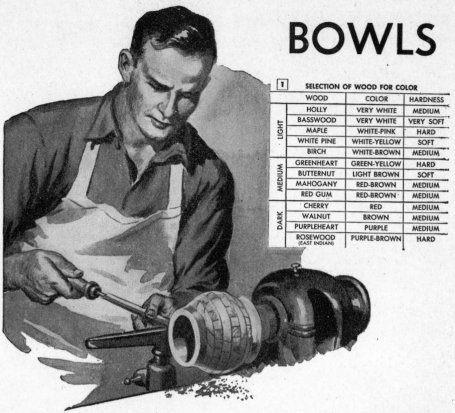

	WOOD	COLOR	HARDNESS
1 SELECTION OF WOOD FOR COLOR			
LIGHT	HOLLY	VERY WHITE	MEDIUM
	BASSWOOD	VERY WHITE	VERY SOFT
	MAPLE	WHITE-PINK	HARD
	WHITE PINE	WHITE-YELLOW	SOFT
	BIRCH	WHITE-BROWN	MEDIUM
MEDIUM	GREENHEART	GREEN-YELLOW	HARD
	BUTTERNUT	LIGHT BROWN	SOFT
	MAHOGANY	RED-BROWN	MEDIUM
	RED GUM	RED-BROWN	MEDIUM
DARK	CHERRY	RED	MEDIUM
	WALNUT	BROWN	MEDIUM
	PURPLEHEART	PURPLE	MEDIUM
	ROSEWOOD (EAST INDIAN)	PURPLE-BROWN	HARD

LAMINATED turned work looks like flush inlay when finished, more especially when you use quality hardwoods of pronounced color contrasts. That's why laminated projects have always been a natural for wood-turning hobbyists. Although finished work of this kind gives the appearance of being very difficult to accomplish, in reality it is quite simple to do.

Almost any wood can be used that will turn well. A typical selection is given in Fig. 1. Two-color pattern effects usually are based on a light-colored wood, such as holly or maple, combined with dark wood, such as cherry or walnut. Best results are obtained when the woods used are approximately the same degree of hardness. Softwoods should not be combined with hardwoods except in the case of thin spacers for laminated work. If woods of equal thickness but of unequal hardness are used the work may turn out-of-round, and sanding will develop flats. The humidor shown in Fig. 2 is made by gluing laminated blocks to the eight sides of a softwood core. This assembly is glued to the unfinished base, Fig. 4. Then you bore out the core after the glue has set, cut the blocks from

the strip either directly across, Fig. 4, B, lengthwise, Fig. 4, A, or at an angle as in Fig. 4, C. A more intricate pattern will be obtained by cutting half the blocks square across and the other half through lengthwise. Then alternate the colors when gluing them to the sides of the core. With the angle blocks, a herringbone pattern can be achieved. In assembling, glue the core to the base, then glue the laminated blocks to the base and sides of the core. This leaves 45-deg. openings between the blocks, which are filled by gluing in triangular filler blocks of contrasting wood the same length as the blocks.

Turn the outside of the bowl to the rough size first, leaving enough stock so that the inside can be bored out to a minimum wall thickness of ¼ in. Finish the outside by sanding while the work is still mounted in the lathe. Finished dimensions of the humidor shown in Fig. 2 are: 6-in. base diameter, 4½-in. outside diameter and 3⅞-in. inside diameter on the shell or body. Of course, it is not necessary to hold these dimensions which can be varied if desired.

The cover is turned from solid wood. Mount the cover in the lathe by gluing to a

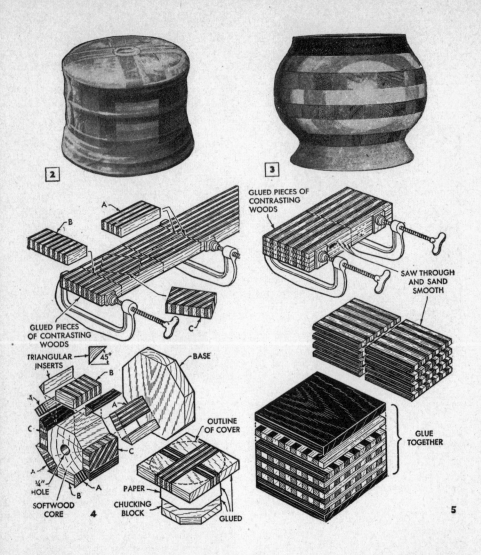

chucking block with a piece of paper in the joint. Rabbet the edge of the cover to fit easily inside the humidor, then turn the outside to the desired contour. Finish with lacquer or varnish.

Another method of lamination which results in an unusually attractive job is detailed in Fig. 5. A turned bowl built up in this manner is shown in Fig. 3. The lamination consists of layers of ¼ by ¼-in. strips of alternately spaced contrasting woods glued together. Alternating layers are placed at right angles and glued together between top and bottom blocks of clear wood. Size of the glued-up block must be somewhat larger than the finished dimensions of the bowl, of course. The top and bottom blocks are one piece as in Fig. 5. Turning the inside and outside to the desired size and contour is just another simple turning job. When undercutting the inside of a bowl or humidor one has to be especially careful that the chisel does not dig in suddenly and damage the work. Keep a firm grip on the chisel handle to prevent the tool from turning and thus presenting the cutting edge to the work at a new angle. Usually this is the cause of the cutting edge digging deeply into the wood and seriously damaging the work.

BRACING

ALL parts of a building that is even slightly out of plumb are subjected to undue stresses, which, if allowed to continue, gradually slacken the normal hold of the nails, cause studding and plates to take a permanent "bend" and unbalance the load on the foundation. Sooner or later wind pressure is likely to combine stresses on the framing to the point where something "lets go." The result is generally an expensive repair job if not a new building. Where the building stands plumb and is of open-frame construction, sheathed and sided on outside walls only, diagonal braces in the four corners, Fig. 1, are good insurance against sagging and wind damage. Where possible, braces always should be of equal length, should extend from the sill to the plate or ceiling line, and should be spiked to each stud. Where braces must be of unequal length, they should be so located that the stresses will be equalized. Carry bracing around a window or door by

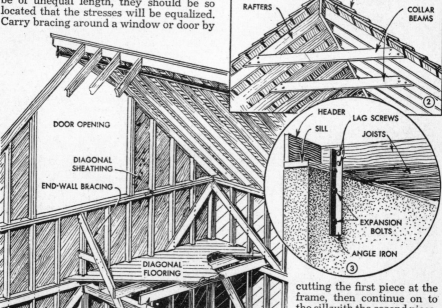

cutting the first piece at the frame, then continue on to the sill with the second piece, the latter being in line with the first. A third member, reaching across at least four studs, is spiked in place parallel with the first two at the top or bottom of the door or window frame.

Usually the weakest points in a roof of conventional framing are at the ridge and

at the plate or ceiling line. If the ridge line is straight you can strengthen the whole roof structure by nailing or bolting in collar beams as in Fig. 2. These should be either of 1 by 8 or 2 by 8-in. stock, whichever is in proportion to the size of the building. Wood-framed structures often are wrecked by windstorms because the frame is not anchored properly to the foundation. Fig. 3 suggests one effective method of anchoring the wall to the foundation where there is a basement or a foundation wall above ground. Another method, somewhat similar in application, is the use of flat-iron ties, bolted to the foundation on the outside and lag-screwed to the studs through the siding.

Fig. 4 shows approved methods of bracing an average-size building of open framing and full two-story height. On a new building diagonal sheathing is desirable but on those already built the bracing indicated will be quite effective. Before nailing or bolting in any bracing, always make sure that walls and corners of the building are plumb, and that the plates and ridge are straight. If a building is out of plumb one way, a common method of jacking it back is shown in Fig. 5. Block under the upper ends of the pressure beams so that when pressure is applied the beam ends will not crush the siding and corner boards. Use at least two pressure beams, one at each corner, to prevent racking. If the plates are curved outward and the ridge sags it will be necessary to apply pressure at the center of the building on both sides and at the same time the ridge must be "eased up" with jacks as in Fig. 12. If the walls sag outward at the plate, a fault which may be due to any one of a number

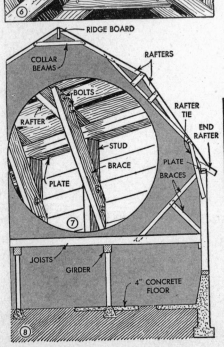

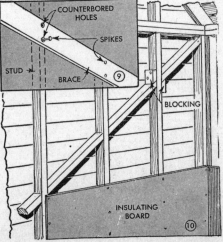

of conditions, and the building is full two-story or is built with hayloft, it's likely that the studs have taken a more or less permanent bend. If any considerable pressure is applied to the wall at the plate or upper-floor ceiling line, the second-floor joists will act as a fulcrum, causing the lower ends of the studs to exert an outward pressure on the foundation wall. If this seems likely to happen, braces from the studs to the floor joists, Fig. 11, will be a good precaution. Install these before bringing pressure on the top of the wall. Once the walls have been plumbed and the ridge straightened give all the jackscrews an extra half turn and then install rafter trusses each way from the center of the building as in Fig. 13. If there's no ridge board, short "collars" nailed to the rafters as in Fig. 6 will strengthen the ridge. Finally, tie the rafters to the studs as in Fig. 7. Ordinarily, one tie and collar to every second stud and rafter will be sufficient, but if the parts were sagged or curved badly, one tie and collar on each stud and rafter will be good insurance. An equal number of joist-to-stud braces, Fig. 11, will take any lateral strains off the foundation walls. Three to five rafter trusses spaced equally usually are sufficient.

It should be remembered that the type of bracing discussed above is applicable in

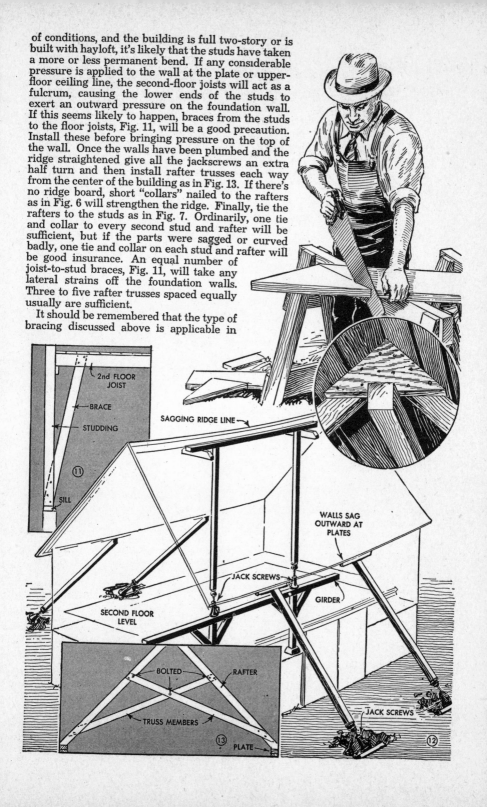

2nd FLOOR JOIST

BRACE

STUDDING

(11)

SILL

SAGGING RIDGE LINE

WALLS SAG OUTWARD AT PLATES

JACK SCREWS

GIRDER

SECOND FLOOR LEVEL

BOLTED   RAFTER

TRUSS MEMBERS

(13)   PLATE

JACK SCREWS

(12)

14
RENAILING
SIDING
STRENGTHENS
WALLS

15 DIAGONAL RAFTER BRACE

ALL PARTS BOLTED

16 END BRACE AT PLATE

general only to those buildings which are framed conventionally, and that the procedure applies only to old buildings and to those of later construction which show faults due to various causes. If the roof is supported by purlin-and-post framing or other older types of "barn-framing" consisting of heavy timbers joined with pinned mortise-and-tenon joints, then, of course, somewhat different methods will apply. However, diagonal corner bracing, extending in both directions from the top or ceiling line of the corner posts to the sills at a 45-deg. angle, will greatly strengthen such a structure.

Fig. 8 shows an approved method of bracing a gambrel-roofed building. Generally, this particular bracing can be installed in both old and new buildings and for greater strength it always should be bolted in place. If loose hay is stored in the mow it is necessary to "part" the hay directly over the brace so that the latter will not carry the weight of the hay above it. Sometimes it is desirable to cover the inner walls of outbuildings with insulating board. To save a lot of angle cutting, bracing can be installed over or under the board lining as in Figs. 9 and 10. Where the bracing is applied over the insulating board it's a good idea to drive the spikes in counterbored holes as shown. The counterbore

should be of a depth equal to half the thickness of the board. Where the bracing is located between studs as in Fig. 10, each piece should be cut to a snug fit, all sections should be kept in line and the ends must be blocked as indicated. Although both methods take more time, the completed job is very nearly as effective as is a brace nailed-directly to the studding.

On old buildings, merely re-nailing the siding, as in Fig. 14, helps materially to strengthen the whole structure. Tighten all old nails and add at least one new nail to each board at each stud. Re-nailing always should be done after plumbing a building by any of the methods shown, as the nails are certain to be loosened on some parts of the structure. Another added precaution against racking wind pressures is the installation of diagonal rafter braces as in Fig. 15. These run from the ridge to the plate or ceiling line as indicated, and are spiked to the underface of each rafter. These braces usually are installed as a part of the general bracing procedure already discussed. Where it is desirable for any reason to have smooth end walls up to the ceiling line the A-brace shown in Fig. 16 may be substituted for the end-wall angle brace shown in Fig. 4. Properly installed, the A-brace is quite as effective. It should be supported at the center by a short angle brace to one stud.

BRASS TAPPING

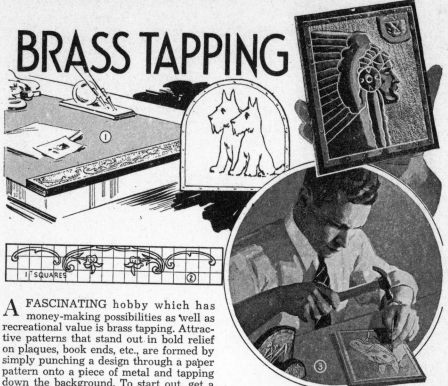

A FASCINATING hobby which has money-making possibilities as well as recreational value is brass tapping. Attractive patterns that stand out in bold relief on plaques, book ends, etc., are formed by simply punching a design through a paper pattern onto a piece of metal and tapping down the background. To start out, get a piece of 30-ga. soft sheet brass, some plywood for mounting it, a light hammer, small round-head brass nails, and a piece of 1/8-in. steel rod about 5 in. long, which is ground to a 1/32-in. point to form a tapping tool. Steel wool, lacquer, etc., are used for finishing. Fig. 6 shows how a design and a piece of sheet brass are fastened to the plywood. Nail holes are made by piercing the design sheet and metal with the tapping tool. Next, the outlines of the design, including the border, are gone over with the tapping tool as illustrated in Fig. 3, striking it firmly but not hard enough to punch holes in the metal. The taps should be so close together that the resulting impressions form a continuous line. When the transferring of the design has been completed, the paper is torn off and the background tapped down. It is best to make the taps about 1/4 in. apart at first, then go over each section, always avoiding a regularity of pattern, until the surface consists of a solid mass of tool marks. After getting the "knack" of doing this work, the job can be speeded up by using two tapping tools at one time. Polishing of the brass comes next. For this you can use either No. "0" or "00" steel wool. By working back and forth in the same direction you will be able to produce a bright surface free from scratches. To preserve the shiny surface apply a coat of clear lacquer, Fig. 5, or if desired, color the background by applying bronze of the desired shade. By wiping off the high spots before the bronze has had a chance to set, it is possible to obtain some attractive effects. Still another finish consists of coloring the metal chemically. To get a black finish, dissolve a small quantity of liver of sulphur in water, and apply it to the background with a small brush. For a red-brown color use a solution of barium sulphide and water. Successful chemical coloring depends to a considerable extent on having the work perfectly clean, so it is advisable to wash the metal with gasoline or benzine. Refrain from touching the cleaned surface until the chemicals have been applied. Colors obtained by chemical action vary somewhat in intensity according to the number of applications. The final application should be followed by a coating of clear lacquer to make the finish permanent.

A simple frame which covers up the

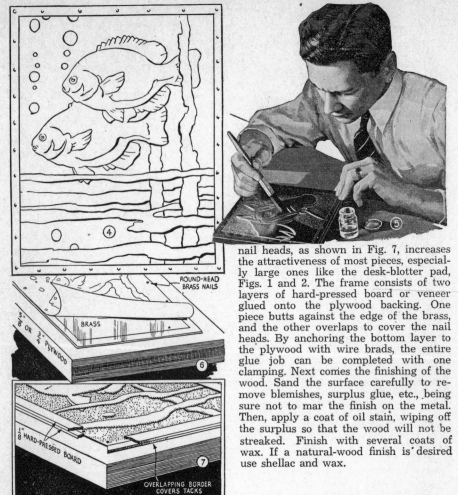

nail heads, as shown in Fig. 7, increases the attractiveness of most pieces, especially large ones like the desk-blotter pad, Figs. 1 and 2. The frame consists of two layers of hard-pressed board or veneer glued onto the plywood backing. One piece butts against the edge of the brass, and the other overlaps to cover the nail heads. By anchoring the bottom layer to the plywood with wire brads, the entire glue job can be completed with one clamping. Next comes the finishing of the wood. Sand the surface carefully to remove blemishes, surplus glue, etc., being sure not to mar the finish on the metal. Then, apply a coat of oil stain, wiping off the surplus so that the wood will not be streaked. Finish with several coats of wax. If a natural-wood finish is desired use shellac and wax.

Brass Pipe Fireplace Rails

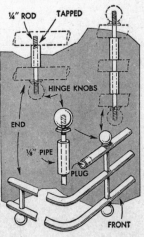

One homeowner added a decorative touch to the hearth of his fireplace by setting these modernistic brass rails in front of the andirons. The rails, cut and bent from lengths of ½-in. brass pipe, are held together with several ball tips taken from loose-pin door hinges. Spacers of ⅛-in. brass pipe are placed between the rails and the tips, after being tapped, are screwed onto the threaded ends of ¼-in. rod. To give the appearance of rod stock, the open ends of the short top rail are plugged with pieces of brass stock, pressed in place and filed flush. All parts are buffed and lacquered.

BRAZING TORCHES

A vacuum cleaner supplies air for operating these simple gas torches, which are designed in two sizes to cover the widest range of light brazing, silver soldering, soft soldering, annealing and hardening

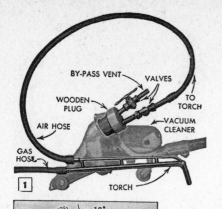

CONNECTED to any source of illuminating gas and supplied with air from a vacuum cleaner, these torches give sufficient heat to handle any ordinary brazing job. Silver soldering, soft soldering, annealing, hardening and tempering also can be done with either size. The torches will not operate on acetylene gas or "bottled" gas.

Both torches are very similar in construction, the only essential difference being in the size of copper tubing used to conduct air and gas to the tips. Figs. 4 and 5 detail the construction. It is impractical to bend tubing to the sharp radius required to form the torch tip, so to save time simply cut an 82-deg. notch in the tube as in Fig. 2. Be careful not to cut into the wall of the tubing at the bottom of the notch. Leave the wall full thickness at this point. Then bend to the position shown by the dotted lines in Fig. 2, and silver solder the joint as in Fig. 3, using a gasoline blowtorch. Place the work on a couple of bricks while heating the joint. The air tubes can be bent by hand to the required radius. Drill a hole just back of the joint in the gas tube for insertion of the air tube. It is important that the air tube project into the tip of the large torch the distance shown in Fig. 5 and that it be exactly centered in the larger gas tube. Wedge it in place before silver soldering the joint at the point where it is inserted

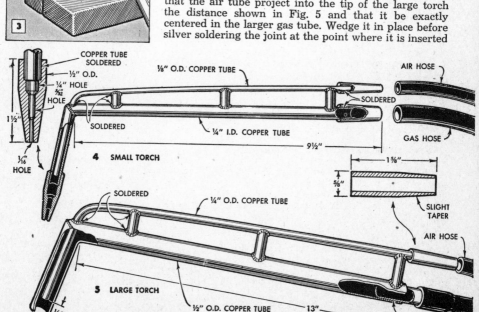

in the gas tube. Joint should be gas-tight.

The three spacers along the length of each torch between the air and gas tubes are short lengths of tubing, silver soldered to both tubes to hold them securely in position. The small torch, Fig. 4, has a separate tip counterbored in four steps. This tip is silver soldered to the gas tube after the latter has been formed.

The air and gas tubes on both the large and small torches are fitted with tapered sleeves turned from thick-walled brass or copper tubing. These are silver soldered to the tubes as in Figs. 4 and 5. Note that one sleeve fits inside the gas tube, Fig. 5. Tapered ends of the sleeves make it easier to connect the lengths of rubber hose which bring gas and air to the torch.

The vacuum cleaner is used without any alteration except for the removal of the dust bag. A wooden plug is turned to fit into the outlet for the dust bag as in Figs. 1 and 8. The tapered end of the plug is covered with felt to prevent air leaks. Two air outlets, each consisting of a pipe nipple, a short length of pipe threaded at one end, and a valve, are turned into holes drilled in the outer end of the plug as in Fig. 8. One serves as a by-pass for excess air. The air hose from the torch is connected to the other. Adjust flame as in Figs. 6 and 7.

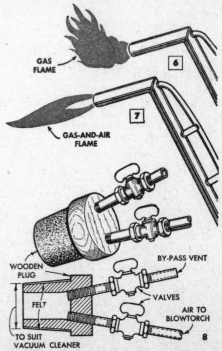

GAS FLAME — 6

GAS-AND-AIR FLAME — 7

WOODEN PLUG

FELT

TO SUIT VACUUM CLEANER

BY-PASS VENT

VALVES

AIR TO BLOWTORCH

8

Breakfast Set Folds into Wall

THIS FOLD-AWAY breakfast set has been designed especially to solve the problem of space in small kitchens. It seats four persons comfortably and when not in use the whole unit folds into the wall behind doors that close flush, leaving the wall and floor space clear. Note in the details below that the width of the table is given as 25 in. and the width of the wall recess as 30 in. The latter dimension is the approximate width of the wall opening before installing the header, false studs and jambs. Locating the breakfast set on an outside wall provides maximum depth for the opening and, if the unit must be installed in exceptionally limited space, some changes in dimensions may be necessary. Finish the wall opening and hang the doors first, then make the table and benches from ¾-in. plywood. Assemble the hinged parts with the special hinge fittings shown in the details. In the original design, the rear end of the table is guided by steel pins sliding in stopped grooves cut at an angle in the jambs. This construction can be simplified by using two hardwood strips nailed to each jamb and spaced to allow the pins to slide freely. Provide stop blocks at the lower ends of the guides.

When not in use, benches and table fold into wall behind doors that close flush, leaving wall space clear

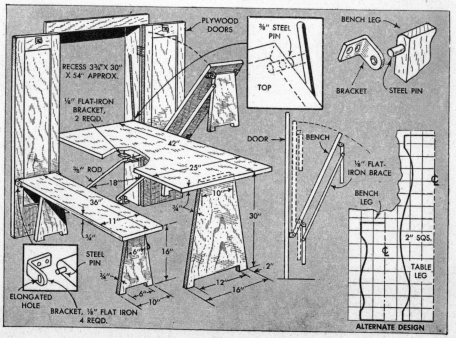

BRUSHES

Will do a better job and last longer if you know how to select, use and care for them

After brush has been spun dry, bristles are combed out as above, to remove kinks. Below, wrap the brush in heavy paper and lay it flat for long storage

Enlarged view of bristles, below, shows "flags" on good brushes. Flags are visible when brush is held up against light. Brush without flags leaves marks

IN PAINTING, as in other types of work, the quality of the finished job depends to a large extent on whether or not you use the proper tools. Economy when purchasing a paintbrush is no substitute for quality, as an inferior brush cannot possibly turn out a good job. And a top-quality brush, when properly handled, will produce a smooth, streakless finish and will outwear several of the cheaper variety.

The best paintbrushes are made of 100 percent pure Chinese hog bristles which have been carefully selected and blended. There are also nylon brushes of excellent quality on the market, which wear well on rough surfaces such as raw lumber. However, they should never be used with shellac, as the alcohol in the shellac will soften the bristles. The bristles can be restored by immersing for 30 min. in boiling water and then drying thoroughly.

To compare brush values, run a pencil through the bristles at the heel of the brush next to the ferrule. Carefully separate the bristles to expose the setting, which is a block set into the ferrule to separate the bristles and to provide a well for the paint. In a good brush this is no wider than absolutely necessary, and is often split into 2 or 3 dividers. This will provide the user with a fully stocked brush and cause the bristles to lie together at the tip to form a good cutting edge. If the block is too thick, the edge of the brush will split lengthwise.

Grasp the brush as for painting and press down with moderate pressure on a flat surface. A good brush will form a sharp chisel edge. Now hold the brush up to the light and examine the bristle tips. Little split ends or "flags" can be seen on a good brush. Without these "flags," a brush will leave streaks in the finished job. A fine brush has flagged bristles in staggered lengths, so that a new set of bristle ends is presented as the longer ones are worn down.

You want not only a good quality brush but also the right brush for the job. The most common types are shown in the accompanying illustration to help in determining your needs.

Having purchased a new brush, it's important to break it in properly. Unwrap

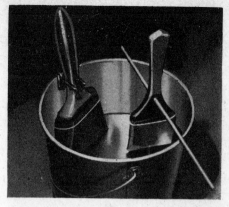

the brush and, holding firmly in one hand, slap the bristles vigorously across the other hand. Then hold it up to the light and remove any loose bristles you see. Spin the handle rapidly between the palms and again remove any loose bristles. Then comb the bristles straight to remove any curl. Now wrap the bristles in heavy paper and suspend the brush in linseed oil for at least 24 hrs. The oil should overflow the top of the wrapper and saturate the bristles. Nylon brushes do not need to be soaked, but this is very important with hog bristles, as they are porous. Soaking in linseed oil seals up the bristles, helping to keep them flexible, and makes the brush easier to clean. Remove most of the oil by dragging the flat side of the brush against a wire fastened across the top of the can. Take out the remaining oil by twirling the handle between the palms, with the brush held well down into an empty can. Then wash in two rinses of clear turpentine and spin dry again. Finally, comb out any kinks.

To use a paintbrush properly, dip about ⅓ to ½ the length of the bristles into the paint. Dip it slowly to allow time to soak up the maximum amount of paint. When removing the excess paint, draw the brush flat across a wire fastened across the top of the can. Never draw it edgewise, as this

Above, two methods of suspending brushes in solvent. Brushes should not be allowed to rest on bottom of can, as resulting curled bristles cannot be straightened

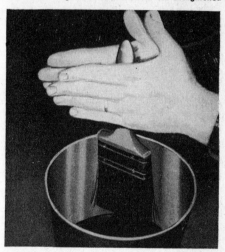

After soaking new brush in linseed oil for 24 hrs., it is spun dry by rolling rapidly between palms. Brush is held well down in empty pail for spinning

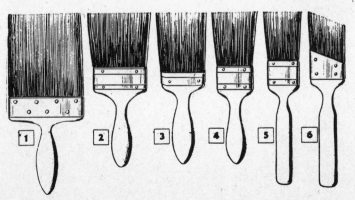

1—Flat wall, long haired, 3-5 in.

2—Flat wall, short haired, 3-5 in.

3—Oval varnish, 2-3 in.

4—Flat varnish, 2-3 in.

5—Flat sash, 1-2½ in.

6—Angular sash, 1-2½ in.

Above, a wire stretched across the paint bucket offers a double advantage. Excess paint is removed by drawing brush across it, and when brush is not in use wire acts as a rest

Proper procedure of dipping brush is shown at the left. One-third to ½ of bristle length is dipped slowly, so that brush can absorb maximum amount of paint. Paint with end of bristles

Never paint with the edge of a brush, as this will cause "fingering." For sash and other narrow places, use a sash brush, which is made to be used edgewise

The photo above shows a badly "fingered" brush which has been used edgewise so often that its normal brushing characteristics have been ruined

When washing out a brush after painting, work it vigorously against the sides and bottom of the solvent container. Change the solvent several times

Use the thumb and forefinger to help remove all of paint. Squeeze from the ferrule down toward the tip of the bristles, dipping in the solvent each time

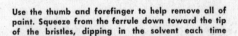

will cause it to "finger" or separate into clumps. Professional painters often prefer to tap the tip of the flat side of the brush lightly against the inside of the can, which leaves the brush more fully loaded.

Brushing varnish, enamel and lacquer calls for a fully loaded brush and a minimum of brush strokes. Brush out the paint in smooth, parallel strokes, and then cross it once to smooth out any brush marks. On vertical work, finish up with long light strokes running the length of the work. Keep checking back for 15 or 20 min. to catch any runs. Hold the brush at a 45-deg. angle and brush with ⅓ to ½ of the bristle length. Don't press down hard, as you will then be painting with the sides of the bristles instead of the ends, causing a streaky job. Never use a brush edgewise, because it will "finger," ruining its good brushing characteristics. If you have narrow surfaces to cut in, use a sash brush, which is made to be used edgewise. If occasionally you have to use the edge of the brush always finish up with a few flat strokes to remove the fingering.

When painting up into a corner, never poke the brush into it. Start the brush a little way from the joint, apply moderate pressure to fan out the bristle, and gradually work the cutting edge into the corner.

If brush cleaning is done immediately after use, it is a comparatively simple task. First wipe off as much of the excess paint as possible and then wash thoroughly in the appropriate solvent by working the brush vigorously against the container sides and bottom. Squeeze the bristle out with the thumb and forefinger, working from the ferrule to the tip. Repeat the process several times, using fresh solvent each time. Then spin the brush dry, between the palms and comb out. If the brush is to be used again in a day or so, wrap in heavy paper, saturate in linseed oil and lay it flat. If the brush is being stored for a longer time, after using the solvent wash thoroughly in warm water and neutral soap. Clean carefully around the ferrule and heel of the brush. Separate the bristles to expose the block and scrape the plug clean of any paint. A wedge of hardened paint will cause the brush to bulge at the ferrule and flare at the tip, making it difficult to spread paint evenly. When the brush is clean, rinse in running water, spin dry and comb out. Then allow it to dry thoroughly. Never dip a paintbrush that is damp into oil or paint, as this will cause the bristles to lose their spring. After the brush is dry, wrap in heavy paper, soak in linseed oil and lay flat in a cool, dry place. If the brush is stored for a lengthy period, unwrap it occasionally and resaturate with linseed oil. ★ ★ ★

A wire brush can be used to scrape dried paint from the handle, around the ferrule and from the heel. In stubborn cases, wire brush is used on bristles

Before storing a paintbrush for a long period, separate bristles as shown above and clean paint from the well with a screwdriver or narrow putty knife

Sometimes a badly-caked brush can be salvaged but it will never be as good as a brush which has been well cared for, and reclaiming it is a lot of work

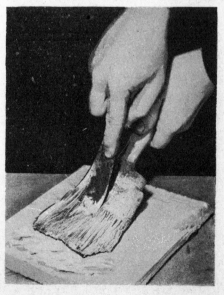

BUNK BEDS

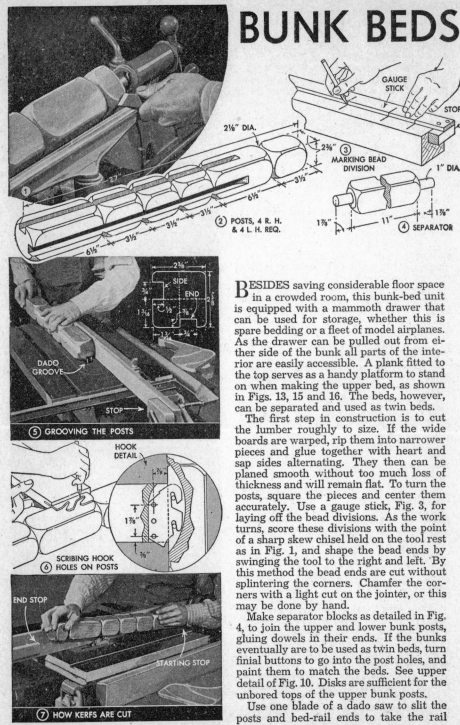

1

2½" DIA.

MARKING BEAD DIVISION ③

2⅜"

3½"

6½"

3½" **3½"** **3½"** **3½"**

6½"

② POSTS, 4 R. H. & 4 L. H. REQ.

GAUGE STICK

STOP

1" DIA.

1⅞"

1⅜"

11"

④ SEPARATOR

2⅜"

SIDE

END

¾"

½" ⅜"

1¾₆"

¾"

1¾₆"

DADO GROOVE

STOP

⑤ GROOVING THE POSTS

HOOK DETAIL

⅞"

1⅞"

⅜"

⑥ SCRIBING HOOK HOLES ON POSTS

END STOP

STARTING STOP

⑦ HOW KERFS ARE CUT

BESIDES saving considerable floor space in a crowded room, this bunk-bed unit is equipped with a mammoth drawer that can be used for storage, whether this is spare bedding or a fleet of model airplanes. As the drawer can be pulled out from either side of the bunk all parts of the interior are easily accessible. A plank fitted to the top serves as a handy platform to stand on when making the upper bed, as shown in Figs. 13, 15 and 16. The beds, however, can be separated and used as twin beds.

The first step in construction is to cut the lumber roughly to size. If the wide boards are warped, rip them into narrower pieces and glue together with heart and sap sides alternating. They then can be planed smooth without too much loss of thickness and will remain flat. To turn the posts, square the pieces and center them accurately. Use a gauge stick, Fig. 3, for laying off the bead divisions. As the work turns, score these divisions with the point of a sharp skew chisel held on the tool rest as in Fig. 1, and shape the bead ends by swinging the tool to the right and left. By this method the bead ends are cut without splintering the corners. Chamfer the corners with a light cut on the jointer, or this may be done by hand.

Make separator blocks as detailed in Fig. 4, to join the upper and lower bunk posts, gluing dowels in their ends. If the bunks eventually are to be used as twin beds, turn finial buttons to go into the post holes, and paint them to match the beds. See upper detail of Fig. 10. Disks are sufficient for the unbored tops of the upper bunk posts.

Use one blade of a dado saw to slit the posts and bed-rail ends to take the rail

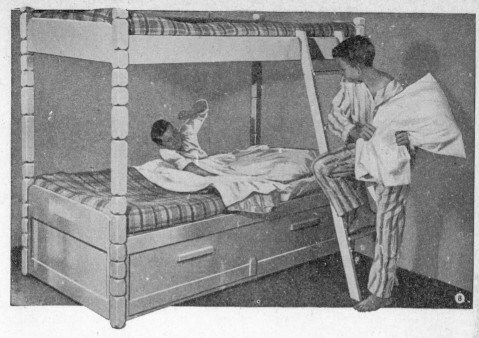

Here's the logical solution to the frequent problem of getting more space in the growing boys' bedroom. Consisting of two separate beds, which can be used individually instead of in bunk formation, this unit is provided with a mammoth drawer that can be pulled out at either side for easy access to its contents

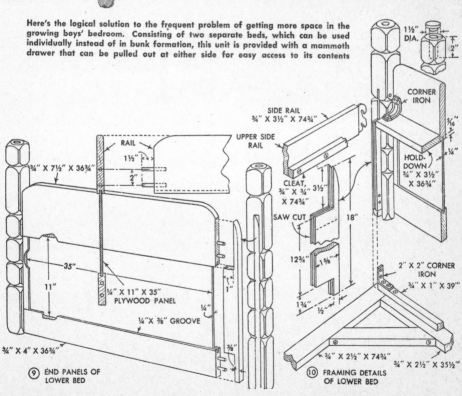

1½" DIA.

2"

CORNER IRON

SIDE RAIL
¾" X 3½" X 74¾"

UPPER SIDE RAIL

RAIL

1½"

2"

¾" X 7½" X 36¾"

HOLD-DOWN
¾" X 3½" X 36¾"

CLEAT,
¾" X ¾" X 3½"
X 74¾"

SAW CUT

18"

5/16"

¼"

35"

11"

¼" X 11" X 35"
PLYWOOD PANEL

¼" X ⅜" GROOVE

1"

¼"

12¾"

1⅝"

1¾"

½"

2" X 2" CORNER IRON
¾" X 1" X 39"

¾" X 4" X 36¾"

⑨ END PANELS OF LOWER BED

⑩ FRAMING DETAILS OF LOWER BED

⅜"

¾" X 2½" X 74¾"

¾" X 2½" X 35½"

hooks. Install the hooks in the rails and secure the pins with wooden wedges to prevent them from dropping out. Use one rail end fitted with a hook as a template for scribing the pin locations on a post as in Fig. 6, taking a pattern from this for the rest. Center the pins where the hooks will bear against them and draw the rail ends tight when the rail is 1/8 in. above level. The joints will be rigid when the rails are driven down to position. Then determine the length of the saw kerfs in the posts, and set start and stop blocks on the circular saw to correspond, as shown in Fig. 7.

Next mount a 3/4-in. dado head and groove the posts 1/2 in. deep to receive the panel stiles as shown in Figs. 2 and 5. Make the stiles, rounding the ends to fit the grooves or chiseling the groove ends square, as preferred. The exact position of the grooves is shown in the detail of Fig. 5. Kerf the ends of the drawer stiles to receive the ends of the hooks that project below the rails.

Bore dowel holes in the end rails and use them as patterns for locating the post dowel holes. As-

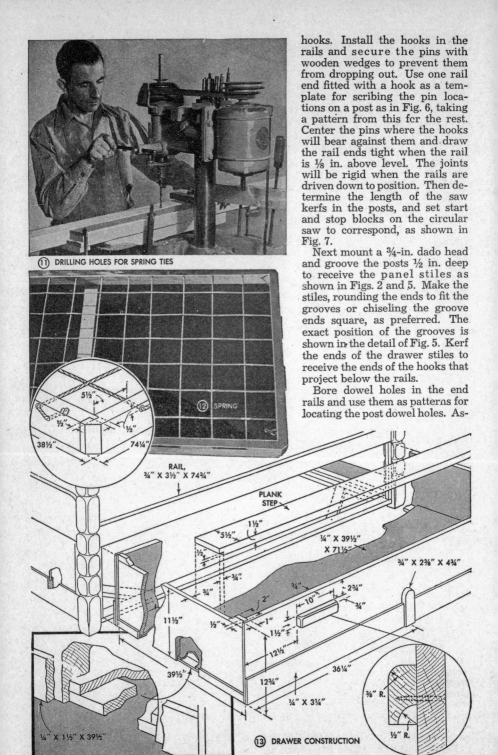

⑪ DRILLING HOLES FOR SPRING TIES

⑫ SPRING

⑬ DRAWER CONSTRUCTION

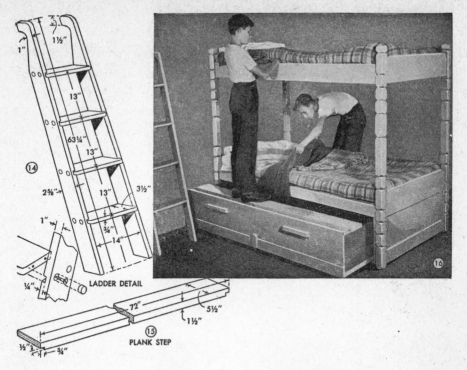

LADDER DETAIL

1½"
1"
13"
63¼"
13"
13"
3½"
2⅝"
1"
¾"
14"
¼"

⑭

72"
5½"
1½"
½"
¾"

⑮
PLANK STEP

⑯

semble the rails and stiles with the end panels and when the glue is dry assemble with the ends and attach the side rails. Build the lower frame to fit, screwing in the corner braces as in Fig. 10 and reinforcing all joints with corrugated fasteners driven into the underside. Wax the upper side of the frame. To support the frame make six blocks of suitable thickness, nailing one under each corner, set well back, and one at the center of each drawer rail. Add the drawer guides, which are flush with the sides of the drawer, since this can be pulled from either side. The four corner irons screwed to the guides and inner surfaces of the drawer stiles prevent the frame from dropping if the bunk is lifted. The corner irons are not intended to take the weight of the drawer, for which purpose the blocks, already mentioned, are provided.

Build the drawer with the sides rabbeted into the fronts and the bottom rabbeted into the front and sides as in Fig. 13. Hardwood strips nailed to the ends and across the center take the wear and provide clearance for easy sliding of the drawer. Use plywood to make overlays for the drawer fronts. A wooden overlay shaped to match the post turning is placed at the center. Both sides are made exactly alike.

Before taking the bunk apart, number the four corners of the drawer, the bed and

rail ends, and the lower frame to facilitate assembly in the proper order. Since the bunk can be carried through an ordinary doorway the ends and rails may be assembled by means of dowels, making a rigid housing for the drawer and eliminating the bother of fitting rail hooks. The upper bunk ends are assembled with two posts and a wide rail, and are put together with the rails like any ordinary bed.

Glue and screw cleats inside the rails near the lower edges to carry the springs. Rope springs, Fig. 12, are quite satisfactory, although they tend to sag like hammocks when the ropes stretch, and the ropes cannot be drawn too tightly or the sides bow in unduly. If tight and flat springs are desired, stiffen the sides by nailing a 1 by 6-in. board lengthwise under each edge, setting it in ¾ in. to allow for the rail cleats. The rope is laced through holes drilled in the spring frames as shown in Fig. 11, the ends of the rope being knotted. Details of frame corner construction and sizes are given in the circular insert of Fig. 12.

A simple four-step ladder is shown in Figs. 8 and 14. Gain the ends of the steps into the sides of the ladder and secure them with screws having heads sunk in counterbored holes. Glue plugs into the holes and dress them flush when dry.

Corner Cabinets

WITH the ever increasing trend toward built-in furniture, the popularity of the corner cabinet is growing every day. From a purely utilitarian standpoint, it transforms a dark corner into something useful and attractive. The shelves will hold either books, or dishes, and display them attractively. Concealed lighting under shelves adds a spot of color to the room at night. In addition, the corner cabinet may take the place of an expensive sideboard in a dining room. This is a great advantage to tenants, as it reduces the number of furnishings. Home owners find it equally desirable from both purely decorative and space-saving viewpoints. The top may be extended to the ceiling or not as desired. Either the natural finish may be used, or the wood painted to harmonize with the surrounding walls. While separate, removable cabinets are generally desirable for those who rent houses and apartments, permanent built-in cabinets are easier and cheaper to build by the home owner. The two adjacent walls in a corner provide sides for the cabinet and many of the frame pieces and shelf cleats can be attached directly to the wall. Either screws or nails can be used for attachment but they should be located so that they can be driven through the plaster and into the studs underneath. Although screws can be driven into lath under plaster where much holding strength is not required, the driving of nails at right angles through plaster and into the lath, frequently causes damage to the wall. Before

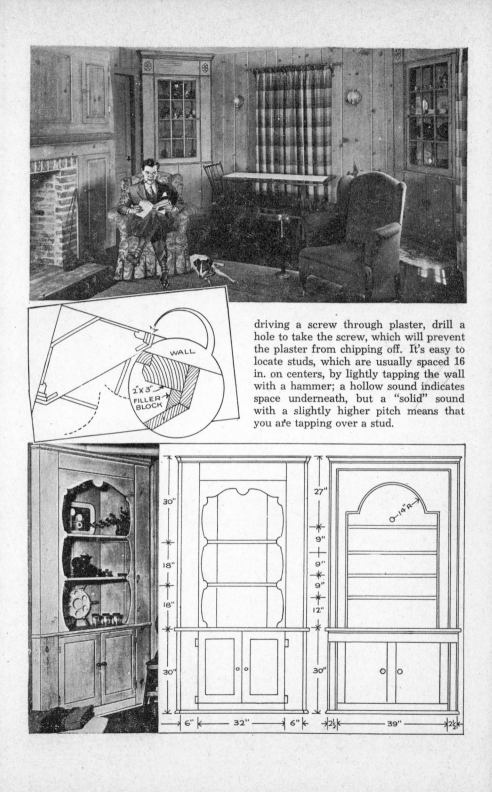

driving a screw through plaster, drill a hole to take the screw, which will prevent the plaster from chipping off. It's easy to locate studs, which are usually spaced 16 in. on centers, by lightly tapping the wall with a hammer; a hollow sound indicates space underneath, but a "solid" sound with a slightly higher pitch means that you are tapping over a stud.

CABINET-TABLE COMBINATION

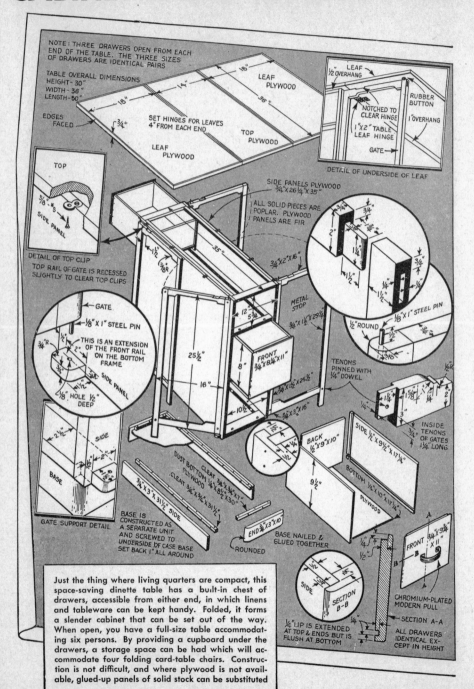

NOTE: THREE DRAWERS OPEN FROM EACH END OF THE TABLE. THE THREE SIZES OF DRAWERS ARE IDENTICAL PAIRS

TABLE OVERALL DIMENSIONS
HEIGHT- 30"
WIDTH- 36"
LENGTH- 50"

EDGES FACED

SET HINGES FOR LEAVES 4" FROM EACH END

LEAF PLYWOOD

TOP PLYWOOD

LEAF PLYWOOD

LEAF ½ OVERHANG

RUBBER BUTTON

NOTCHED TO CLEAR HINGE

1" OVERHANG

1"X2" TABLE LEAF HINGE

GATE

DETAIL OF UNDERSIDE OF LEAF

TOP

SIDE PANEL

DETAIL OF TOP CLIP

TOP RAIL OF GATE IS RECESSED SLIGHTLY TO CLEAR TOP CLIPS

SIDE PANELS PLYWOOD ¾"X 26½"X 35"

ALL SOLID PIECES ARE POPLAR. PLYWOOD PANELS ARE FIR

GATE
⅛" X 1" STEEL PIN

THIS IS AN EXTENSION OF THE FRONT RAIL ON THE BOTTOM FRAME

SIDE PANEL

⅛" HOLE ½" DEEP

METAL STOP
¾"X1½"X 29¼"

FRONT
¾"X 8¼"X 11"

⅛"X 1" STEEL PIN

½" ROUND

TENONS PINNED WITH ¼" DOWEL

INSIDE TENONS OF GATES ¼" LONG

SIDE
½" X 9½" X 17¼"

BACK
½"X 9½"X 10"

BOTTOM PLYWOOD

DUST BOTTOM ¼"X 8½"X 30"
PLYWOOD

CLEAT ¾"X 3¾"X 1"

CLEAT ¾"X 3¾"X 31½"

¾"X 3"X 31½" SIDE

BASE IS CONSTRUCTED AS A SEPARATE UNIT AND SCREWED TO UNDERSIDE OF CASE BASE SET BACK 1" ALL AROUND

GATE SUPPORT DETAIL

END ¾"X 3"X 10"
ROUNDED

BASE NAILED & GLUED TOGETHER

SIDE

SECTION B-B

½" LIP IS EXTENDED AT TOP & ENDS BUT IS FLUSH AT BOTTOM

FRONT ¾"X 5¾" X 11"

CHROMIUM-PLATED MODERN PULL

SECTION A-A

ALL DRAWERS IDENTICAL EXCEPT IN HEIGHT

Just the thing where living quarters are compact, this space-saving dinette table has a built-in chest of drawers, accessible from either end, in which linens and tableware can be kept handy. Folded, it forms a slender cabinet that can be set out of the way. When open, you have a full-size table accommodating six persons. By providing a cupboard under the drawers, a storage space can be had which will accommodate four folding card-table chairs. Construction is not difficult, and where plywood is not available, glued-up panels of solid stock can be substituted

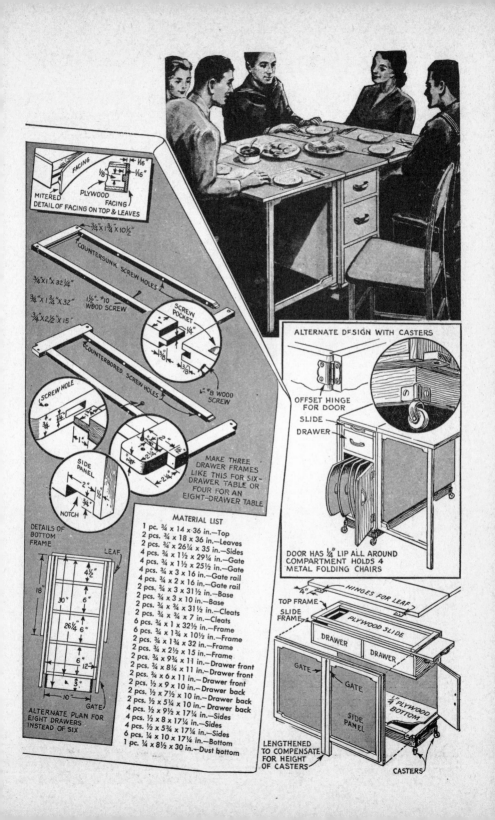

DETAIL OF FACING ON TOP & LEAVES

FACING

PLYWOOD FACING

MITERED

1/16" 1/8" 1/16"

3/4" x 1 3/4" x 10 1/2"

COUNTERSUNK SCREW HOLES

3/4" x 1" x 32 1/4"

3/4" x 1 3/4" x 32"

1/2"-#10 WOOD SCREW

3/4" x 2 1/2" x 15"

SCREW POCKET

1/4"

1/16" 1 3/8" 1 3/8"

COUNTERBORED SCREW HOLES

-#8 WOOD SCREW

SCREW HOLE

3/4" 1/4" 1"

SIDE PANEL

2" 1/2"

NOTCH 3/4"

MAKE THREE DRAWER FRAMES LIKE THIS FOR SIX-DRAWER TABLE OR FOUR FOR AN EIGHT-DRAWER TABLE

DETAILS OF BOTTOM FRAME

LEAF

4 1/2"

18"

30" 6"

26 1/4" 6"

6"

12"

3"

10"

GATE

ALTERNATE PLAN FOR EIGHT DRAWERS INSTEAD OF SIX

MATERIAL LIST

1 pc. 3/4 x 14 x 36 in.—Top
2 pcs. 3/4 x 18 x 36 in.—Leaves
2 pcs. 3/4 x 26 1/4 x 35 in.—Sides
4 pcs. 3/4 x 1 1/2 x 29 1/4 in.—Gate
4 pcs. 3/4 x 1 1/2 x 25 1/2 in.—Gate
4 pcs. 3/4 x 3 x 16 in.—Gate rail
2 pcs. 3/4 x 2 x 16 in.—Gate rail
2 pcs. 3/4 x 3 x 31 1/2 in.—Base
2 pcs. 3/4 x 3 x 10 in.—Base
2 pcs. 3/4 x 3/4 x 31 1/2 in.—Cleats
2 pcs. 3/4 x 3/4 x 7 in.—Cleats
6 pcs. 3/4 x 1 x 32 1/2 in.—Frame
6 pcs. 3/4 x 1 3/4 x 10 1/2 in.—Frame
2 pcs. 3/4 x 1 3/4 x 32 in.—Frame
2 pcs. 3/4 x 2 1/2 x 15 in.—Frame
2 pcs. 3/4 x 9 3/4 x 11 in.—Drawer front
2 pcs. 3/4 x 8 1/4 x 11 in.—Drawer front
2 pcs. 3/4 x 6 x 11 in.—Drawer front
2 pcs. 1/2 x 9 x 10 in.—Drawer back
2 pcs. 1/2 x 7 1/2 x 10 in.—Drawer back
2 pcs. 1/2 x 5 1/4 x 10 in.—Drawer back
4 pcs. 1/2 x 9 1/2 x 17 1/4 in.—Sides
4 pcs. 1/2 x 8 x 17 1/4 in.—Sides
4 pcs. 1/2 x 5 3/4 x 17 1/4 in.—Sides
6 pcs. 1/4 x 10 x 17 1/4 in.—Bottom
1 pc. 1/4 x 8 1/2 x 30 in.—Dust bottom

ALTERNATE DESIGN WITH CASTERS

OFFSET HINGE FOR DOOR

SLIDE

DRAWER

DOOR HAS 1/4" LIP ALL AROUND
COMPARTMENT HOLDS 4
METAL FOLDING CHAIRS

4" HINGES FOR LEAF

TOP FRAME

SLIDE FRAME

PLYWOOD SLIDE

DRAWER DRAWER

GATE

GATE

SIDE PANEL

1/4" PLYWOOD BOTTOM

LENGTHENED TO COMPENSATE FOR HEIGHT OF CASTERS

CASTERS

CABINETS
Save Space

FOR those who live in small apartments, this clothes cabinet, which is attached to the inner side of a door, will increase storage space and permit shoes, ties, linens and similar articles to be stored neatly within easy reach. The cabinet frame is made of ½-in. stock cut to fit a door, and is grooved for shelves and a partition as shown. Staggered holes are drilled in the side members of the frame to take lengths of dowel, which form shoe racks, and the ends of the members are rabbeted for top and bottom pieces. Flush doors of ¼-in. plywood are provided with friction catches and glass knobs. A wooden disk and a spacer made by cutting a spool in half are screwed into the underside of the top to hold ties, nails being driven into the edge of the disk for this purpose. When assembled and finished as desired, the cabinet is attached to the door with angle brackets screwed to top and bottom pieces.

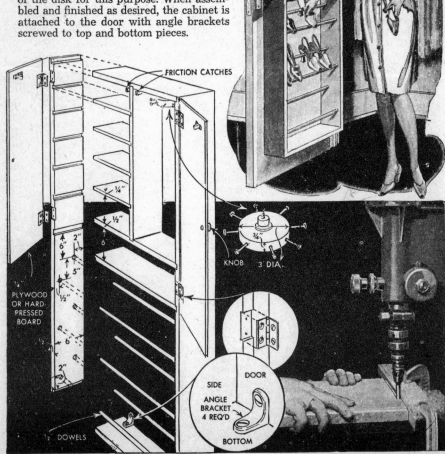

FRICTION CATCHES

¼"

½"

2"
6"
5"

¼"
PLYWOOD
OR HARD-
PRESSED
BOARD

½"

6"

2"

½ DOWELS

KNOB   3 DIA.
¾"

SIDE   DOOR
ANGLE
BRACKET
4 REQ'D

BOTTOM

CURIO CABINET

Colonial both in design and finish, this little curio cabinet provides an appropriate setting for displaying your treasured bits of bric-a-brac. Typical cabinet joinery is used, a right and left-hand side member being cut first from maple or birch and rabbeted along the rear edges for a ¼-in. plywood panel. Except for the shelf above the door, all others, including the top and bottom of the cabinet, are cut the same size. The scrolled valance, which frames the open shelves, is built-up from four separate pieces, the side strips being bandsawed from stock 2 in. wide. The side pieces are joined to the top and bottom scrolled pieces with mortise-and-tenon joints and then nailed to the face of the cabinet flush with the sides. Finally, the top is finished off with a cove molding, and the bottom is fitted with a raised-panel door, being built-up as detailed and hung with wrought-type hinges. A bullet friction catch holds the door shut.

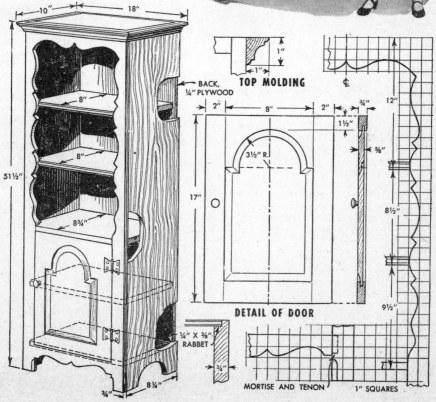

BACK, ¼" PLYWOOD

TOP MOLDING

DETAIL OF DOOR

¼" X ⅜" RABBET

MORTISE AND TENON

1" SQUARES

CACTI
All-season house plants

BECAUSE there are so many varieties and shapes, raising cactus is a kind of indoor gardening that will not easily become monotonous. In shape, some plants are globular, some cylindrical and some columnar, while others are flattened, or ribbed like a cantaloupe. Several species, including the prickly pear, are edible, and others serve as forage for cattle, while still others are cultivated solely for their showy, delicately colored flowers.

Possessed with a camel-like ability to store water in their fleshy protuberances, cacti are plants that not only survive in the desert but in some instances attain unusual size. The giant cactus of Arizona and other southwestern states, for example, attains a height of 40 to 70 ft. with a diameter of about 2 ft. However, there are many smaller varieties that are suitable for cultivation in the home conservatory. Some of these are shown in Figs. 5 to 10, and 12 to 15.

Such plants usually can be purchased from nurseries and florists. Wild cacti sel-

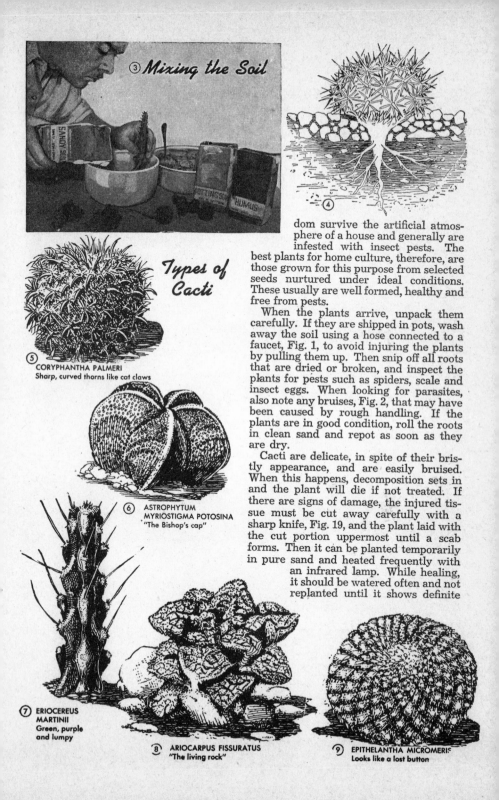

③ *Mixing the Soil*

④

Types of Cacti

⑤ CORYPHANTHA PALMERI
Sharp, curved thorns like cat claws

⑥ ASTROPHYTUM
MYRIOSTIGMA POTOSINA
"The Bishop's cap"

⑦ ERIOCEREUS
MARTINII
Green, purple
and lumpy

⑧ ARIOCARPUS FISSURATUS
"The living rock"

⑨ EPITHELANTHA MICROMERIS
Looks like a lost button

dom survive the artificial atmosphere of a house and generally are infested with insect pests. The best plants for home culture, therefore, are those grown for this purpose from selected seeds nurtured under ideal conditions. These usually are well formed, healthy and free from pests.

When the plants arrive, unpack them carefully. If they are shipped in pots, wash away the soil using a hose connected to a faucet, Fig. 1, to avoid injuring the plants by pulling them up. Then snip off all roots that are dried or broken, and inspect the plants for pests such as spiders, scale and insect eggs. When looking for parasites, also note any bruises, Fig. 2, that may have been caused by rough handling. If the plants are in good condition, roll the roots in clean sand and repot as soon as they are dry.

Cacti are delicate, in spite of their bristly appearance, and are easily bruised. When this happens, decomposition sets in and the plant will die if not treated. If there are signs of damage, the injured tissue must be cut away carefully with a sharp knife, Fig. 19, and the plant laid with the cut portion uppermost until a scab forms. Then it can be planted temporarily in pure sand and heated frequently with an infrared lamp. While healing, it should be watered often and not replanted until it shows definite

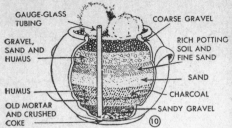

GAUGE-GLASS TUBING — COARSE GRAVEL

GRAVEL, SAND AND HUMUS — RICH POTTING SOIL AND FINE SAND

— SAND

HUMUS — CHARCOAL

OLD MORTAR AND CRUSHED COKE — SANDY GRAVEL

10

11 Pest Control

signs of recovery. The period of convalescence may be two or three months.

Growing cacti in the house is not a very difficult job; however, the right kind of container is important. Terra cotta flowerpots are not desirable because they absorb too much water, causing the soil to pack. This in turn will cause the roots to dry out and die. Also, as water evaporates from the outside of the pot, a cooling effect is obtained which may chill the roots. Wooden tubs are the best containers, but glazed pottery or porcelain will be most ornamental. Bean pots, mixing bowls and Mexican cooking ware add a touch of color to a living room and are entirely suitable to the needs of cacti.

Soil, too, is important. No cactus will thrive in sand alone, even though many species grow in the desert. Desert soil is light and fluffy, rich with wind-blown leaf dust and other nutrient elements, and there is enough moisture—enough for the cactus. Therefore, when growing cacti at home, these conditions must be duplicated as closely as possible. The soil can be made to order by mixing easily obtained ingredients: humus (decomposed leaves and other vegetation), potting soil (a composite of black, sandy loam and humus), gravel, old plaster, charcoal and crushed coke. These are placed in layers in the pot, Fig. 10, so the soil will be loose and porous as it is in the desert. The roots of cacti must have air.

Under no conditions must the soil be more than slightly damp. To determine the moisture content, press a length of glass tub-

12 ECHINOCEREUS REICHENBACHI
Delicate white spines intermeshed like dainty lace

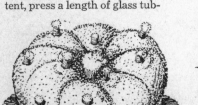

13 LOPHOPHORA WILLIAMSII
Mescal, or dumpling cactus

14 CEPHALOCEREUS SENILIS
The "Old Man" Cactus

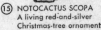

15 NOTOCACTUS SCOPA
A living red-and-silver Christmas-tree ornament

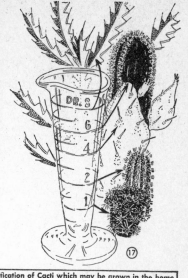

ing down through the soil, Fig. 10, and insert a water-color brush in the tube. If the brush is damp when withdrawn, the soil is too wet. Another function of the tube is to act as a vent or breather tube for the roots.

To set plants in filled pots, scoop out a depression for the root and, holding the plant erect, pack a cushion of gravel under it as in Fig. 4. The gravel will keep the plant dry and free from mildew. Usually four or five plants can be set together in one pot at the beginning, but, as they grow, some may have to be transplanted to avoid crowding. Since some species grow quite large while others mature and die when they reach the size of a man's thumb, it is best before planting to determine which types to group. The table under Fig. 17 will guide you.

The growth pattern for the different species varies widely. For example, the Astrophytum shown in Fig. 6 develops very slowly; a spine will start in the center of first one, then another, of the five lobes and gradually advance toward the edge, but there is little evidence of growth from month to month. Growth of Echinocereus, Fig. 12, starts as a tuft of soft down and slowly develops into a crown. In selecting types of cacti, it is best not to mix jungle varieties with the desert types such as the large growing species shown in the table. As a general rule, jungle cacti bloom quite frequently, but so-called fancy types rarely do, except when growing in their natural state.

From time to time the plants should be inspected under a magnifying glass. Soot and dust collect in the deep creases and under the spines to hide the sleek shine of a healthy plant. The best means of removing this accumulation is a long-haired showcard brush, Fig. 11. This is also an effective tool for exterminating insect pests which, if allowed to feed and multi-

General classification of Cacti which may be grown in the home			
Large Growing	**Jungle**	**Tiny Plants**	**Fancy Cacti**
Echinocactus	Echinopsis	Astrophytum	Cephalocereus
Carnegiea	Epiphyllum	Echinocereus	Coryphantha
Cleistocactus	Eriocereus	Epithelantha	Espostoa
Ferocactus	Heliocereus	Frailea	Hamatocactus
Gymnocalycium	Hylocereus	Lobivia	Leuchtenbergia
Lemaireocereus	Monvillea	Mamillaria	Notocactus
Melocactus	Nyctocereus	Rebutia	Periskia
Opuntia	Peniocereus		Stenocactus
Oreocereus	Rhipsalis		
Rathbunia	Selenicereus		
Trichocereus	Zygocactus		

ply, will in time devour an entire plant. To kill such pests, dip the brush in alcohol and apply it under the spines and along the crevices that show signs of parasitic destruction.

In watering plants, the schematic guide shown in Fig. 17 indicates their widely varying needs. For small plants, one dram usually will be sufficient, while larger ones will need 8 drams, or one-half oz. The water is poured gently along the edge of the pot, Fig. 16, and allowed to soak into the soil. Water should never be poured directly on the cactus because a wet, soggy plant molds rapidly. For this reason, too little water is preferable to too much. Cactus will store up a year's supply of moisture and water should be added only to replace that consumed.

Strong light can be harmful; contrary to popular belief, cacti do not thrive in hot sunlight but prefer shady areas or locations where the sun will strike them only for part of the day. Jungle cacti, as the name implies, grow almost entirely in deep shade. Too much light, like too much water, destroys the color and leaves a bleached, drab-looking plant. However, in the house, a northern exposure is not likely

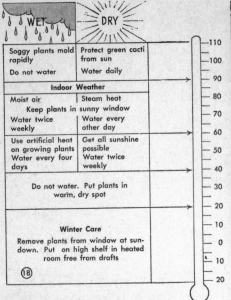

WET | DRY

Soggy plants mold rapidly	Protect green cacti from sun
Do not water	Water daily
Indoor Weather	
Moist air	Steam heat
Keep plants in sunny window	
Water twice weekly	Water every other day
Use artificial heat on growing plants Water every four days	Get all sunshine possible Water twice weekly
Do not water. Put plants in warm, dry spot	
Winter Care	
Remove plants from window at sundown. Put on high shelf in heated room free from drafts	

⑱

(Thermometer scale: 110, 100, 90, 80, 70, 60, 50, 40, 30, 20, 10, 0, 10, 20)

⑲

to harm cacti, even in summer.

In regard to growing temperatures, heat is preferable to cold. If chilled, the plant will stop growing and the buds will wither. A temperature of 100 deg. for an hour or two a day will speed the growing process. High humidity is dangerous because it promotes the development of fungi. When the weather is damp or chilly, an infrared heat lamp can be directed at the plants, or they can be placed on a shelf near a hot-water tank or boiler. The chart, Fig. 18, will serve as a guide for wet and dry weather at various temperatures.

Barrel of Small Insect Sprayer Provides Good Calking Gun

For an occasional calking job around the home, the barrel of an old insect sprayer makes a good gun. After removing the sprayer tank, the pointed end of the barrel will enable you to force the compound into cracks around windows, doors and other openings. If desired, a short piece of tubing threaded at one end can be soldered to the gun for attaching nozzles of various shapes.

CALKING COMPOUND →

SPRAYER (TANK REMOVED)

CAMPER'S KITCHEN

Being the camp cook is a real pleasure when everything you need is right at your finger tips. Note how the hinged front of the portable cabinet opens to provide a worktable at a convenient height

THERE WAS A TIME when camping out meant roughing it, and eating camp food was a test of endurance. That picture has changed considerably and camping has become the art of living as comfortably as possible under all kinds of conditions. For family camping, this compact portable kitchen will provide the answer to the problem of a place for everything. It also can be used by hunters and fishermen who are going to spots that are accessible by car. The cabinet is designed to hold a cooking kit, eating utensils, and enough canned and dehydrated foods to feed six people for a week. Removable legs make it easy to stow the cabinet in the trunk of your car.

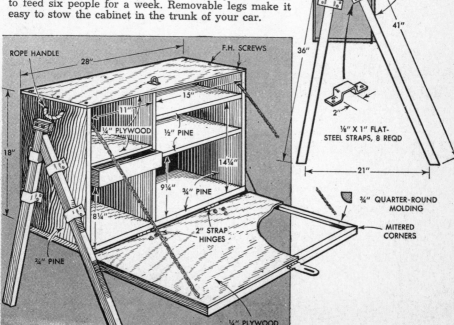

CAMPING OVEN
and
ACCESSORIES

While the biscuits are shown in a pan for convenience in handling, food can be placed directly on the shelf

L IKE ANY reflector-type oven, this one is designed to be placed in front of an open fire where two inclined covers reflect heat waves against a center shelf on which food is placed. While the oven itself can be made of almost any sheet metal, the two reflecting surfaces should be of bright metal, such as polished aluminum or tinned sheet metal. Although not as good, bright galvanized iron will do for the reflecting surfaces. To help hasten heat absorption, it sometimes is helpful to blacken the underside of the center shelf with shoe polish.

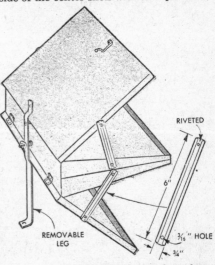

RIVETED

REMOVABLE LEG

6"

3/16" HOLE

3/4"

Folded, the oven resembles a neat, metal brief case. Pivoted arms fold flush with sides of oven proper

This rear view of oven shows supporting leg and arms which snap in place to hold reflecting covers open

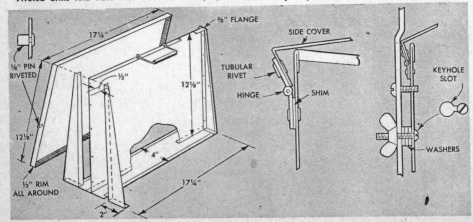

3/8" FLANGE

17 1/4"

1/8" PIN RIVETED

1/2"

12 1/8"

12 1/8"

1/2" RIM ALL AROUND

4"

17 1/4"

2"

SIDE COVER

TUBULAR RIVET

HINGE

SHIM

KEYHOLE SLOT

WASHERS

Cooking accessories, such as hamburger grill, fork and toaster, plus oven leg, all store inside the oven

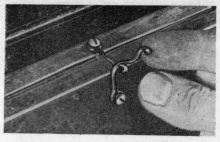

The latch is formed of stiff wire, each part being attached to respective covers with sheet-metal screws

Leg which supports oven is made removable by means of horizontal keyhole slot which disengages screw

Commercial hamburger grill is used and the handles shortened so that unit can be stored inside the oven

The basket-type toaster holds two slices. Cotter pin in pivoted handle permits removal for storing

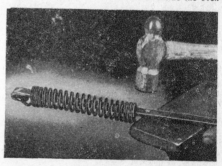

Toaster handle is fitted with "cool" grip formed by riveting coil spring to looped end of flat steel rod

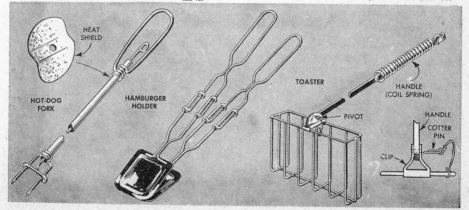

HEAT SHIELD

HOT-DOG FORK

HAMBURGER HOLDER

TOASTER

HANDLE (COIL SPRING)

PIVOT

HANDLE

COTTER PIN

CLIP

CANDLE HOLDERS

BY A SIMPLE half turn of the ball, which is mounted on a concealed pivot pin, these novel candlesticks are adapted for use either on a table or a wall. Turning them is an interesting job for the craftsman who likes to work at the wood lathe. Use a fine cabinet wood such as maple, walnut or mahogany. Turn the ball candle sockets first, using a special template made from heavy cardboard or thin hardwood. Work slowly, checking the work frequently to assure that the balls are turned to true spheres. Drill each ball as indicated in the sectional view. The tapered hole forming the candle socket is drilled while the ball is still in the lathe. To finish the ball, apply a thin coat of shellac. Then immediately moisten a pad with alcohol and polish the work with the lathe running. Proceed in a similar manner when making and finishing the base, using a special template to bring the concave cut to exactly the same radius as that of the ball. Drill meeting holes from the bottom of the base to provide space for an L-hook, and counterbore for the pivot pin. Then glue felt to the base.

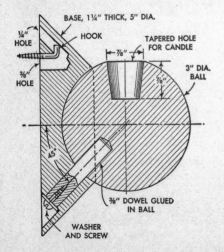

BASE, 1¼" THICK, 5" DIA.

¼" HOLE

HOOK

TAPERED HOLE FOR CANDLE

⅜" HOLE

7/8"

7/8"

3" DIA. BALL

45°

⅜" DOWEL GLUED IN BALL

WASHER AND SCREW

Antique Candleholder for Basement Playrooms

HOSTESSES will like this candleholder because it is especially suitable for the informal table, and home craftsmen with limited spare time will find that it's easy to build and requires the use of only a few simple tools. Although sheet copper can be used for all the parts, pieces of tin cut from coffee cans and used with the bright side out are the next best. If you use tin, be extra careful when cutting that the material is not sharply bent or dented in the process. Start with the base which consists of two sheet-metal disks and an encircling band, the ends of which overlap ⅛ in. The decoration on the band is stamped into the metal with a short piece of pipe. Care must be taken to get the indentations of uniform size and equally spaced. Note that the same decoration is carried out on the four sides of the drip-tray support, except that here the full-circle indentation is made.

Cone-shaped sections which make up into the center ornament are formed separately and soldered together before soldering to the base. Form the drip-tray support over a block of hardwood, then shape the drip tray by beating down a sheet-metal disk into a circular recess cut in a block of wood. Use a wood mallet with a rounded end. The band of tin holding the candle is formed to the cylindrical shape by bending over a rod or pipe and is soldered to the center of the drip tray.

With all the parts made up, cut or file the drip-tray support to fit the curvature of the tray. Then solder all parts together. Use a small torch for soldering. The needle flame will get into those places where it is impossible to use an iron effectively. Final part in the assembly is the handle, which is a strip of metal bent to a scroll shape and

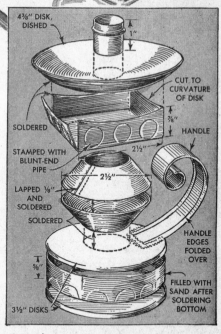

soldered to the base and the drip tray as shown in the photo. Note that the edges of the strip are turned or folded over to add strength. This is done before bending to the scroll shape. Smooth all edges bright, wash in a soda-water solution to remove the soldering flux and finish with a coat of water-white lacquer.

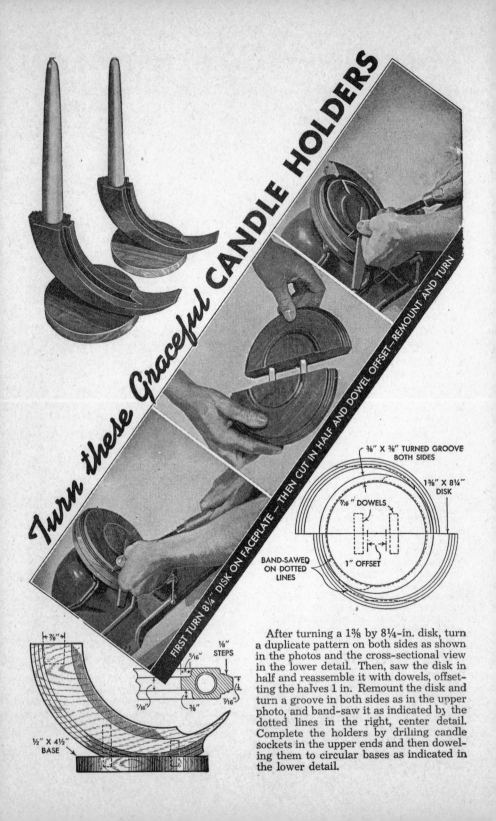

Turn these Graceful CANDLE HOLDERS

FIRST TURN 8¼" DISK ON FACEPLATE — THEN CUT IN HALF AND DOWEL OFFSET — REMOUNT AND TURN

⅜" X ⅜" TURNED GROOVE BOTH SIDES

1⅜" X 8¼" DISK

⁷⁄₁₆" DOWELS

BAND-SAWED ON DOTTED LINES

1" OFFSET

⅛" STEPS

⅝"

⁵⁄₁₆"

⁷⁄₁₆"

⅜"

⁷⁄₁₆"

½" X 4½" BASE

After turning a 1⅜ by 8¼-in. disk, turn a duplicate pattern on both sides as shown in the photos and the cross-sectional view in the lower detail. Then, saw the disk in half and reassemble it with dowels, offsetting the halves 1 in. Remount the disk and turn a groove in both sides as in the upper photo, and band-saw it as indicated by the dotted lines in the right, center detail. Complete the holders by drilling candle sockets in the upper ends and then doweling them to circular bases as indicated in the lower detail.

Plastic CANDLESTICKS

A PPROPRIATE on smart tables, these colorful modern candlesticks are assembled from standard pieces of sheet, rod and tube plastic. The style shown in Figs. 1 and 7 has a chromium base and a plastic ring drilled on opposite sides to take a candle. The model shown in Figs. 2 and 8 is pleasing because of its simplicity. Figs. 4 and 5 show how the sockets are bored to size. Crescent-shaped bases, each carrying a trio of candles, Figs. 3 and 9, are particularly effective. Slotting, Fig. 6, can be done with a hacksaw and file if you have no motorized equipment.

④ DRILLING THE CANDLE SOCKET

⑤ BORING SOCKETS TO ⅞" INSIDE DIAMETER

⑥ SLOTTED SOCKETS ARE EASILY CUT ON THE SHAPER

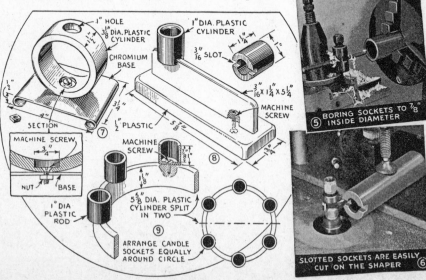

Build Your

WITH its low ends and flat bottom, which extends well up into bow and stern, this 16-ft., Canadian-type canoe is well adapted to the needs of the average builder. It is used by the forestry service because of its steadiness on the water, ease of paddling and the fact that it is little affected by cross winds on account of its wide beam which is 33 in. amidships. The weight of the finished canoe will be about 70 or 80 pounds.

Construction begins with a temporary framework consisting of a set of molds and a backbone, to which the molds are fastened. Paper patterns are made from the squared drawings, Figs. 1 and 2, to trace the outline of the molds on the stock. Each mold is made in two halves, fastened together temporarily with cleats. As both ends of the canoe are identical, two molds of each size, with the exception of the cen-

ter one, are required. The backbone is a piece of ¾-in. stock 5¼ in. wide and 14 ft. 6 in. long on the upper edge and 14 ft. 4½ in. on the lower edge. See Figs. 3 and 7. The keelson is a piece of clear, straight-grained ash or oak, cut to size and tapered at each end as shown in Fig. 7.

Bending canoe stems is a cranky job, even with special equipment for the business, so you use stems built up from regular stock as in Fig. 6. The grain should run nearly at right angles as in Fig. 7, and casein glue and dowels should be used in the joint.

Assembly is started by locating and nailing the molds in position along the backbone, as in Figs. 3 and 7. The frame is then turned over and the keelson nailed temporarily to each of the molds, after which the stem pieces are screwed between the cleats at the ends of the backbone, Fig. 7.

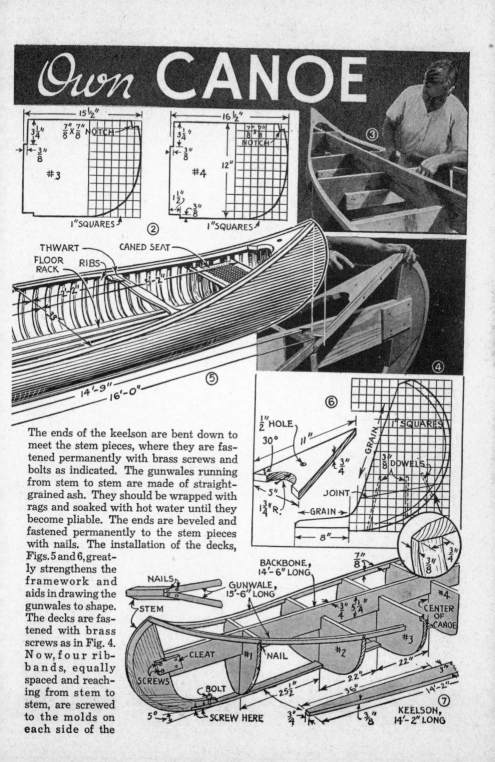

Own CANOE

③

② 1" SQUARES   #3   #4   1" SQUARES

THWART   CANED SEAT
FLOOR RACK   RIBS

④

⑤ 14'-9"   16'-0"

⑥ 1" SQUARES   1" HOLE   30°   11"   GRAIN   3/4   3/8 DOWELS   JOINT   GRAIN   5"   1 3/4" R.   8"   3/4   3/8

The ends of the keelson are bent down to meet the stem pieces, where they are fastened permanently with brass screws and bolts as indicated. The gunwales running from stem to stem are made of straight-grained ash. They should be wrapped with rags and soaked with hot water until they become pliable. The ends are beveled and fastened permanently to the stem pieces with nails. The installation of the decks, Figs. 5 and 6, greatly strengthens the framework and aids in drawing the gunwales to shape. The decks are fastened with brass screws as in Fig. 4. Now, four rib-bands, equally spaced and reaching from stem to stem, are screwed to the molds on each side of the

NAILS   STEM   CLEAT   SCREWS   BOLT   SCREW HERE   5°   #1   NAIL   BACKBONE, 14'-6" LONG   GUNWALE, 15'-6" LONG   #2   #3   #4   CENTER OF CANOE   25 1/2"   36"   22"   22"   3"   14'-2"   KEELSON, 14'-2" LONG   ⑦

saw is equipped with a ripping fence you will be able to save money on the ribs and planking by resawing them yourself, as shown in Fig. 10. The planks are soaked for several hours, then the first full-length plank is laid with the edge parallel with the center line of the keelson, Fig. 11, using clamps to draw it into place. Copper nails are used for fastening the planking to the ribs and all nails must be clinched across the grain on the inside of the ribs, Fig. 12. Fig. 11 shows the arrangement of the planking. Notice that the first five bilge planks run from stem to stem on each side of the keelson. The freeboard planks run out to points fore and aft as shown.

To remove the backbone, take out the cleats and saw it through at the center. Take out all but the No. 3 molds. Bolt the maple thwarts, Figs. 5 and 16, to the underside of the gunwales to prevent the hull from springing out of shape. The seat frames, Figs. 5 and 18, also may be fitted at this time. Actual measurement must determine the length of the seat stretchers. The rear stretchers are bolted direct to the keelson as shown in Figs. 8 and 9.

Although the 2-in. white-cedar ribs are ³⁄₁₆ in. thick instead of the usual ¼ or ⁵⁄₁₆ in., this variation does not weaken the construction as the ribs are spaced 1 in. apart to compensate. Steaming, Fig. 13, is necessary to make them sufficiently pliable to take the bends. Each rib should be long enough to reach from gunwale to gunwale over the outside of the ribbands. Begin at the center and install each rib as shown in Fig. 14, drawing it into position with C-clamps and nailing at the keelson and gunwales, starting at the center of the canoe and working toward the ends. The ribs in front of the first mold are bent so sharply that it is practically impossible to prevent them from splintering. Where a rib comes over a mold, it is simply spaced out and omitted temporarily, Fig. 15, until the molds have been removed.

When the ribs are all in place, the ribbands are taken off, making the job ready for the ⅛-in. cedar planking. If your band

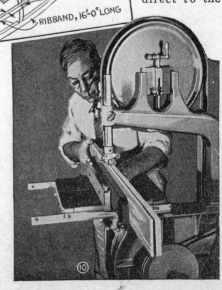

gunwales but the two forward are lowered 3 in. by means of hardwood spacers as in Fig. 18.

For canvassing you need two pieces of 8-oz. canvas, long enough to reach from stem to stem with about a foot to spare, and wide enough to reach from the gunwale to the keel with allowance for a lap. Start by spreading the canvas over half of the canoe, tacking temporarily near the center of the gunwale. Pull the covering tightly around the bilge and place a few tacks along the keel, near the center. Wet the canvas and pull it lengthwise over the stems, and tack. As it dries, the fabric will stretch and take the shape of the hull. When dry, pull out the tacks at one end and fit the canvas neatly around the stem,

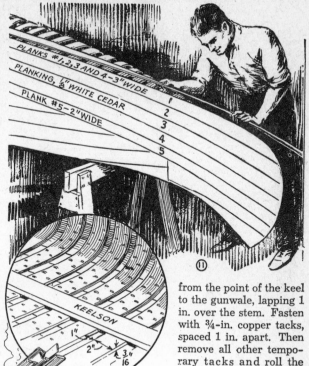

PLANKS #1, 2, 3 AND 4 - 3" WIDE

PLANKING, ⅜" WHITE CEDAR

PLANK #5 - 2" WIDE

1 2 3 4 5

KEELSON

1"

2"

3/16

⑪

⑫

NAILS ARE CLINCHED ACROSS THE GRAIN

⑬

C-CLAMPS

RIBBANDS

TRIM OFF NAIL HERE

RIB

⑭

⑮

from the point of the keel to the gunwale, lapping 1 in. over the stem. Fasten with ¾-in. copper tacks, spaced 1 in. apart. Then remove all other temporary tacks and roll the canvas back off the canoe.

Beginning at the tacked end, apply a coat of waterproof canvas cement to a section of the planking along the keel, using a stiff brush, Fig. 17. Do not cover a large area as the cement dries quickly. Unroll the canvas over the cemented area, pull tightly lengthwise and fasten the loose end temporarily while tacks are placed closely along the gunwale and keel of the cemented portion. As you tack be sure that the cloth lies flat without any wrinkles. Then squeegee the canvas with the palm of the hand to make sure that it is in contact with the cement at all points. Take the next section of the hull in the same manner continuing by successive stages until you finish at the opposite stem. The second half is stretched and tacked in the same manner as the first allowing for the lap under the keel. This done, you trim the canvas along

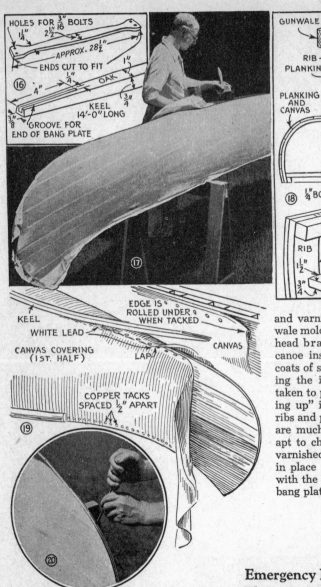

HOLES FOR 3/16" BOLTS

1 1/4" 2 1/2"

APPROX. 28 1/2"

ENDS CUT TO FIT

1"

⑯ 4" 1/4" OAK

3/4"

KEEL 14'-0" LONG

3/8" GROOVE. FOR END OF BANG PLATE

GUNWALE

1/4" X 1" MOLDING

RIB NAILS

PLANKING CANVAS

PLANKING AND CANVAS KEEL SCREW

KEELSON

12" 2" X 3/16" RIBS

THWART

⑱ 1/4" BOLT 3/4" X 2 1/8"

RIB 3" 1 3/4" MORTISE JOINT

1/2"

3/4" CANE

⑰

KEEL

EDGE IS ROLLED UNDER WHEN TACKED

WHITE LEAD

CANVAS COVERING (1ST. HALF) LAP CANVAS

COPPER TACKS SPACED 1/2" APART

⑲

⑳

Emergency Repair for Canoes

and varnished. Apply the gunwale molding, Fig. 19, with round-head brass nails, and finish the canoe inside and out with two coats of spar varnish. In varnishing the inside, care should be taken to prevent the varnish "piling up" in corners between the ribs and planking. Two thin coats are much more durable and less apt to check. Finally the keel is varnished separately and screwed in place as in Fig. 19. Finish up with the 1/4-in. half-round copper bang plates.

the gunwales and finish tacking the stems, using copper tacks, which should be spaced about 1/2 in. apart.

Allow a few days for drying, then apply a coat of canvas cement over the entire surface. When dry, sand smooth and finish with one coat of deck paint and one of flat color after which it is again sanded

Emergency Repair for Canoes

When spruce gum is available, a leaking canoe can be repaired even though you do not have a repair kit with you. After the leak has been located, clean the area and allow it to dry thoroughly. Then fasten a piece of spruce gum the size of a hickory nut on the end of a stick. Heat the gum with a match and allow the drippings to fall on the leak. Spread the gum around the area with a heated knife. When the patch has dried the canoe is ready for the water.

CAR BODY REPAIR

Plastic material is applied to small scratches and dents with a wide putty knife as pictured at left. Although material works like ordinary putty, it sets very fast. Usually no more than one stroke of the putty knife is possible and for this reason material is built up above the surrounding surface and later ground off

Heretofore a gash like this in the body metal required a major repair, but with new plastic patching materials it is reduced to just a few simple steps

First step is to remove all paint and rust, exposing bare metal in and around the break. Then the metal is thoroughly cleaned to remove any loose particles

Next, a fiber patch is cut to size, dipped in solvent and laid over the opening. It is pressed quickly into place so that it will adhere to edges of opening

Then the fiber patch is coated with plastic which is built up above the surrounding surface and allowed to harden. It is then ground down to contour

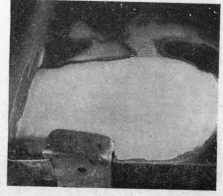

HAVE YOU BEEN wondering what to do about repairing the dents, dimples, deep scratches and breaks that appear in the body and fenders of a car after a year or so of ordinary use? The gash pictured in the center left-hand photo on the opposite page is an example of the minor damage to car bodies and fenders that can be repaired easily with new sheet-metal repair kits now available. The first step in repairing such a break is to remove all paint and rust with emery cloth or an aluminum-oxide abrasive and expose bare metal all around the break. Then a special fiber patch, included with the kit, is dipped in solvent and laid over the opening. After pressing the patch into close contact with the metal, it is coated with plastic applied with a wide putty knife. When dry, the built-up repair is smoothed and feathered at the edges with abrasive so that it takes the same contour as the original shape. Any similar break or small spot where rust has eaten through can be repaired by this method. Breaks that extend to an edge must have additional support. Such a break is shown in the upper right-hand photo which shows a cracked fender bead before repairing. This break is reinforced with a repair iron attached with stove bolts as in the detail below. The iron must be bent to the curve of the fender at the point of the break so there will be no distortion when the bolts are drawn tight. Note that the holes in the iron are countersunk, but that the holes drilled in the body metal are not. Where possible, clamp the iron in place and drill the holes in the sheet metal as at A. Then the screw or stove bolt is inserted as at B and drawn down as at C, so that the bolt head countersinks the sheet metal in the manner shown. As a final step, the bolt head is filed flush as in detail D. Ordinarily the bolts should be spaced about 1 in. apart. After filing the break flush with the surface, the repair is finished with an application of the plastic which is smoothed

A break in the metal that extends to an edge, such as this one in a fender bead, requires reinforcing with a repair iron. The latter is attached with stove bolts driven through from the outside of the fender

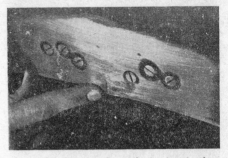

Above, after fastening the reinforcing iron in place, the bolt heads are filed flush before applying plastic. Below, here's the finished job all ready for metal primer and enamel or lacquer. Note the true contour

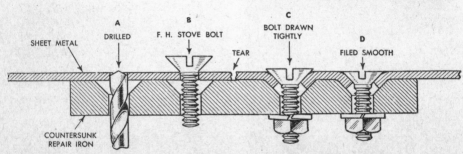

A DRILLED   B F. H. STOVE BOLT   C BOLT DRAWN TIGHTLY   D FILED SMOOTH

SHEET METAL   TEAR

COUNTERSUNK REPAIR IRON

FOUR STEPS IN MENDING TORN SHEET METAL WITH COUNTERSUNK REPAIR IRON

Above, a straightedge or flat file can be used to determine the contour. Below, although finish can be applied with a brush as shown, it is recommended that metal primer and finishing coats be sprayed on

After building up the patch with plastic on a large area check with the straightedge to locate any low spots. Level these by applying small dabs of plastic. These are ground down to contour after drying

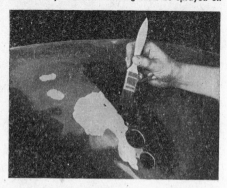

may remain from grinding. It is important that the surface of the patch be as smooth as the surrounding metal. After applying two coats of finishing material over the primer, allow it to dry thoroughly, then polish with a rubbing compound. ★ ★ ★

to contour after drying. In most cases it will be necessary to remove paint and rust from the surrounding metal in order to assure a perfect bond of the plastic filler. On some types of breaks due to rust or collision it will be necessary to straighten the metal or bring it back into contour with a dolly and bumping hammer before reinforcing and finishing with plastic. Before applying the plastic, read the directions on the container and follow these in all details. Generally you will be instructed to build up deep scratches and breaks with two or more applications. Where a repair is made on a contour, the material must be built up slightly above the surrounding surface to permit feathering the patch into the curve by grinding.

After surfacing, the patch is ready for metal priming and finishing to match the body color. This can be done with brush application but, for a professional job, rent a paint-spraying unit from your dealer and spray both the primer and the finishing coats of enamel or lacquer. Before applying the primer, go over the surface of the patch lightly with fine emery cloth, rubbing at an angle with any fine scratches that

Repairing Holes in Car Bodies Without Removing Upholstery

Small holes remaining in car and truck bodies after the removal of identification lights or spotlights can be repaired quickly from the outside without the necessity of taking off the upholstery or trim. To provide a backing for the solder which is used to fill the hole, carefully cut a sheet-metal disk slightly smaller than the diameter of the hole, and solder a 6-in. length of wire to the center of the disk. Using the

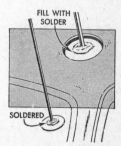

FILL WITH SOLDER

SOLDERED

wire as a handle, hold the disk in the hole barely below the outer surface of the body metal. Then fill the hole with solder and, after the solder has cooled, file or cut off the wire. Finish the new surface flush with the car body prior to painting.

CAR BRAKES

MODERN car-braking systems have been so simplified and standardized in construction that any car owner who likes to tinker can easily make ordinary repairs and adjustments himself. A simple adjustment of one or more of the four braking units, Fig. 1, renewal of shoes, adding fluid or bleeding air out of the system are usually all that is necessary. The most common symptoms of defects in the system are brakes that squeal on application, a "soft" pedal or a pedal that requires pumping in order to make a quick stop. Operation of the hydraulic service brake is quite simple and the parts are easily reached for servicing. When the brake pedal is depressed, a piston in the main, or master, cylinder, Fig. 7, exerts pressure on the fluid in the brake lines. This transfers an equalized pressure to pistons in each of the wheel cylinders, Figs. 3, 5 and 6. Each wheel cylinder contains two pistons, the purpose of the two being to distribute hydraulic pressure equally to the two brake shoes in each braking unit. As the pedal is released, the pressure is relieved and the brake-shoe retracting springs release the shoes from contact with the brake drums and, at the same time, force the pistons of the wheel cylinder inward. This movement forces fluid out of the cylinders and back into the brake lines.

Before servicing the brakes, check the

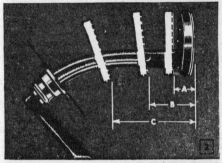

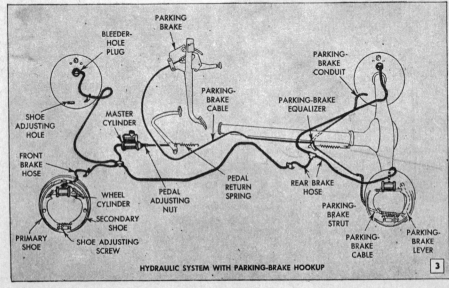

HYDRAULIC SYSTEM WITH PARKING-BRAKE HOOKUP

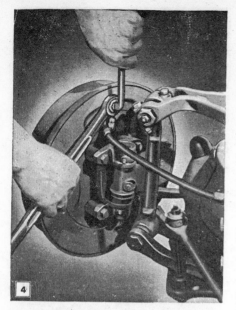

4

When new brake shoes are installed at the time of servicing, it's necessary to adjust anchor bolts. Although methods vary with different makes of brakes, the method shown above is typical of regular procedure

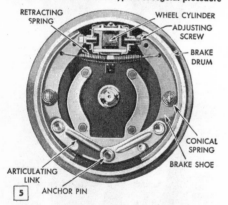

RETRACTING SPRING

WHEEL CYLINDER

ADJUSTING SCREW

BRAKE DRUM

CONICAL SPRING

BRAKE SHOE

ARTICULATING LINK

ANCHOR PIN

5

Sectional view, above, shows the hydraulic wheel cylinder and other parts of the brake unit. Below is a pull-apart view of the wheel cylinder, showing the various parts. Shown at the right is the master cylinder

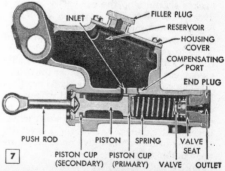

INLET

FILLER PLUG

RESERVOIR

HOUSING COVER

COMPENSATING PORT

END PLUG

PUSH ROD

PISTON

SPRING

VALVE SEAT

PISTON CUP (SECONDARY)

PISTON CUP (PRIMARY)

VALVE

OUTLET

7

ADJUSTING SCREW

COVER

PISTON

CUP

SPRING

HOUSING

CUP

PISTON

COVER

ADJUSTING SCREW

6

pedal for free movement and toeboard clearance. There should be from ¼ to ½ in. of free movement, A in Fig. 2. Full braking pressure should be available between the positions B and C. A soft, spongy pedal can mean that there is air or gas in the system or insufficient fluid. Check the fluid level in the master cylinder, add fluid if necessary and then, before bleeding the system, examine the lines carefully for leaks. In bleeding the system to remove air, it is a common rule that the longest pipe line should be bled first. Remove the bleeder valve screw, Figs. 8, 9 and 10. Then attach the bleeder drain, Fig. 8, being careful to keep the end of the bleeder drain hose below the level of fluid in the jar. Unscrew the bleeder valve one-half to three-quarters turn, depress the foot pedal by hand and then allow it to return slowly. Air in the system will show as bubbles on the surface of the fluid in the glass jar. Continue movement of the pedal until bubbles cease to appear. Then tighten the bleeder valve, remove the drain hose and replace and tighten the screw at the bleeder valve.

To adjust the brake shoes, jack up the car and block the axles so that the wheels can be turned freely. Disconnect emergency-brake pull rods and remove the adjusting-hole covers from the flange plates. On one common type of brake, these holes are located at the bottom of the flange plate as in Fig. 1. Insert a flat tool or a screwdriver in the hole. The end of the tool should engage the lugs on the adjusting cover or star wheel. Lift up on the adjusting tool to turn the star wheel to the right. Continue the adjustment on both star wheels until the brake shoes drag slightly when the road wheel is turned. Then back off the star wheel the required number of notches to give the brakes the proper running clearance. The service manual gives the proper number of notches to back the adjusting mechanism to get the correct clearance. The emergency or parking brake should be adjusted each time the service brakes are adjusted and, on some cars, it is necessary to adjust the parking brake before backing off the star wheels in the rear brakes. When new brake shoes have been installed at the time of servicing the brakes, it will be necessary to adjust all anchor bolts, Figs. 4 and 10. Although the methods will vary with different cars and makes of brakes, Fig. 4 shows the typical procedure in making this adjustment. After servicing the brakes, be sure that there is sufficient brake fluid in the master cylinder. The recommendations generally specify that it should be nearly full. Use only the brake fluid specified by the manufacturer of the car. On some late-model postwar cars, the brakes are of the self-centering, self-adjusting type. Under normal wear, this brake will not require servicing until replacement of the brake shoes is necessary. The brake automatically adjusts itself to compensate for each .005 in. of wear on the linings, keeping the running clearance always approximately the same.

To check performance of the brakes under the average driving conditions, road-test the car after the servicing has been completed. On dry, smooth concrete, the brakes should stop the car easily within a distance of 30 ft. at a speed of 20 m.p.h., Fig. 11, assuming, of course, that the tires are in good condition and have sufficient tread to grip the surface of the road effectively. This is a fair measure of brake efficiency but it is well to remember that other mechanical defects will affect good braking. Incorrect wheel alignment and wheels out of balance, worn tires, underinflation or overinflation of the tires, and worn wheel bearings are defects to look for if carefully serviced brakes do not give good performance under test.

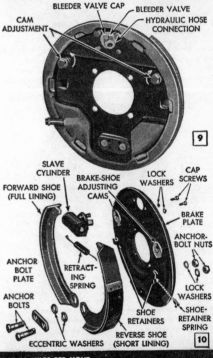

BLEEDER VALVE CAP — BLEEDER VALVE

CAM ADJUSTMENT — HYDRAULIC HOSE CONNECTION

SLAVE CYLINDER — FORWARD SHOE (FULL LINING) — BRAKE-SHOE ADJUSTING CAMS — LOCK WASHERS — CAP SCREWS — BRAKE PLATE — ANCHOR-BOLT NUTS — ANCHOR BOLT PLATE — RETRACTING SPRING — LOCK WASHERS — ANCHOR BOLTS — SHOE RETAINERS — SHOE-RETAINER SPRING — ECCENTRIC WASHERS — REVERSE SHOE (SHORT LINING)

WILL IT STOP WITHIN 30 FT. AT 20 MILES PER HOUR

CAR CLEANING

CLEANING and waxing your car must be done correctly if the results are to be satisfactory If the surface is coated with road grime or dried mud, wash it thoroughly, Fig. 3. Don't use a stream of water under high pressure. This will drive the dirt and fine grit right into the finish. Use a sprinkler head on the hose and open the valve less than halfway, directing the spray against the body at an angle. If you don't have a hose, an ordinary sprinkling can will do. It's better and quicker than a cloth or sponge, and there's no danger of scratching the finish.

Immediately after washing and before the water dries on the surface, take up the surplus water with a chamois, Fig. 4. Then let the surfaces dry and you're ready for the wax. Use either the liquid or paste form. If you have time to polish your car frequently, liquid wax is your best bet as it takes less time to apply. However, it may not last as long as the paste. If you clean up the car occasionally, the paste wax is best as it leaves a thick coating that will protect the finish longer than the liquid wax. Both the applicator cloth and the polishing cloth should be of a coarse mesh, such as cheesecloth, or open-mesh polishing material which is woven especially for the purpose. You can obtain this cloth inexpensively at service stations and auto accessory stores. Never use an or-

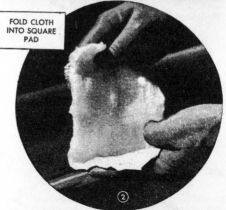

FOLD CLOTH INTO SQUARE PAD

THOROUGH WASHING IS IMPORTANT

Dry with a chamois

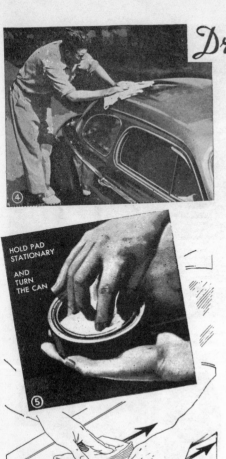

HOLD PAD STATIONARY

AND TURN THE CAN

WAX

POLISH

POLISHING STROKES SAME DIRECTION AS WAXING STROKES

ILLINOIS 1941
292·092

⑦ BE SURE THE CHROMIUM IS DRY

dinary cloth of tight weave for the surface will quickly glaze over, making it impossible to apply the wax or polish it to a high luster. The applicator cloth should be folded into a pad of five or six thicknesses and about 4 in. square, Fig. 2. Take care that no abrasive particles get on the cloth and scratch the finish.

Apply the liquid wax according to the manufacturer's directions. A cloudy, humid day is best for waxing a car as the wax does not dry too rapidly. If you must do it on a clear, dry day, work in the shade. While polishing, shake out the cloth pad frequently to remove the powdery accumulation, refolding to the same size and thickness. Polish with long, uniform strokes as in Fig. 8. Excessive pressure while rubbing is unnecessary. Both liquid waxes and polishes have the property of removing a certain amount of road film and dust as they are applied. Unless the car is badly spotted with mud it will not be necessary to wash it each time you shine it. Simply wipe off the dust with a soft, dry cloth of the open-mesh kind; tightly woven cloth rubbed over grit is likely to cause scratches. Tightly-woven cloth has more of a tendency to pick up and retain tiny particles of grit, which then act as an abrasive.

Applying the paste waxes is just as simple and easy, if you watch the details carefully. There's no necessity for making a hard, tiresome job of it. You use the same applicator and polishing cloths, but with the paste waxes the applicator pad must be wet with water and then wrung out. In picking up the wax with the pad, hold the latter stationary and turn the can as in Fig. 5. Don't press hard on the pad, just lightly, so that it will pick up only a small quantity at a time. Now apply the wax in light, straight strokes as in Fig. 6, covering only a small panel; never more than 2 or 3 sq. ft. at a time. Then immediately— and this is the trick—follow with a dry cloth to spread the film of wax uniformly, picking up any excess. Have the applicator pad in one hand and the "following cloth" in the other as in Fig. 1. Let the wax stand for a minute or so while you're applying some to another small area. Then

Polish with long strokes

rub down the first with a clean, dry, polishing cloth. You'll find that it takes only a few long, sweeping strokes to give a glass-smooth surface and a high luster. Don't bear down hard on the polisher. Continue the same procedure and watch the timing between operations. That's the important thing in handling paste wax. If it gets a bit too dry before polishing, simply go over the area lightly with the applicator and polish down immediately. Or, if it does not dry fast enough, causing the cloth to stick and drag slightly, wait a little longer before polishing. On curved surfaces such as in Fig. 10, you can save yourself a lot of extra work by rubbing across them at right angles to the curve instead of up and down, or the long way of the curve.

Chromium-plated surfaces are waxed in the same way as the body, Fig. 7. If you've washed the car, be sure the chromium is thoroughly dry, otherwise you'll have trouble in getting a uniform coating. Drops of water will collect on the lower edges and overhanging surfaces, and keep the wax from adhering and spreading uniformly over the plated surfaces.

Wax and polish the dash and interior trim last, Fig. 9. Use a smaller pad and apply the wax sparingly. On older cars that have not been polished for some time, and the finish is dulled and roughened, you'll have more work renewing it. First comes a thorough washing. Follow with a prepared cleaner, which comes in both paste and liquid forms, to remove the loosened pigment and discoloration. Cleaners are usually mild abrasives, so handle them carefully on corners and edges. Apply with a pad of the same cloth you use for the wax, rub lightly, and stop when the finish begins to brighten up to its original color. After you've gone over the car, wash it with a gentle spray from the sprinkler head and dry with a chamois. If there are still some dull spots use some cleaner and again wash away all traces of it. Washing with a sponge and neutral soap after the first cleaner application often helps. Then wash the whole car thoroughly to remove the soap. Although it will still be dull the finish should come back to a fairly uniform color after this treatment. Under

WAX THE INTERIOR LAST

ON CURVED SURFACES RUB ACROSS NOT UP AND DOWN

these conditions the paste wax is best, although either the liquid wax or the polishes will give good results. Likely it will take two or more applications to build up a uniform luster. Proceed in the same way as you would with a newer car, except that possibly you will have to change applicator cloths more often as they are likely to become charged with loosened pigment and glaze over.

CAR COOLING SYSTEM

GET RID OF WINTER'S RUST AND SCALE

✓ CHEMICAL FLUSH THE RADIATOR

✓ REVERSE FLUSH RADIATOR CORE

✓ REVERSE FLUSH ENGINE JACKET

✓ CHECK THERMOSTAT OPERATION

✓ EXAMINE WATER HOSE FOR DEFECTS

✓ INSPECT THE FAN BELT FOR PLAY

✓ BLOW OUT THE RADIATOR CORE

✓ LOOK FOR WATER-PUMP LEAKAGE

Check ✓

SPRING means cooling system time—time to "clean house" on rust and scale and to take this eight-point precaution against **overheating** —the costly penalty of engine neglect. It's corrosion—rust, lime and grease left by hard winter driving—that retards heat dissipation and becomes the unsuspected cause of scored pistons, bearings and cylinder walls, burned valves and warped and cracked engine blocks. So play safe and guard the motor against these costly repairs by cleaning the cooling system regularly.

Chemical flushing: Draining the radiator of antifreeze and then simply flushing with water is not enough. A good cleaner is needed first to loosen the rust and scale. Such deposits act as an insulator and, if allowed to build up, may in time clog the fine water passages of the radiator. There are a number of efficient cleaning compounds on the market. Alkali-type cleaners, such as washing soda, are not entirely effective. They cut grease and sludge but have no solvent action on hard rust. Be cautious and select one that does not contain strong acids or caustics which might be harmful to the radiator core, and be especially careful if your motor is fitted with aluminum cylinder heads. Some chemicals used in cleaning preparations to loosen scale will also attack aluminum and damage the heads severely in a short time. After the cooling system has been drained, close both drain cocks and add the cleaner as in Fig. 1. Then refill and clean according to the directions.

Reverse-flushing core: The loosened particles are removed from the radiator most effectively by reverse flushing, that is, flushing in the direction opposite to that of the normal flow of water through the cooling system. This is done by first replacing the radiator cap, opening both drain cocks and disconnecting the lower and upper hoses. As shown in Fig. 5, the flushing is done from below and a drain hose is attached to the top. A satisfactory job of flushing can be done with a garden hose as shown in Fig. 2, although a more thorough cleaning is assured with a flushing gun which combines air pressure with water to

Don't be a Mr. Put-it-off. Make this eight-point inspection now and be ready for hot months ahead with a "cool" cooling system

increase the scouring action and send the water through the system in forceful spurts. If such a gun is not available, a garageman will do the flushing job for you. However, be sure that you remove the thermostat beforehand, as cold water will cause it to close and build up harmful pressure. Flush until the water runs clear.

Reverse-flushing jacket: The same thing is done now to the water jacket, Fig. 3, which flushes the particles out through the water pump in the manner shown in Fig. 5. Attach a drain hose to the water-pump inlet, insert the gun at the top and flush as before. Some cars require removal of the water pump before pressure flushing to avoid unseating the pump sealing washer and forcing water into the pump bearings. If the car has a water heater, it should be flushed out too, as rust particles will form in the heater core as they do in the radiator.

Thermostat test: After flushing, make sure that the thermostat is functioning properly. Normally, this can be checked by the gauge, but an accurate test can be performed by suspending the thermostat in water heated somewhat above the rated temperature, which is usually

Here's how rust, boiled out of water jacket, can build up to obstruct the radiator tubes

Test thermostat's working order. Gummy one that fails to open causes overheating

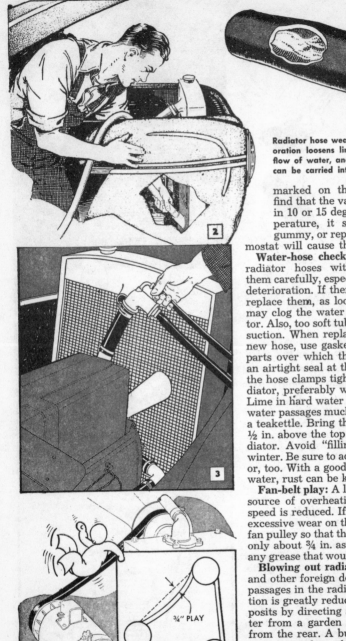

Radiator hose wears out too. Gradual deterioration loosens lining which may retard the flow of water, and particles of rotted rubber can be carried into radiator water passages

marked on the thermostat. If you find that the valve fails to open within 10 or 15 degrees of the rated temperature, it should be cleaned, if gummy, or replaced, as a faulty thermostat will cause the engine to overheat.

Water-hose checkup: Don't replace the radiator hoses without first examining them carefully, especially on the inside, for deterioration. If there are signs of rotting, replace them, as loose particles of rubber may clog the water passages of the radiator. Also, too soft tubing may collapse from suction. When replacing either the old or new hose, use gasket shellac on the metal parts over which the hose slips to assure an airtight seal at this point, and draw up the hose clamps tightly. Now, refill the radiator, preferably with soft or rain water. Lime in hard water causes scale to form in water passages much the same as it does in a teakettle. Bring the water level to about ½ in. above the top of the tubes in the radiator. Avoid "filling" either summer or winter. Be sure to add a can of rust inhibitor, too. With a good active inhibitor in the water, rust can be kept to a minimum.

Fan-belt play: A loose fan belt is another source of overheating. If it slips, the fan speed is reduced. If it is too tight, there is excessive wear on the bearings. Adjust the fan pulley so that the belt can be depressed only about ¾ in. as in Fig. 4, and wipe off any grease that would cause the belt to slip.

Blowing out radiator: With dirt, insects and other foreign deposits clogging the air passages in the radiator core, heat dissipation is greatly reduced. Force out such deposits by directing a strong stream of water from a garden hose through the core from the rear. A bug screen is a good investment to keep these passages open.

Water-pump leakage: The water pump can be guilty of rust formation, too, by allowing air to enter the cooling system through a leaking packing gland. Oxygen in the air mixing with the cooling water in-

Cooling system suffers when fan belt is too loose. Both fan and water pump do their best when belt has ¾-in. play. Tight belt wears bearings prematurely

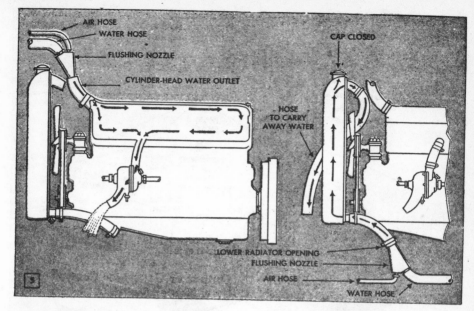

AIR HOSE
WATER HOSE
FLUSHING NOZZLE
CYLINDER-HEAD WATER OUTLET
CAP CLOSED
HOSE TO CARRY AWAY WATER
LOWER RADIATOR OPENING
FLUSHING NOZZLE
AIR HOSE
WATER HOSE

creases rusting of the metal parts. Also, besides losing water along the pump shaft, air sucked in at this point causes a turbulent bubbling action of the water which results in loss through the overflow pipe and consequent overheating. Check for leakage while the engine is running, and repack the gland if necessary. Don't overlook grease and dirt on the engine. Even a thin accumulation acts as insulation and reduces heat radiation. Use a good grease remover, but avoid inflammable solutions and do the job outdoors. Don't start the engine before it has dried thoroughly. A loose cylinder head or a damaged gasket will allow gases, which contain strong corrosive acids, to enter the cooling system and speed the formation of rust. A telltale indication that leaks have developed is the presence of a rusty stain along the seam. Tightening the cylinder-head bolts sometimes will stop such a leak. However, if the gasket is actually broken, it should be replaced. In taking up on the bolts, care should be used to avoid cracking the head by tightening it unevenly. Check the front and rear of the engine water jacket and cylinder-head joint, and also the underside of the bottom tank of the radiator. Internal leaks may not be serious enough to cause loss of liquid into the cylinder or crankcase, but they may allow loss of gas from the combustion chamber into the water jacket. While this is not too serious, it's the gas bubbles in the water jacket that displace liquid and consequently raise the water level above the overflow.

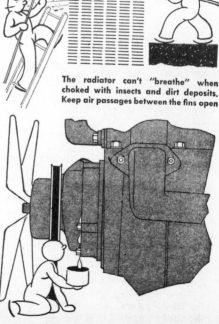

The radiator can't "breathe" when choked with insects and dirt deposits. Keep air passages between the fins open

Watch for possible leaks at the water-pump packing gland. Air sucked in at this point causes water to foam excessively, resulting in loss through overflow

CAR'S ELECTRICAL SYSTEM

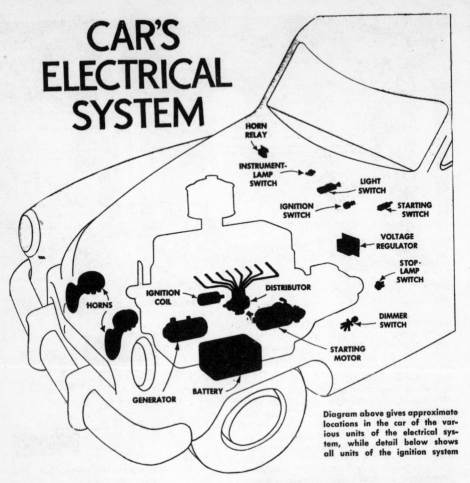

HORN RELAY

INSTRUMENT-LAMP SWITCH

LIGHT SWITCH

IGNITION SWITCH

STARTING SWITCH

VOLTAGE REGULATOR

STOP-LAMP SWITCH

IGNITION COIL

DISTRIBUTOR

DIMMER SWITCH

HORNS

STARTING MOTOR

GENERATOR

BATTERY

Diagram above gives approximate locations in the car of the various units of the electrical system, while detail below shows all units of the ignition system

KEEPING the electrical system of your car operating at peak efficiency makes a "healthy car" just as a healthy nervous system in your own body makes you feel well; the two are comparable as they both produce the stimulus to make other parts function. Also, both are highly complex and sensitive and are easily thrown out of balance with detrimental results to the parts that depend on them.

Unlike the human nervous system, however, the car electrical system can be understood, adjusted and repaired by the car owner to keep it at peak efficiency.

Often the terms "electrical system" and "ignition system" are confused. Actually the ignition system is only a branch of the electrical system. The diagram above shows the approximate locations of the parts of

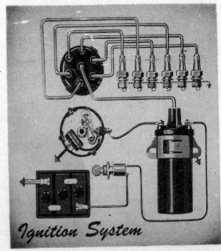

Ignition System

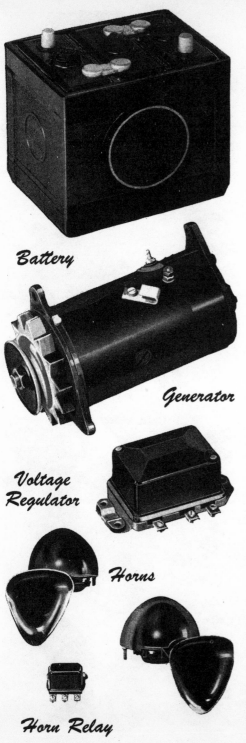

Battery

Generator

Voltage Regulator

Horns

Horn Relay

the electrical system and the diagram below it shows the part of the electrical system that is called the ignition system. The units composing the basic electrical system, which are pictured on this and the following page, are the battery, generator, coil, distributor, condenser, starting motor, voltage regulator, spark plugs, switches and relays. To these basic units are added the horns, lights, radio and other accessories.

The ignition system, which handles the job of actually firing the fuel charge in the engine cylinders, includes the battery, coil, distributor, condenser, spark plugs and wiring. With the exception of the battery, these units carry high-voltage current, stepped up from a low six volts by the coil to more than 14,000 volts. This high voltage is necessary in order to make the current jump the gap between the spark-plug electrodes and produce a hot spark to fire the gasoline.

Again, comparing the electrical system to the human body, the battery and generator can be considered the heart of the system, the battery storing the electrical energy and the generator producing it.

The battery performs three functions. First, it supplies current for the starting motor and the ignition system when cranking the engine. Second, it intermittently supplies current for lights, radio, heater and other accessories when the electrical demand of these devices exceeds the output of the generator, or when generator output is not available. Third, the battery acts as a voltage stabilizer in the electrical system. Your car cannot operate dependably unless the battery performs each of these functions satisfactorily. Since the battery can supply the electrical needs only for relatively short periods, it is necessary to provide some other means of carrying the electrical load most of the time. This job is handled by the generator, which performs two functions. It supplies all the current needed for operation of the engine and accessories, and produces the electrical energy stored in the battery.

Since the battery and the generator act as a team to provide electrical current whenever needed, it is essential that some type of control be provided between them to coordinate their efforts. This service is performed by the voltage regulator, which is known as the policeman of the electrical system. This unit protects voltage-sensitive units of the electrical system and prevents the battery and generator from damaging each other. When the generator is operating at charging speed, the regulator permits current to flow to the battery to recharge it, but it limits the voltage of the generator so that the battery will not be overcharged. It also limits the total output of the generator, when necessary, to prevent overloading. When the generator slows below charging speed, the regulator automatically breaks the battery-generator circuit to prevent a reverse flow of current from the battery to the generator.

The ignition coil acts as the booster for the system. Its job is simply to step up the primary voltage supplied by the battery or the generator into a high-voltage surge, capable of igniting the gasoline vapor in the cylinders. Essentially, it is a transformer.

The ignition distributor is the brain of the system. It times the high-voltage surge supplied by the coil and directs it to the proper spark plug at exactly the right instant to fire each cylinder in its proper turn.

Included in the distributor is a small but indispensable item known as the condenser. It has but one duty and that is to provide a place where primary current can flow until the distributor contact points are safely apart each time they open. This is necessary to prevent a voltage-sapping arc as the points first begin to separate.

The cranking motor, or starter, as it is commonly called, performs only one job—that of cranking the engine.

The spark plugs provide an electrical gap in the firing chamber of each cylinder, across which the high-voltage surge can jump, igniting the gasoline vapor, which explodes and drives the piston.

In modern gasoline engines the task performed by the ignition system is staggering to the imagination. For instance, on an eight-cylinder passenger car, the system must produce and distribute 12,-000 high-voltage surges per car mile. At 90 miles per hour the ignition system is delivering 300 ignition sparks every second. This means that the entire system must go through its complete cycle of ignition each 3/100 part of a second.

It is readily apparent, therefore, that anything which can be done to keep the electrical-system units in tiptop condition will be a tremendous aid to better car performance. You will be surprised how much you can do, at home, along this line. The first unit to be described next month will be the storage battery.

A knowledge of how the battery operates will enable you to care for it properly, thus increasing its life as well as making car-starting much easier.

Photos and information courtesy Delco-Remy Division, General Motors Corp.

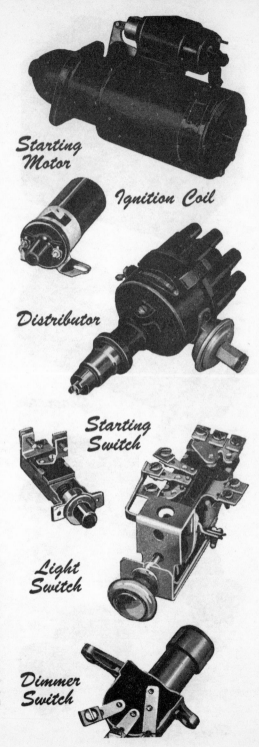

Starting Motor

Ignition Coil

Distributor

Starting Switch

Light Switch

Dimmer Switch

Car Key Pops Out

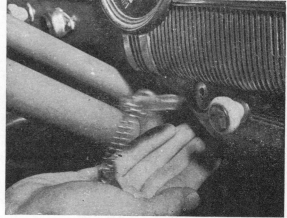

Homemade spring ejector tosses it into your hand when you turn off ignition.

LEAVING the ignition key in your car invites theft—and may lock you out. But this ejector won't let you forget. It pops the key out into your hand when you switch off the ignition.

The ejector can be made from plastic tubing having an inside diameter 1/16" larger than the width of the key blade. The length can vary, but it should be about 2".

Starting ¼" from the end of the tube, cut two longitudinal slots, one directly opposite the other. A hand grinder is ideal for this, but a knife with a good point can be used. Make the slots wide enough so the key will not bind. Smooth the edges.

Using a drill slightly larger than the tubing, countersink a blind hole in a piece of scrap wood. Heat the end of the tube in hot water and press it into the wood hole with a twisting motion. Repeat until the tube is crimped enough to keep a compression spring from falling through.

Assemble the ejector by inserting the spring, compressing it, and then sliding in the key. Put a key chain into a hole drilled through the tubing near the back end.

When you put the key into the ignition, you automatically compress the spring. With the ignition on the key stays in.

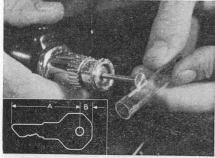

A HAND GRINDER makes quick work of forming slots in plastic tubing. Dimension A of key determines slot length. At distance B from end of slot, drill hole for key chain.

INSERT KEY through short compression spring. End of plastic tube must be crimped to retain spring. If the spring you have is too long, cut it to about six turns.

CAR PAINTING

Painting makes the old car a lot easier to look at and adds many dollars to its trade-in value

TO PAINT, or not to paint. Likely you've considered the question, but after another studied look at the battered old bus, you decided that a commercial paint job was too expensive and a home job too complicated. But the motor and other mechanical parts seem to be in good condition, so maybe it does deserve a new paint job. Also keep in mind that painting will add a hundred dollars or so to trade-in value. So, if you are willing to take a little extra care in the preparation of a good painting surface, use the right paint and approved methods of application, you'll finish up with a paint job that'll make you wonder for a while whether this is really your car.

Preparation's the thing. At the start, take off all parts that can be readily removed such as the radiator grille, Fig. 1, and cover all other areas you don't want the paint to hit, with masking tape, Figs. 6, 7 and 9. Perhaps the most tedious part of the whole job is "bumping" out deep scratches and dimples that every car body suffers after several years of use. Usually it will pay to have the worst of the bends and dents taken out by a reputable body shop. But you can level shallow fender dents with a bumping hammer and dolly block. This job gets easier after you try it. In treating an ordinary shallow fender dent, the trick is to begin at the edge of the depression and work inward. Easy on the hammer does it. No hard blows, just a light tapping, and always taking the hammer blow on the dolly held against the opposite side of the metal. With this simple procedure you can iron out ordinary body and fender dents without leaving a trace. Usually there'll be rust spots along the lower edges of the fenders and doors. These can be sanded out by hand, Fig. 3, or removed with a motor-driven disk sander, Fig. 2. For hand work

First step in preparation is to remove all the bright work, such as radiator grille, head-lamp rims and hub caps

A motor-driven disk sander helps a lot in preparing a good surface for either enamel or lacquer

You can do all the sanding and smoothing by hand where the body and fender metal is in good shape

After sanding do a thorough job of cleaning body and fenders, using a cleaner made especially for the purpose

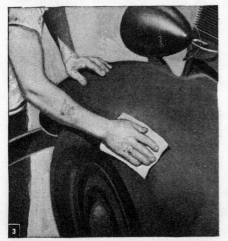

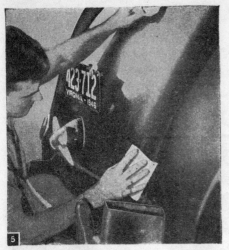

5

In cleaning up, pay special attention to exposed portions of the rear deck, for here's where dirt collects

6

Above, mask glass and trim, using masking tape to cover small parts and to hold newspapers as below

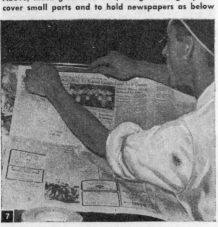

7

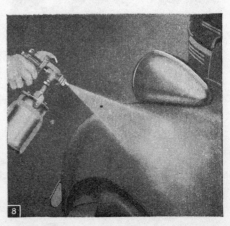

8

use No. 100 dry sandpaper and for the machine No. 80 grit. In using the machine, watch the work closely for the high-speed disk cuts very fast. Finish all sanded areas with No. 240 grit. Then go over the whole body with a prepared cleaner as in Figs. 4 and 5 to remove the accumulated road grime and loose pigment from the original paint coats and also any grease that may be on the surface. Next, any areas where the metal has been bared in the preparatory steps will need to be primed before the final painting or lacquering. Use either an enamel or lacquer primer depending on which you are going to use for the finish.

Most ordinary quick-drying, self-leveling enamels used in car finishing can be applied with a brush without any trouble with brush marks or laps. It takes these finishes nearly an hour to dry dust free so precautions against dust must be taken. One of the best ways to do this is to work with the car in the garage. Then, just before you begin painting, spray the floor with water and go over the car with a painter's tack rag. Plan the procedure so that you can finish all the large surfaces without any lapse of time. In painting the top, for example, keep working back and forth across the width. Don't paint half the top area and then the other, because the edge of the painted area you have just covered will have started to set and you'll likely have some trouble getting a smooth lap. On the large surfaces always finish the work to the edge before you stop. Lay the enamel on with a well-filled brush, using short strokes and light pressure and do not brush it out as you would an oil paint. Be careful at the lower edges of the fenders that the brush does not pick up dirt or sand. It's a good idea to wipe or brush these lower edges before you bring the enamel down to them. Although enamel sets dust free in an hour or so, the job

should not be touched or the car moved for at least 48 hours after you've finished enameling. Then wait two weeks before you do any polishing, or "compounding" as it is sometimes referred to in body shops. Actually, there's little need for a preparatory rubbing on an enameled job. Just wipe it with a soft cloth at the end of a couple weeks and wax in the regular way.

A lacquer job requires application of a lacquer undercoater or sealer, made especially for the purpose. Both the undercoater and the lacquer are applied with a spray gun, Fig. 8. In spraying you don't have to be quite so particular about laps as the sprayed coat is much thinner. However, there are several tricks in handling a spray gun that one should know about. First, dilute both the undercoater and the lacquer exactly as the manufacturer directs for spray-gun use, be sure that the gun is clean and properly adjusted, then, in spraying vertical surfaces, hold the gun level about 6 to 8 in. from the surface and make sweeping back-and-forth strokes, releasing the trigger at the end of each stroke to avoid "piling" up the sprayed material at the edges of the area being covered.

Don't use a circular or zigzag stroke except possibly where it is necessary to cover small irregular-shaped objects. Hold the gun at an angle of about 45 degrees when working on horizontal surfaces. As in hand brushing, finish up small areas at a time. Don't spray-paint one side of the car from end to end and then the other side the same way, but rather finish the hood, a fender or a door panel separately. Take the same precautions against dust as in hand brushing. If you work inside the garage even more elaborate precautions are sometimes necessary as the air blast from a spray gun will raise dust several feet away. Sprinkle everything nearby thoroughly and go over every part of the car with a tack rag before beginning work. If you work inside, wear an approved respirator. Although the quick-drying lacquers permit application of a second or third coat almost immediately, be sure that the material is thoroughly dry before applying another coat. Finish the whole car with one coat before applying the second to any part. Two to three coats of lacquer will be sufficient to produce a good job. Finish up by waxing in the regular way.

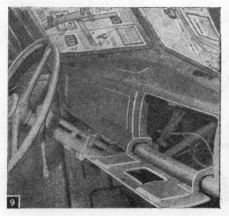

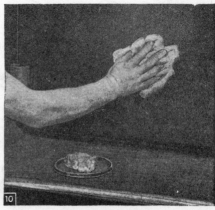

CAR SPRINGS

ALTHOUGH repairing or replacing a broken or damaged spring is a simple job, waiting for your turn to have it repaired may take several days. Rather than have your car or light truck out of service for this length of time, why not install the spring yourself? Figs. 2 to 6 inclusive detail the usual procedure in removing a spring. If the spring is to be replaced, or if it is necessary to replace the main leaf, it's important to know the exact length. Fig. 1 shows how to measure it correctly. Before loosening any of the parts or jacking up the car, block both the front and rear wheels securely. Use a roll-away jack if the work is done on a level floor. Assuming that a rear spring is to be removed, place the jack against the frame about 6 in. ahead of the spring. Raise the car until the spring assumes the normal "free" arch when tension due to weight of the car is removed. Wheels should not leave the floor. Block up under the frame at a point near the jack. Disconnect the shock absorber if it interferes. Then remove the U-bolts, Fig. 2, and the front and rear shackle pins to free the

eyes of the spring. On some late-model cars, such as Nash and Hudson, the emergency-brake cable is clipped onto the spring. In this case it will be necessary to cut the clip bolt and replace it with a new one when the spring is installed.

Installing a spring after servicing or repairing it is just as easy as the removal if the correct procedure is followed. Figs. 7 to 10 inclusive detail the first steps. Arrange the spring leaves on a table according to size and length. If the center holes of the leaves are not equally distant from the ends, be sure before installing the center bolt that the long ends face the same way. Align the leaves with a straight pin or rod of the same diameter as the bolt, Fig. 7. Don't attempt to draw up the loose leaves with the center bolt; you are very likely to strip the threads. With the pin in place, tighten the spring in a heavy vise as in Fig. 8, or with C-clamps as in Fig. 9. Remove the pin and install the

1 LENGTH OF SPRING   MAIN LEAF

7

2 U-BOLT

SHACKLE

4

CHAIN

PRY BAR

8

SEPARATOR

5

SHACKLE BUSHINGS

9

6

3 PROPER POSITION OF WHEEL

10

bolt as in Fig. 10. On overslung springs, the head of the center bolt should be on the short-plate side of the spring, but on underslung springs the head of the bolt should bear on the main leaf. Any projection of a new bolt beyond the nut after tightening, Fig. 10, should be cut off. Align the center-bolt head as in Fig. 18. The spring clips may now be installed, Figs. 11 to 14 inclusive. Place the U portion of the clip in proper position, with the nib fitting into the rivet hole. Apply the saddle so that the ends of the lower plate extend through the upper openings. Hammer down both ends firmly. Remove the clamps and the job is done.

When placing the spring back in position, be sure that you have it "right end to" so the car or truck axle will be in the correct position, Fig. 3. If the center bolt is in the center of the spring, and the eyes or bushings are the same at both ends, then there's nothing to worry about. But one must watch for springs with different eyes or bushings which must be matched with the shackles, to get the right end forward. Also some springs are made with the center bolt off-center. Sometimes this off-center distance is so small you won't notice it unless you measure carefully. Ex-cept in a few instances, the short end of such a spring is always installed toward the front. Generally, the swinging shackle has ample freedom of movement so that assembly is easy. But for cars with U-shackles a separator must be used to keep the eye of the spring in position, Fig. 5. Also, it sometimes is necessary to place a jack under the spring near the center bolt and spread or flatten the spring sufficiently to bring the eye within reach of the shackle. Then with a pry bar and chain arranged as in Fig. 4 the spring can be brought into position so that the shackle will slip in place. If shackles are of the type shown in Fig. 6, place the shackle link on the stud of the perch bushing and line up with the spring-bushing stud. With a wrench turn the spring stud so that the opening in the link will fit over the squared section of the stud. Then turn on the nuts, tighten, and install cotter pins.

On Ford, Lincoln and Studebaker cars it is necessary to use a spring spreader made from a length of pipe and a threaded rod as in Fig. 16. When removing worn or defective perch bushings on Ford, Mercury and Lincoln cars use a bushing remover made from a cold chisel, Fig. 17. Regrind the edge as indicated. Install the rebound clips, Fig. 18. Tighten the U-bolt nuts in the order given in Fig. 19, drawing each nut a little at a time until tight.

Courtesy Maremont Automotive Products, Inc.

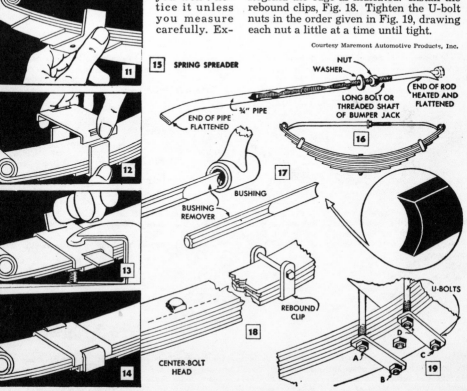

11

12

13

14

CENTER-BOLT HEAD

15 SPRING SPREADER

END OF PIPE FLATTENED

¾" PIPE

NUT
WASHER

LONG BOLT OR THREADED SHAFT OF BUMPER JACK

END OF ROD HEATED AND FLATTENED

16

17

BUSHING

BUSHING REMOVER

REBOUND CLIP

18

U-BOLTS

A   B   C   D

19

12-POINT SPRING INSPECTION

In most cases auto or truck springs do not break suddenly or unexpectedly. Rather they tend to deteriorate gradually by processes of metal fatigue. Usually a "tiring" spring will give you plenty of warning with such common symptoms as you see illustrated in detail below

Courtesy Maremont Automotive Products, Inc.

A low corner is almost sure to mean a broken spring or one that allows the body of the car to sag because of several cracked leaves

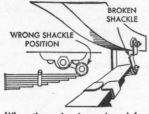

When the spring is weakened for any reason it pushes the shackle out of position. A broken shackle will eventually result from this

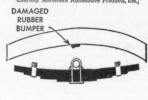

"Striking through" damages the rubber frame bumper. This not only indicates spring fatigue but sooner or later ruins the bumper entirely

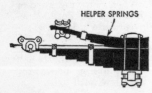

Should the helper springs touch the brackets when the truck is empty, the main springs should be replaced or repaired immediately

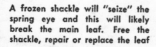

A frozen shackle will "seize" the spring eye and this will likely break the main leaf. Free the shackle, repair or replace the leaf

A "wrapped" spring is usually due to "rabbit" starts or repeated sudden, violent stops. Causes rapid axle wear due to misalignment

Worn bushings cause annoying knocks and rattles that are hard to locate unless you know symptoms. New bushings are the remedy

If the ends of the spring leaves cut in due to heavy loading, the spring will be weakened because of reduced thickness of the metal

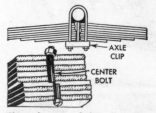

Sheared center bolts allow the spring leaves to shift. This quite often loosens the axle clip and causes breakage of entire spring

Broken rebound clips also permit the leaves to shift. This often has the effect of shifting the loading, causing springs to wrap or break

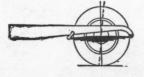

A sagged or broken front spring amounts to much the same thing as a shift in wheel alignment. It results in excessive wear on the tires

Defective shock absorbers can cause plenty of spring troubles, too. Keep them in good working order by periodic service and inspection

Keep Your Car Riding Like New

Straight-line steering and smooth riding qualities built into your car are retained by regular servicing of springs

CAR CHASSIS AND BODY

WHEELS AND AXLES

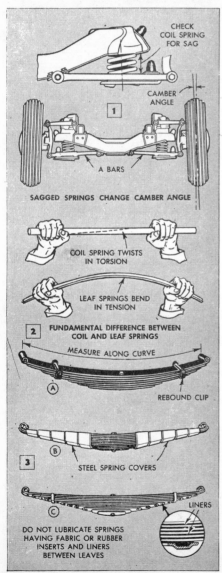

CHECK COIL SPRING FOR SAG

CAMBER ANGLE

1

A BARS

SAGGED SPRINGS CHANGE CAMBER ANGLE

COIL SPRING TWISTS IN TORSION

LEAF SPRINGS BEND IN TENSION

2 FUNDAMENTAL DIFFERENCE BETWEEN COIL AND LEAF SPRINGS

MEASURE ALONG CURVE

(A)

REBOUND CLIP

3

(B)

STEEL SPRING COVERS

(C)

LINERS

DO NOT LUBRICATE SPRINGS HAVING FABRIC OR RUBBER INSERTS AND LINERS BETWEEN LEAVES

WHEN YOU hit a hole in the pavement or a bump in a side road the shock absorbers snub out rebound of the car axle but the springs take the real punishment by preventing the shock from reaching the car frame and body. Even when you're cruising on a smooth highway, the springs soften the ride by constantly flexing to equalize irregularities in the road surface. Lack of lubrication can cause rapid wear in leaf springs, and rust and metal fatigue combine to cause a slow loss of "life" in a coil-spring suspension of the type shown in Fig. 1. Under normal load conditions, spring suspensions of this type are designed to operate with the A-bars, or control arms, in approximately a level position. After years of service the springs may weaken and, in effect, shorten slightly under the body load which, of course, remains the same. This changes the normal position of the control arms and, in some cases, may even change the front-wheel camber as in the lower detail in Fig. 1. This condition can cause a serious loss in steering response and it also results in rapid wear on the tires. Often the defect can be corrected by shimming the springs with spacing washers which fit into the retaining cups at the top and bottom ends. However, if body sag is excessive, or if one spring is lower than the other, then both springs should be replaced. On some older cars it will be necessary to check steering and possibly to realign the front wheels after shimming or installing springs. On certain newer cars, coil springs may be shimmed or replaced without changing the wheel alignment. Coil springs are simply torsion bars, upper detail in Fig. 2, and any surface flaws caused by rust will weaken them. To protect coil springs against rust, keep them well painted or coated with any of the rust preventives which are available.

Leaf springs and shackles on nearly all older-model cars and trucks require lubricating at regular intervals. The method of lubricating depends on the type of spring and the provisions made by the manufacturer for applying lubricant. All leaf springs bend under tension as in the lower detail in Fig. 2 and on nearly all cars more than 10 years old the springs are of the type shown at A in Fig. 3, the ends of the spring leaves being cut square or diamond pointed as in Fig. 7. Some, however, were made with round, tapered ends on all the leaves except the top leaf, Fig. 7. On later-model cars, and on some light trucks, the leaf springs either are fitted with steel covers as at B in Fig. 3, or are of the nonlubricated type detailed at C. On the older-type springs, Fig. 3,A, it may be necessary to loosen the rebound clips and pry the leaves apart in order to apply lubricant between the leaves. Whenever such springs are lubricated always make the checks detailed in Figs. 4, 5 and 6. If measurement from the top of the spring to the lower side of the frame varies more than ¾ in., check the low spring carefully for a broken leaf or excessively worn shackle bolts. Renew faulty parts, as otherwise lubrication of the spring may increase leaf deflection and result in breakage of adjacent leaves. If possible, use the lubricant specified by the manufacturer of the car. Otherwise use chassis grease to which a small quantity of powdered graphite has been added, or use penetrating oil.

Lubrication of covered springs is easily done, without removing the metal cover, by the use of the special spring-lubricating fitting detailed in Fig. 8. On some of the late-model cars the need for lubrication of the leaf springs has been eliminated by the use of waxed fabric liners between the adjacent leaves, detail C in Fig. 3. On others, rubber "buttons" are placed under the tips of the spring leaves. The only service required on springs of this type is replacement of worn liners or buttons. This is done by jacking up the car body to take the weight off the springs. Then the leaves are pried apart with a screwdriver or a special spring spreading tool, and the worn liners or buttons are removed from the depressions in the leaf tips and replaced. On some liners, only the worn ends are renewed. This is done by wedging the leaves apart and cutting off the worn portion of the liner with a hacksaw blade. Replace with new end sections of liner fabric. When the rebound clips are removed for any reason, be especially careful when replacing them to see that they fit with the correct clearance, Figs. 5, 6 and 9. This clearance is important as it allows the main leaf to twist when the car or truck is driven diagonally across a low culvert or onto a ramp.

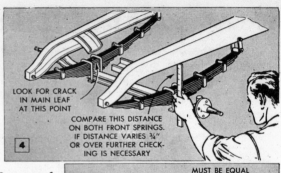

LOOK FOR CRACK IN MAIN LEAF AT THIS POINT

COMPARE THIS DISTANCE ON BOTH FRONT SPRINGS. IF DISTANCE VARIES ¾" OR OVER FURTHER CHECKING IS NECESSARY

4

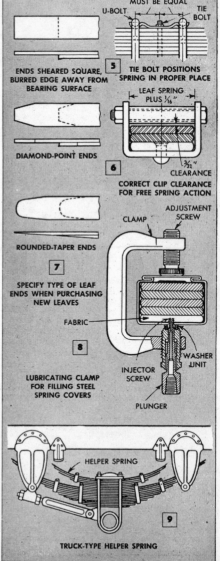

MUST BE EQUAL

U-BOLT   TIE BOLT

5 TIE BOLT POSITIONS SPRING IN PROPER PLACE

ENDS SHEARED SQUARE, BURRED EDGE AWAY FROM BEARING SURFACE

LEAF SPRING PLUS 1/16"

DIAMOND-POINT ENDS

6 CLEARANCE 3/32"

CORRECT CLIP CLEARANCE FOR FREE SPRING ACTION

ROUNDED-TAPER ENDS

7

SPECIFY TYPE OF LEAF ENDS WHEN PURCHASING NEW LEAVES

ADJUSTMENT SCREW

CLAMP

FABRIC

8

WASHER UNIT

INJECTOR SCREW

PLUNGER

LUBRICATING CLAMP FOR FILLING STEEL SPRING COVERS

HELPER SPRING

9

TRUCK-TYPE HELPER SPRING

CAR STARTER

The Electric Starter—
Operation, Care and Repair

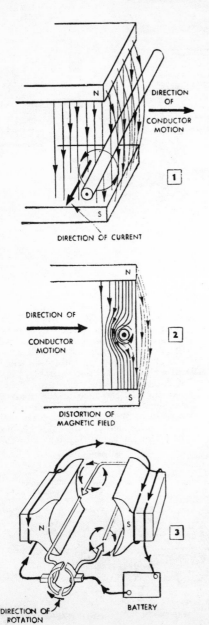

DIRECTION OF CONDUCTOR MOTION

[1]

DIRECTION OF CURRENT

DIRECTION OF CONDUCTOR MOTION

[2]

DISTORTION OF MAGNETIC FIELD

[3]

DIRECTION OF ROTATION

BATTERY

PROBABLY ONE of the units of the automotive electrical system most taken for granted is the cranking motor, or starter. Although it operates only for short periods of time compared with other parts of the car, its successful performance definitely depends on regular checking and maintenance procedures. The armature in this highly specialized unit rotates at about 1500 r.p.m. in order to crank the car engine at 100 r.p.m.

It operates on the principle that opposing magnetic fields tend to attract each other while similar magnetic fields repel each other. Fig. 1 is a simple sketch of a magnetic field from a permanent magnet in which a single conductor has been placed. Current flowing through the conductor in the direction indicated by the heavy arrow causes a magnetic field to circle the conductor as shown by the circular arrows. As a result a force is exerted on the conductor which tends to move it to the right.

Fig. 2 explains this force. The circular magnetic field around the conductor (indicated by the circular arrow) opposes the permanent magnetic field on the right side of the conductor while it aids the magnetic field to the left of the conductor. Opposition to the magnetic field on the right tends to cancel it, so there is less magnetism to the right of the conductor than there is to the left. The magnetic lines of force are thus distorted around the conductor and exert a thrust on it.

Fig. 3 is a drawing of a simple electric motor with a one-turn armature which indicates how the sidewise thrust on the conductor causes it to rotate and crank an engine. The armature is a single loop of wire suspended between two magnetic poles. The magnetic field of each pole is reinforced by the field coil wound around it. When the circuit between the battery and the motor is closed, current flows from battery through the armature loop, then through the field-coil windings and back to the battery as shown by arrows. On the left-hand side of the armature loop current is flowing in the direction of the loop arrows, which causes an upward thrust on that half of the armature. Since the current is flowing in the opposite direction through the other half of the armature, the thrust on it is downward. These opposing thrusts

The Starter

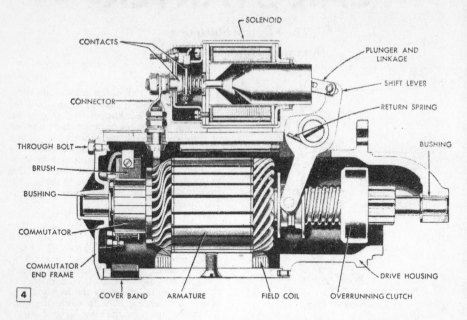

4

SOLENOID
CONTACTS
CONNECTOR
THROUGH BOLT
BRUSH
BUSHING
COMMUTATOR
COMMUTATOR END FRAME
COVER BAND
ARMATURE
FIELD COIL
PLUNGER AND LINKAGE
SHIFT LEVER
RETURN SPRING
BUSHING
DRIVE HOUSING
OVERRUNNING CLUTCH

cause the armature to rotate in a clockwise direction.

A powerful cranking torque is produced by using many windings in the armature, instead of the single loop of wire, thus multiplying the thrusts on the armature. Fig. 4 is a sectional view of a typical modern passenger-car starter.

All passenger-car starters are much the same in general design and operation, differing mainly in the type of drive used. The drive mechanism has two functions—to transmit the cranking torque to the engine flywheel and to disconnect the starter from the flywheel after the engine has started. Most passenger cars use either the Bendix or the overrunning-clutch type of drive.

A typical Bendix-drive starter is shown in Fig. 5. This drive depends upon inertia to mesh and unmesh the starter drive pinion from the engine-flywheel ring gear. When this type of starter is not operating, the pinion is out of mesh with the flywheel ring gear. As soon as the starter switch is closed, the starter armature begins to rotate and moves the pinion into mesh with the flywheel.

The overrunning-clutch type of drive, Fig. 4, is shifted

mechanically into mesh with the flywheel. This may be done directly by foot pressure on a pedal or by a solenoid switch controlled from the dashboard. Completion of the shift in either case closes the circuit between the starter and the battery. The pinion maintains contact with the flywheel ring gear until the pedal or switch is released.

Briefly, the overrunning clutch consists of a shell-and-sleeve assembly—in which is fitted a pinion-and-collar assembly, Fig. 7— that rotates with the armature. Four tapered slots in the face of the shell take spring-loaded steel rollers. When the shell is rotated by the starter motor, the rollers move into contact with the collar, jamming tightly against it and forcing it to rotate

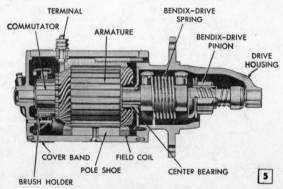

TERMINAL
COMMUTATOR
ARMATURE
BENDIX-DRIVE SPRING
BENDIX-DRIVE PINION
DRIVE HOUSING
COVER BAND
FIELD COIL
POLE SHOE
CENTER BEARING
BRUSH HOLDER

5

6

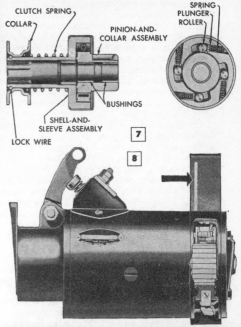

CLUTCH SPRING
COLLAR
PINION-AND-COLLAR ASSEMBLY
SPRING
PLUNGER
ROLLER
BUSHINGS
SHELL-AND-SLEEVE ASSEMBLY
LOCK WIRE

7

8

with the shell, thus cranking the engine. When the engine flywheel rotates faster than the shell, the rollers move back in the slots, disengaging the collar and shell so the shell overrides the collar and disengages the starter from the engine.

Obviously, as soon as the engine begins to operate, the starter switch or pedal should be released. Otherwise the drive pinion remains in mesh and continues to overrun the armature, which will cause overheating.

Quick checks and maintenance procedures: Armed with a working knowledge of the operation of his car's starter, a motorist can do much to assure a long and dependable life for the starter. The following trouble shooting, inspection and maintenance procedures can be followed easily without specialized equipment or tools.

To make a quick check of the starter system, turn on the headlights. If they do not burn with normal brilliance, the battery should be checked. If the battery is in a charged condition and the lights burn brightly, operate the starter. One of these things will happen to the lights: They will go out, dim considerably or stay bright with no cranking action taking place.

1. If the lights go out, there is a poor connection, which usually will be found at the battery terminals, between the battery and the starter. Correction is made by removing the cable clamps and cleaning both the clamps and terminals. After reconnecting and tightening the clamps, a corrosion inhibitor such as petroleum jelly should be applied.

2. If the lights dim considerably, the battery may be discharged or there may be some mechanical fault in the engine or starter which is throwing a heavy burden on the starter. Check the battery first. If it is in good condition, the trouble is in either the engine or the starter. In the engine, tight bearings or pistons or extra-heavy oil may be causing the added strain on the starter. Low temperatures cause engine oil to thicken and make the engine more difficult to start. Low temperatures

9

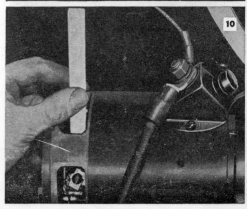

10

also lessen the effectiveness of the battery. In the starter, look for a bent armature shaft, loose pole-shoe screws or worn bearings. Any of these will cause the armature to drag and reduce starting performance.

Occasionally, more serious internal damage may be found. Thrown armature windings or commutator bars, which sometimes occur on overrunning-clutch-type starters, usually are caused by excessive overrunning after starting.

On Bendix-drive starters, broken Bendix housings and "wrapped up" Bendix springs may result if the driver closes the starter switch during engine "rock back," which occurs when the engine starts automatically, then stops again. Another cause may be engine backfire resulting from ignition timing being too far advanced. To avoid such failures, the driver should pause a few seconds after a false start to make sure the engine has come to rest completely.

Frequently, a worn pinion gear in a Bendix drive will jam into mesh with the flywheel ring gear and refuse to unmesh. If this happens, put the car in gear and manually rock it forward and backward.

3. If the lights stay bright and no starting action takes place, an open circuit at some point is indicated. This may be in the starter, in the starter switch or in the control circuit. Where the starter is operated by a solenoid switch, temporarily eliminate the solenoid circuit by placing a heavy jumper lead across the solenoid's main terminals to see if the starter will operate. This connects the starter directly to the battery. If the starter operates, the control circuit is not functioning normally. If the starter does not operate, the trouble most likely will be found in it.

Every 5000 miles, under normal operating conditions, inspect the mounting, wiring and connections to make sure they are in good condition. The magnetic switch or solenoid should be mounted firmly and should operate freely, without binding.

Next, remove the cover band so the commutator, brushes and internal connections can be checked, Fig. 6. Examine the cover band for thrown solder, Fig. 8 (arrow), which results if the starter is subjected to such excessively long cranking periods.

Check the brushes to see that they are not binding and that they are resting on the commutator with sufficient tension to give good, firm contact. Make sure brush leads and screws are tight. If the brushes are worn down to half their original length, they should be replaced.

Note the condition of the commutator. If it is glazed or dirty, it can be cleaned quickly by holding a strip of No. 00 sandpaper against it with a piece of wood, Fig. 10, while the starter is operated. A brush-

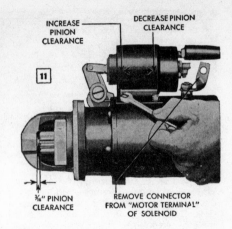

INCREASE PINION CLEARANCE

DECREASE PINION CLEARANCE

11

3/16" PINION CLEARANCE

REMOVE CONNECTOR FROM "MOTOR TERMINAL" OF SOLENOID

seating stone may be used for the same purpose. Move the sandpaper or stone across the face of the commutator as it spins. Blow out all dust after the commutator is cleaned. Always remember never to operate any starter for more than 30 seconds to maintain an accurate adjustment of the pinion clearance. Fig. 11 shows the proper method of making this adjustment. Remove the connector from the "motor" terminal of the solenoid. Place a piece of 3/16-in. bar stock or a 3/16-in. gauge between the pinion and the housing. Connect a six-volt battery across the "switch" terminal of the solenoid and the solenoid base (ground) and push the solenoid plunger in by hand. Battery current will hold the plunger in the "bottomed" position while the pinion clearance is adjusted. Loosen the solenoid-switch mounting and pull the switch away from the shift lever until play is taken out of the lever and the clutch mechanism. *Be careful not to compress the overrunning-clutch spring.* Moving switch toward the lever increases clearance; moving switch away from the lever decreases pinion clearance. Then tighten the switch-mounting screws and replace connector at "motor" terminal of the solenoid.

This adjustment must be made each time after the armature is removed from the starter for any reason. Unless it is correctly adjusted, the solenoid cannot operate properly. Starters equipped with hinge-cap oilers should have 8 to 10 drops of light oil each 5000 miles.

Some models are equipped either with oil wicks to lubricate the center and drive-end bushings or with oilless bushings. Oilless bushings should be supplied with a few drops of light engine oil whenever the starter is disassembled for repair or service.

★ ★ ★

Photos and information courtesy Delco-Remy Division, General Motors Corp.

CAR WHEELS

Like any fine mechanism, wheel bearings need attention to withstand constant use. Proper adjustment, cleaning and lubrication keep them in top condition

Kaiser-Frazer Corp. photo

Testing front-wheel bearings for looseness by rocking wheel. Do not mistake kingpin movement for wheel-bearing looseness

ROLLING contact bearings on each of the four wheels support the entire weight of a car. These bearings are expertly designed and engineered for extremely long service, and with only occasional attention they usually last for the life of the car. Under ordinary conditions, it is advisable to remove the wheels and inspect and clean the bearings at least once a year—oftener under extreme conditions.

The most common causes of bearing malfunction are: (1) rust due to worn or defective seals or condensation inside the housing; (2) worn, galled or abraded surfaces resulting from too loose a fit or dirt lock; (3) broken or bent inner ring, shields, seals or separators caused by improper or careless installation, and (4) damaged raceways, balls or rollers due to dirt or pitting by corrosion. Badly discolored balls and races indicate inadequate lubrication. Dirt or pitting by corrosion is indicated by a general roughness, and excessive looseness or end play is evidence of lapping by dirt or abrasive. Parts are a dull-gray color when lapped or abraded by dirt.

The principal parts of a ball bearing are shown in Fig. 4. Variations of this bearing will be found in the different makes of cars, but basically they are the same. Wear is virtually absent unless foreign matter finds its way into the bearing. However, any

Soft brush assists cleaning of bearings in gasoline. After washing, handle parts only when necessary

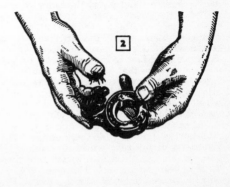

Bearing is packed with wheel-bearing grease made especially for purpose. Substitutes should not be used

abrasion or injury to the surfaces may lead to bearing failure, and hitting or dropping a bearing is likely to damage it beyond repair. Also, incorrect kind or amount of lubricant may cause heating or corrosion.

Fig. 3 shows a typical bearing arrangement for the front wheels. To service these bearings, jack up the wheel and remove the ornamental cover and hub cap, if any. Next, remove the cotter pin from the spindle nut and unscrew the nut. Pull the wheel off slightly to loosen the outer bearing and then push the wheel back in place. Carefully remove the outer bearing and place it on a clean piece of paper. The wheel can then be completely removed from the axle. Now, slip the inner bearing and grease retainer from the hub and place them on the paper also. After this, all parts, including the wheel hub and axle spindle should be thoroughly washed in white gasoline and allowed to dry, Fig. 1. Do not handle the bearings more than necessary after cleaning, as perspiration tends to corrode them. Inspect the grease retainer and brake assembly for grease leakage. As this retainer keeps the lubricant within the bearing area and away from the brakes, it should seal tightly. Inspect the bearings for wear and damaged balls or rollers and check for play between the balls and races. However, do not spin the bearing before it has been lubricated. Coat the bearings and the axle spindle with wheel-bearing grease, Fig. 2, but do not use ordinary chassis lubricant or other substitutes. If new bearings are necessary, be sure to get duplicates of the ones being discarded.

To reassemble the parts, first press the inner bearing and grease retainer into the hub. Mount the wheel on the spindle, being careful not to damage the grease retainer, and insert the outer wheel bearing, applying the spacer washer and castle nut. Rotate the wheel slowly, tighten the nut until the wheel just binds and then back off the nut slightly to insert the cotter pin. Check for bearing looseness by rocking the wheel, but first block the kingpin or have someone watch it, so that kingpin movement is not confused with bearing looseness. With the bearing properly adjusted there will be a slight drag when the wheel is turned slowly by hand. When the adjustment is right, secure the cotter pin.

The rear-wheel bearings, Fig. 5, do not require attention as frequently as those on the front wheels. The parts of the rear-wheel assembly are cleaned and the bearing checked in much the same way as those of the front wheel. However, a wheel puller will be necessary to remove the wheel. Probably a puller will also be needed for the bearing. If the bearing is lubricated by high-pressure grease fittings, be careful not to apply too much grease.

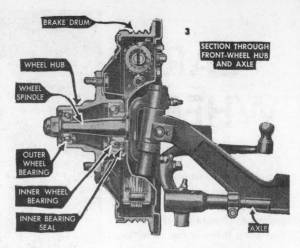

General Motors Corp. photo

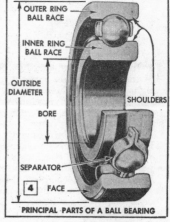

PRINCIPAL PARTS OF A BALL BEARING

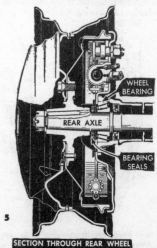

SECTION THROUGH REAR WHEEL
Diagram courtesy Packard Motor Car Co.

Carbide Tools

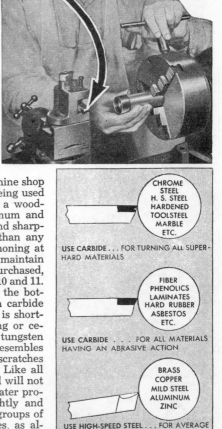

Photo courtesy Carboloy Co.

IF YOU have had the edge of a high-speed bit fold up when making the first "skin" cut on cast iron, you'll appreciate the way a carbide-tipped tool peels off the metal. This high-production cutting tool of industry can be put to work in the small machine shop as well as the home workshop. For besides being used in a tool post, it can be used freehand like a wood-turning chisel, Fig. 9, to turn brass, aluminum and plastics at wood-lathe speeds. Once ground and sharpened, carbide tools will stay sharp longer than any other cutting tool. They require only light honing at long intervals with a silicon-carbide stone to maintain the edge. Tools tipped with carbide can be purchased, or you can assemble chisels as shown in Figs. 10 and 11.

What is cemented carbide? The sketch at the bottom of the page explains cemented tungsten carbide graphically. The full-name description often is shortened to just "carbide." Cobalt is the bonding or cementing agent that binds the particles of tungsten carbide into a compact mass, which closely resembles polished steel. This metal is super hard—it scratches glass, Fig. 1, and it will cut the hardest file. Like all very hard materials, it tends to be brittle and will not stand excessive shock loads. By adding a greater proportion of cobalt, hardness is reduced slightly and toughness is increased. There are two main groups of carbide tools: The straight tungsten carbides, as already described and illustrated, and the combined

CHROME STEEL
H. S. STEEL
HARDENED
TOOLSTEEL
MARBLE
ETC.

USE CARBIDE . . . FOR TURNING ALL SUPER-HARD MATERIALS

FIBER
PHENOLICS
LAMINATES
HARD RUBBER
ASBESTOS
ETC.

USE CARBIDE . . . FOR ALL MATERIALS HAVING AN ABRASIVE ACTION

BRASS
COPPER
MILD STEEL
ALUMINUM
ZINC

USE HIGH-SPEED STEEL . . . FOR AVERAGE TURNING UNLESS YOUR LATHE IS POWERED WITH AT LEAST ¾-HP. MOTOR

TUNGSTEN (A RARE METAL)   CARBON (LAMPBLACK)   HEAT   =   TUNGSTEN CARBIDE   WITH PRESSURE AND HEAT   COBALT   =   CEMENTED TUNGSTEN CARBIDE BLANKS

4-PLACE TURRET WITH ONE CARBIDE AND 3 H. S. S. TOOLS MAKES GOOD SETUP

* SURFACE FEET PER MINUTE

SECONDARY GRINDING ANGLE

8° SIDE RAKE

END

7° SIDE CLEARANCE

10°

CARBIDE TIP — SIDE — STEEL SHANK

7° FRONT CLEARANCE

10°

TOOL BIT IS NORMALLY MOUNTED LEVEL

3

2

A rule-of-thumb speed for carbide tools is 200 s.f.m. Table at right converts this to r.p.m.

200 S. F. M.	
WORK DIA.	R. P. M.
¼	3056
½	1528
¾	1016
1	764
1¼	612
1½	508
1¾	436
2	382
2½	306
3	254
4	191
5	153
WORK 6" TO 12" DIAMETER CAN BE RUN AT 100 R. P. M.	

WORK CENTER LINE

COLLARS

4

⅜" AND ½" BITS CAN BE MOUNTED DIRECT IN TOOL POST

LEVEL TOOL HOLDER

SHIM AS NEEDED

5

STANDARD TOOL BIT SHOULD BE USED IN LEVEL-TYPE HOLDER

8° POSITIVE RAKE TOOL HOLDER

6

POSITIVE RAKE IS RECOMMENDED FOR LIGHT CUTTING

carbides, which are tungsten carbide with titanium or tantalum added. The straight tungsten carbides are used for turning all materials except steel; the combined carbides are used for steel only. The difference is that steel tends to stick or build up on straight tungsten carbide, and the addition of tantalum or titanium helps to overcome this fault. However, for light turning, any kind of carbide tool can be used successfully on any type of material.

What can carbide do? Being extremely hard, carbide turns all materials at high speeds not possible with other cutting tools. Consider a sample job: In turning 1-in. mild steel it is an easy job for carbide to turn this at 300 ft. per minute with a .010 feed and ⅛-in. depth of cut. In other words, with the lathe running at 1150 r.p.m. the tool will peel off 4½ cubic inches of metal per minute. But such a heavy cut requires a lathe powered with a 2½-hp. motor. As the average home-workshop lathe is powered with a fractional-horsepower motor, it is apparent that the full cutting capacity of carbide cannot be utilized as even a high-speed steel bit will tax the capacity of the motor.

However, there is another side to the picture. Very often you will encounter a hard piece of steel which resists turning with high-speed bits. A good example of this is where a broken high-speed drill with Morse shank is turned down to make some other tool. That's where you can use carbide. Again, take a seemingly simple job like turning a ring in phenolic plastic. Most of these plastics are filled with metal, asbestos, wood flour or other material, all very abrasive and quick to turn the edge of carbon or high-speed steel tools. Here, again, the carbide tool does the job perfectly.

Carbide is excellent, too, for turning cast iron. Cast iron does not offer the resistance of steel, hence a fair bite can be made with the work running at 200 s.f.m.

How is carbide used? Just forget you have anything special in the way of a tool bit and use carbide the same as you would high-speed steel. Assuming your

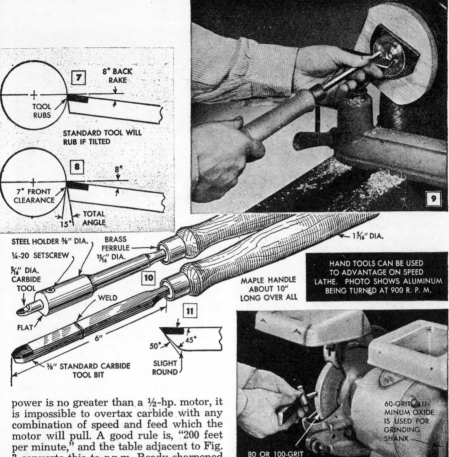

7 8° BACK RAKE

TOOL RUBS

STANDARD TOOL WILL RUB IF TILTED

8 8°

7° FRONT CLEARANCE

TOTAL ANGLE 15°

STEEL HOLDER ⅝" DIA.   BRASS FERRULE   1⅜₆" DIA.

¼-20 SETSCREW

⁵⁄₁₆" DIA. CARBIDE TOOL

10

WELD

FLAT

11

6"   50°   45°

¾" STANDARD CARBIDE TOOL BIT   SLIGHT ROUND

1⅝₆" DIA.

MAPLE HANDLE ABOUT 10" LONG OVER ALL

HAND TOOLS CAN BE USED TO ADVANTAGE ON SPEED LATHE. PHOTO SHOWS ALUMINUM BEING TURNED AT 900 R. P. M.

9

80 OR 100-GRIT SILICON CARBIDE USED FOR GRINDING TIP

60-GRIT ALUMINUM OXIDE IS USED FOR GRINDING SHANK

12

GRINDING IS PREFERABLY DONE FREEHAND AND DRY ON SUITABLE GRINDING WHEELS

power is no greater than a ½-hp. motor, it is impossible to overtax carbide with any combination of speed and feed which the motor will pull. A good rule is, "200 feet per minute," and the table adjacent to Fig. 3 converts this to r.p.m. Ready-sharpened tool bits, available in various sizes and shapes, are intended to be mounted on-center and horizontal as shown in Fig. 3. Figs. 2, 4, 5 and 6 show various mountings. Although industry uses the standard shape, Fig. 4, best results on light equipment are obtained if tool-bit angles closely pattern those of high-speed steel. A good setup is shown in Fig. 7 where the tool is given 8 degrees back rake by the angle of the tool holder. In this case, it is necessary to provide more front clearance, as can be seen in Fig. 8.

How is carbide ground? Use a silicon-carbide wheel for grinding the tip, Fig. 12, and forget anything you may have heard about carbide being tough to grind. True, it is a super-hard metal and grinds slowly, but if you keep the tool moving to grind off small facets, the carbide wheel does the trick quickly. Double angles are commonly used in grinding carbide bits. Grind the tip at the required angle and then back off

the metal shank an extra two or three degrees. With this system, light sharpening can be done on the silicon-carbide wheel without running into the shank. Use an aluminum-oxide wheel if it is necessary to undercut or grind the shank.

Hand tools: Carbide hand tools do excellent work in turning brass, aluminum and plastics, as in Fig. 9, and can be purchased ready-made in square and round-nose patterns. It is also practical to make your own tools from standard tool bits, as shown in Figs. 10 and 11. Once ground and sharpened, these turning tools will stay sharp indefinitely and require only light honing on a silicon-carbide oilstone.

CARD TABLE

Where to play when the gang comes in for an evening of cards is solved in a hurry when you have this auxiliary top, which is designed to set over an ordinary card table. Hinged at the center, it takes up little storage space in a closet, and when open, it forms a large-size playing surface. which seats eight persons comfortably. Construction consists of adding trough-like compartments around the edge of an octagon-shape centerpiece. The whole thing can be assembled as one unit and later sawed in half, or each half can be made up separately. Start by laying out and sawing the eight-sided centerpiece. The compartments are added to the edge of this by first fitting and nailing ½ by 3-in. pieces all around, mitering them where they meet at the corners. Next, the 3-in. pieces forming the bottom of the trough are nailed to the lower edge of the previous piece, mitering it as before. This is followed by fitting the outside piece, and then the trough is divided into compartments by inserting partitions at the eight points. A continuous (piano) hinge makes the neatest job, although two or three butt hinges will do. Complete the job by gluing felt to both top and bottom. Finish with enamel or varnish to match your furniture.

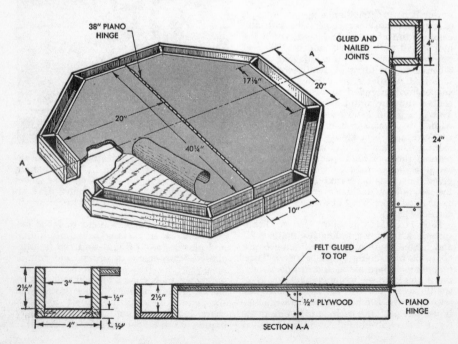

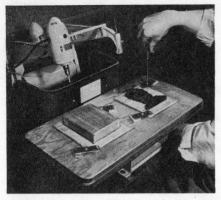 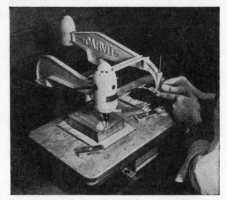

Hobbycrafters who like to do fine wood carving will get a kick out of this unusual power carver. It's set up as in the left-hand photo with a template and blank attached to a worktable. Then, as guide pin is moved over the template contour, the high-speed router duplicates detail by relief cuts in the blank

Above, left, a vibrator-type engraving tool doing a beautiful job of etching on glass. It is supplied with accessories for wood carving, embossing and tooling on leather, etc. Above, right, power carver nearing finish of the job on the blank. Below, right, the hand grinder is supplied with many accessories

CARVING

IF YOU LIKE to do wood carving or embossing and tooling on wood, glass, leather or plastic, you'll get a big kick out of these tools. The first one, a power carver, is pictured in the two upper photos and in the center, right. The tool consists of a high-speed router mounted on a parallel-arm frame so that its movement follows that of a guide pin moving over a template. By simply moving the pin over the template as shown in the upper right-hand photo, a duplicate cut is made in the blank. The contour and relief of the template is faithfully reproduced in all details as you can see from the center right-hand photo. In the center left-hand photo you see a vibrator-type engraving tool etching fine traceries on glass. This unit is supplied with accessories which enable you to do wood carving, embossing and tooling on leather and etching and engraving on plastics and metals. Several hand-grinder units of the type pictured at the lower right are supplied with accessories for grinding, drilling, wire brushing, polishing, carving, filing and buffing on small parts of wood, metal and plastic. A wide assortment of rotary files and grinding wheels is available for use with these hand-held units.

CATAMARAN

ARE you wondering what to do with those old tire tubes? There's a way to use them profitably by building this novel catamaran. It keeps you high and dry above the water and won't tip over easily.

The tubes are slipped over wooden frames after inflating, the valves being on the inside. Ample space is provided for action of the paddle. A foot-operated rudder, used in conjunction with the paddle, enables the passenger to make short turns. Although the rudder can be made of wood, using outdoor plywood for the blade, a slotted seamless-steel tube and galvanized sheet-metal blade make a better, more durable job. Curved brackets, bandsawed from ¾-in. pine, support the seat. If you want a more durable job make the whole frame from oak. In either case use screws for joining all parts. The rear brackets, being set at an angle, serve to reinforce the entire structure. Paint the wood lemon yellow, or finish hardwood in the natural color with black striping. Either way you will have a smart craft.

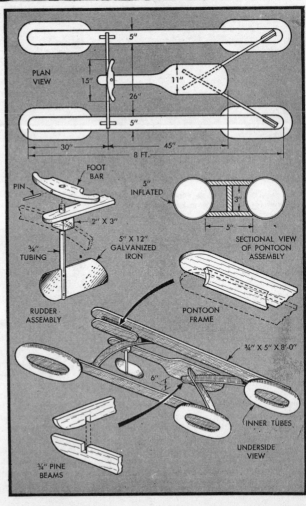

PLAN VIEW

5"
15"
26"
11"
5"
30"
45"
8 FT.

FOOT BAR

PIN

5" INFLATED

3"

5"

2" X 3"

¾" TUBING

5" X 12" GALVANIZED IRON

RUDDER ASSEMBLY

SECTIONAL VIEW OF PONTOON ASSEMBLY

PONTOON FRAME

¾" X 5" X 8'-0"

6"

INNER TUBES

UNDERSIDE VIEW

¾" PINE BEAMS

CEDAR CHEST

CLEAN, UP-TO-DATE lines and an extra storage drawer distinguish this roomy cedar chest. The unit is built primarily of cedar-faced plywood or solid cedar plus your choice of cabinet wood, the end grain of the plywood at the front corners of the chest being hidden by two beveled posts. The top, which is of 13⁄16-in. plywood, is given a heavier appearance by a 1¼-in. molding applied to the front and both ends. The molding is laid in a mitered rabbet for an invisible joint and is also mitered at the corners. A ¼ x ½-in. sponge-rubber gasket is cemented along the top edges of the side panels to form an airtight seal when the top is closed. When fitting the tray, be sure that sufficient clearance is allowed between the tray ends and the end panels of the chest to permit mounting combination hinges and lid supports on the inside of the panels. Note in section A-A that the front edges of the end panels are tenoned to fit the corner posts and that the panels are grooved to take tenons on the ends of the front panel. The rear edge of each end panel is mitered and joined to the rear panel with a spline as in the lower right-hand detail. Both back and end panels are grooved 4¼ in. from the lower edge to support the bottom panel.

MATERIAL YOU WILL NEED

Cedar-faced plywood
1 pc.—13/16" x 19" x 48"—Top
2 pcs.—13/16" x 18⅛" x 19-15/16"—Ends
1 pc.—13/16" x 19-15/16" x 48"—Back
1 pc.—13/16" x 15-5/16" x 46⅜"—Front
1 pc.—¾" x 16⅝" x 46⅜"—Bottom

Solid cedar
2 pcs.—¾" x 5" x 15¼"—Tray ends
2 pcs.—¾" x 5" x 44⅝"—Tray sides
1 pc.—½" x 4¾" x 43⅞"—Tray partition
2 pcs.—1" x 1¼" x 16¼"—Tray supports

Plywood
1 pc.—¼" x 15" x 43⅞"—Tray bottom
1 pc.—¼" x 3" x 47¼"—Front-base overlay
1 pc.—¼" x 16⅛" x 42⅞"—Drawer bottom

Cabinet wood
2 pcs.—5/16" x 1¼" x 19"—Top end molding
1 pc.—5/16" x 1¼" x 48"—Top front molding
1 pc.—7/16" x ¾" x 47⅜"—Top front filler
2 pcs.—¾" x 1¾" x 19"—Posts
1 pc.—¾" x 1¾" x 46½"—Top drawer rail
1 pc.—¾" x 1¾" x 47¼"—Front drawer rail
2 pcs.—¾" x 3¼" x 18"—End base
1 pc.—¾" x 3" x 46½"—Front base
1 pc.—¾" x 3½" x 43¾"—Drawer front

Lumber
2 pcs.—½" x 3½" x 16¾"—Drawer sides
1 pc.—½" x 3¼" x 42⅞"—Drawer back
1 pc.—¾" x 1¾" x 46½"—Back drawer rail
2 pcs.—¾" x 3" x 16⅜"—Side drawer rail
1 pc.—¾" x 3" x 46½"—Back base
1 pc.—¾" x 1½" x 16½"—Drawer guide
1 pc.—9/16" x 3" x 16⅛"—Drawer slide

Miscellaneous
2—combination hinges and lid supports
2—2" dia. brass drawer knobs
1—chest-lid lock
1—drawer lock
4—⅝" dia. furniture glides
7'—¼" x ½" sponge-rubber gasket

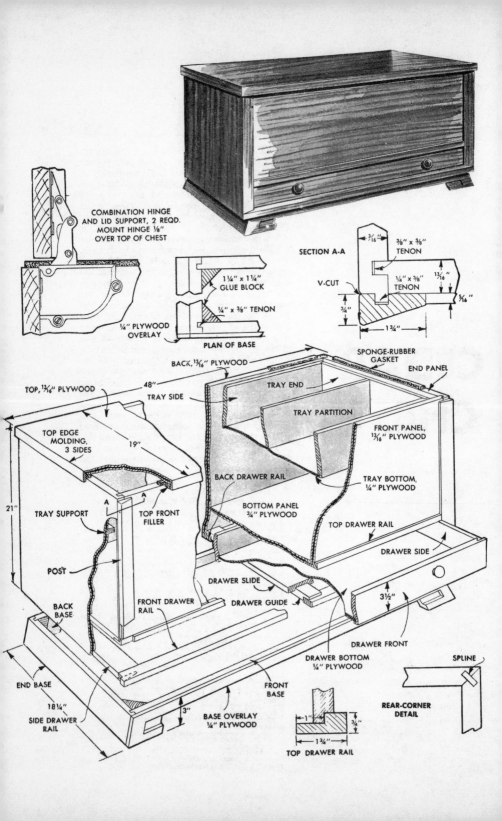

COMBINATION HINGE
AND LID SUPPORT, 2 REQD.
MOUNT HINGE ⅛"
OVER TOP OF CHEST

SECTION A-A

³⁄₁₆"

³⁄₈" x ³⁄₈"
TENON

V-CUT

¼" x ³⁄₈"
TENON

1³⁄₁₆"

⁵⁄₁₆"

¾"

1¾"

1¼" x 1¼"
GLUE BLOCK

¼" x ³⁄₈" TENON

¼" PLYWOOD
OVERLAY

PLAN OF BASE

SPONGE-RUBBER
GASKET

BACK, 1³⁄₁₆" PLYWOOD

END PANEL

TOP, 1³⁄₁₆" PLYWOOD

48"

TRAY END

TRAY SIDE

TRAY PARTITION

FRONT PANEL,
1³⁄₁₆" PLYWOOD

TOP EDGE
MOLDING,
3 SIDES

19"

BACK DRAWER RAIL

TRAY BOTTOM,
¼" PLYWOOD

21"

TRAY SUPPORT

A   A

TOP FRONT
FILLER

BOTTOM PANEL
¾" PLYWOOD

TOP DRAWER RAIL

POST

DRAWER SIDE

BACK
BASE

FRONT DRAWER
RAIL

DRAWER SLIDE

DRAWER GUIDE

3½"

END BASE

DRAWER FRONT

18¼"

SIDE DRAWER
RAIL

FRONT
BASE

BASE OVERLAY
¼" PLYWOOD

3"

DRAWER BOTTOM
¼" PLYWOOD

1"

¾"

1¾"

TOP DRAWER RAIL

SPLINE

REAR-CORNER
DETAIL

Cement Mixer

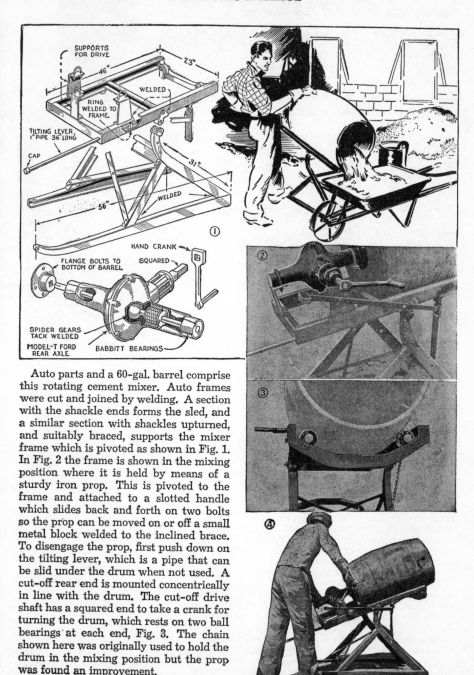

Auto parts and a 60-gal. barrel comprise this rotating cement mixer. Auto frames were cut and joined by welding. A section with the shackle ends forms the sled, and a similar section with shackles upturned, and suitably braced, supports the mixer frame which is pivoted as shown in Fig. 1. In Fig. 2 the frame is shown in the mixing position where it is held by means of a sturdy iron prop. This is pivoted to the frame and attached to a slotted handle which slides back and forth on two bolts so the prop can be moved on or off a small metal block welded to the inclined brace. To disengage the prop, first push down on the tilting lever, which is a pipe that can be slid under the drum when not used. A cut-off rear end is mounted concentrically in line with the drum. The cut-off drive shaft has a squared end to take a crank for turning the drum, which rests on two ball bearings at each end, Fig. 3. The chain shown here was originally used to hold the drum in the mixing position but the prop was found an improvement.

CERAMICS
EQUIPMENT AND TECHNIQUES

Although ceramics, or pottery making, is one of the oldest of the arts, hobbyists still can turn a neat profit from custom work in original designs. Anyone can build the equipment at small cost

A S OUTLINED by Miss Jane Poyer, nationally known authority on ceramic sculpture, there are two methods of making pottery. One method is casting in plaster molds and the other is turning or throwing on a potter's wheel. The former process permits a great variety of design ranging from a simple dish to intricate groups of figures. Also, there are many minor variations of both processes. In casting, a clay model of the subject is first made and plaster of paris is poured over it to form a two-part mold. For the more intricate shapes the mold is often made in several parts. When the plaster has set, the mold is opened and the model removed. The mold is again assembled and is filled with liquid clay, or slip. When this has set or solidified sufficiently to hold its shape, the mold is again opened and the clay casting removed. Rough edges are carefully scraped off and the entire surface of the casting is smoothed with a wet sponge. Then it is placed in a kiln for bisque or hard firing. Following this, color is applied with brush or spray, the piece is dipped in a glaze solution and is then glaze-fired in the kiln, giving it the glossy surface of the finished product. In the process of throwing on the potter's wheel, the object is shaped freehand without use of either a pattern or mold.

For general work in ceramics the hand tools required are spatulas, scrapers, a sharp-pointed knife, several soft brushes, a spray gun, and a mortar and pestle for mixing colors. If the firing is done in a home kiln, special kiln furniture will be needed such as shelves, shelf supports and saddles and stilts on which the work is supported while being fired.

Modeling clay can be purchased from dealers already prepared for use, or it may be prepared by the user from the raw clay. Liquid clay or slip also can be obtained from dealers, but if required in quantity,

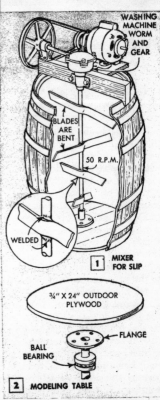

An efficient mixer for slip is made from a hardwood barrel and a reduction gear from an old washing machine. At top of page, Miss Poyer, nationally known ceramics artist, with examples of her work

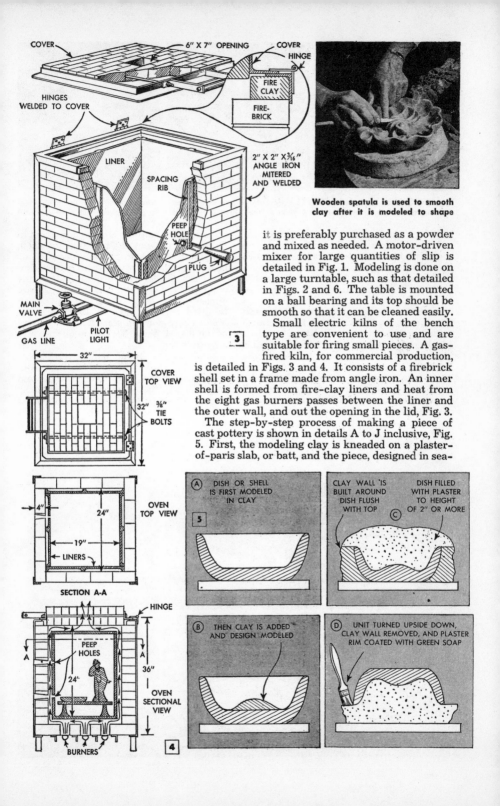

Wooden spatula is used to smooth clay after it is modeled to shape

it is preferably purchased as a powder and mixed as needed. A motor-driven mixer for large quantities of slip is detailed in Fig. 1. Modeling is done on a large turntable, such as that detailed in Figs. 2 and 6. The table is mounted on a ball bearing and its top should be smooth so that it can be cleaned easily.

Small electric kilns of the bench type are convenient to use and are suitable for firing small pieces. A gas-fired kiln, for commercial production, is detailed in Figs. 3 and 4. It consists of a firebrick shell set in a frame made from angle iron. An inner shell is formed from fire-clay liners and heat from the eight gas burners passes between the liner and the outer wall, and out the opening in the lid, Fig. 3.

The step-by-step process of making a piece of cast pottery is shown in details A to J inclusive, Fig. 5. First, the modeling clay is kneaded on a plaster-of-paris slab, or batt, and the piece, designed in sea-

Plaster is brushed on lower half of mold. Coating must be uniform

Clay ring makes pouring cup on bottom of shell. Ring is removed

After trimming at the joint, mold is pried open and shell removed

shell motif with a fish ornament at the center, is roughly shaped with the hands on the turntable to the sectional shape shown at A. Then, a clay roll is added to the bottom from which the fish is to be modeled. Both shell and fish are gradually molded into shape with the fingers, which are kept moist with a sponge. Wooden spatulas and wire cutting tools are used in the finish modeling of both parts. Plaster of paris is brushed over the surface and a clay wall is built around and under the shell and brought up flush with the rim. Then build up the plaster on the model until about 2 in. thick, detail C, as a thinner mold will not absorb moisture sufficiently to dry the casting properly. In preparing plaster of paris, pour the dry powder into a basin of water until an island is formed. When this absorbs the water and begins to settle, mix with the hands, squeezing out the lumps.

Now turn the piece upside down, detail D, remove the clay wall around the shell, and apply either a plaster separator or green soap to the rim of the plaster so that the fresh plaster of the other half of the mold will not adhere. Notch the edges on opposite sides so that the two halves can be fitted together again in exact register. Make a clay ring and place it on the bottom of the model, detail E. This is formed into a pouring cup.

Build up the second half of the plaster mold as in detail F. When it has hardened, trim around the joint with a knife and carefully pry the mold open. Remove the clay model or pattern, clean the mold and put it together again. The halves are held in place with strong rubber bands, Fig. 6. Slip is now poured in as in detail G until it fills the mold nearly to the top of the pouring cup. As the plaster mold absorbs

E PLASTER NOTCHED ON EACH SIDE CLAY RING FOR POURING CUP

F CLAY RING MODELED FOR POURING CUP AND TOP HALF OF PLASTER MOLD SET IN PLACE

G CLAY MODEL REMOVED, MOLD PUT TOGETHER AND FILLED WITH SLIP

H WHEN SLIP SOLIDIFIES TO DEPTH OF 3/16", POUR OUT THAT REMAINING TESTING FOR THICKNESS

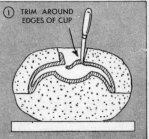
I TRIM AROUND EDGES OF CUP

J WHEN CASTING SHRINKS FROM MOLD, PRY IT OPEN GENTLY

Left, mold is assembled and slip is poured in. Above, after bisque firing and coloring, piece is dipped in glaze

water rapidly, the slip in contact with it will solidify and the level of the slip in the cup will recede. After it has gone down ¼ in. or so, make a knife cut near the top, detail H, to test for thickness and when the solidified slip is from ⅛ to ¼ in. thick, invert the mold and pour out the unsolidified slip. Now carefully trim around the edges of the cup, as in detail I, so that the mold can be opened without breaking the shell-like casting, which shrinks away from the mold sufficiently so that removal will be comparatively easy when the mold is opened. Castings with thin edges should be removed with care to avoid breakage.

Finally pry the mold open with a knife blade and lift out the casting very carefully. Scrape off any fins and smooth the piece with a damp sponge. It is now ready for bisque or hard firing and is placed in the kiln on stilts to raise it off the floor. Pyrometric cones, Fig. 8 are placed just opposite the peephole. These are numbered for various temperatures and the cone marked 04 is used for bisque as it bends or "wilts" at 1922 deg. F. The cone becomes red hot and is easily seen in the dark interior of the kiln through the peephole. When it begins to bend, the heat is turned off. Length of firing time depends on the

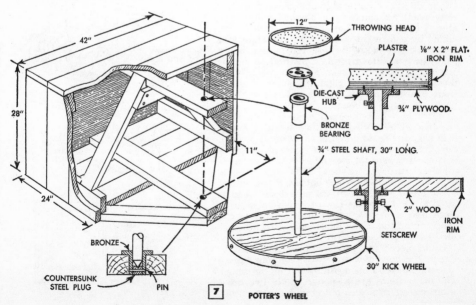

42"

28"

24"

11"

BRONZE

COUNTERSUNK STEEL PLUG

PIN

7

POTTER'S WHEEL

12"

THROWING HEAD

PLASTER

⅛" X 2" FLAT IRON RIM

DIE-CAST HUB

¾" PLYWOOD.

BRONZE BEARING

¾" STEEL SHAFT, 30" LONG.

2" WOOD

IRON RIM

SETSCREW

30" KICK WHEEL

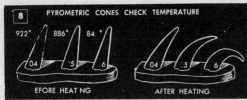

922° 886° 84°

04 5 6

04 5 6

EFORE HEAT NG

AFTER HEATING

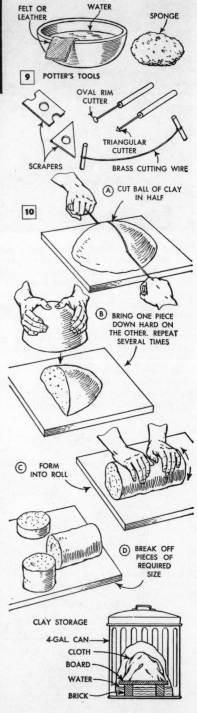

FELT OR LEATHER

WATER

SPONGE

9 POTTER'S TOOLS

OVAL RIM CUTTER

TRIANGULAR CUTTER

SCRAPERS

BRASS CUTTING WIRE

10

(A) CUT BALL OF CLAY IN HALF

(B) BRING ONE PIECE DOWN HARD ON THE OTHER. REPEAT SEVERAL TIMES

(C) FORM INTO ROLL

(D) BREAK OFF PIECES OF REQUIRED SIZE

CLAY STORAGE

4-GAL. CAN

CLOTH

BOARD

WATER

BRICK

gas pressure. the type of kiln used and other factors. In regular practice, the heat is turned on at lowest adjustment for two hours or so to warm the kiln. Then it is turned up full. Four to eight hours at full heat are required in hard firing.

Coloring with engobe, or colored slip, is the next step. The colored engobe comes in dry form and is prepared according to the directions supplied. Engobe is laid on in a uniform coating but is not brushed out like paint. It will appear flat and colorless before firing, but the application of heat brings out the true color. Colors also are applied with a spray gun. After coloring, the glaze solution is applied, either by spraying or dipping. In dipping, the piece is immersed in the solution. and the portions held by the fingers are later painted over with the solution. The piece is now placed in the kiln and fired for about an hour to set the glaze and impart a glossy finish.

In its simplest form the potter's wheel consists of a rotating disk propelled by means of a kick wheel. A refinement is the electrically driven wheel with variable speeds. A simple design employing the kick wheel is shown in Fig. 7. Essential features are a strongly braced frame, with an easy-turning kick wheel and throwing head, or disk. upon which the subject is modeled. Distance between top of bench and kick wheel either should be adjustable or fixed at the most convenient and comfortable height for the operator, who straddles the shaft and rotates the wheel by a forward motion with the right foot and backward with the left, the motion being from the knees downward. Construction details are shown in Fig. 7, 2-in. material being used throughout to make a rigid structure. The two shaft bearings are flanged bronze sleeves, the lower one having a countersunk plug of brass or cast iron on which the shaft rotates. Ordinarily, the kick wheel is made from wood with a heavy iron rim, or tire. to give the effect of a flywheel. For the throwing head, many potters prefer a plaster surface as the clay adheres well and surplus moisture is absorbed. This type is made with an outdoor-plywood bottom fitted with a sheet-metal rim. When assembled the head is filled to the top of the rim with plaster of paris. Both disk and kick wheel are fastened to the shaft with flanges, the lower one being adjustable by means of setscrews.

Other necessary equipment is illustrated in Fig. 9. The bowl of water always contains a piece of leather or felt for smoothing clay on the wheel. The other items are a sponge, cloth, two brass scrapers, an oval and a triangular rim cutter,

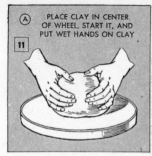

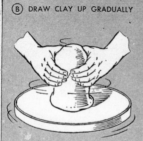

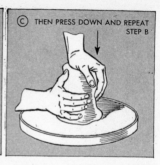

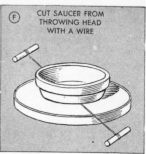

and a brass cutting wire with two wooden handles. Some potters prefer to dig and prepare the clay themselves. Others purchase refined clay from dealers to save time and labor. Clay freshly dug from the pit should be seasoned through the winter. Then, the clay is powdered and mixed with water until it is thin enough to pass through a fine sieve into a large container. It is allowed to settle for several days, then the excess water is poured off. When dry enough to handle, spread it on a clean floor and allow to dry until stiff enough to knead. This can be done by hand, with the bare feet or in a pugmill. Further seasoning in a cool, damp place will improve its quality. Unused clay is kept in a covered can with about 2 in. of water in the bottom. The clay is placed on a board supported above the water on bricks. A cloth is then thrown over the mass, with the ends in the water.

Fig. 10, details A to D inclusive, shows how to prepare clay for the wheel. Work it into a ball the size of a round loaf of bread and place on a clean board. Cut in half with the brass wire, A. Then pick up one piece and bring it down hard on the other as at B. This is known as wedging. Repeat several times, finally forming the mass into a roll, C. Break off pieces of the sizes required, D, and mold them into balls.

In throwing a simple dish, a clay ball is placed firmly in the center of the throwing head, Fig. 11, and the hands are dipped in water. Start the wheel in motion and cup the hands over the clay, pressing down on the disk, A. Now draw the clay upward with a slight pressure of the hands as at B, and then force it down again with the palm of the left hand. Repeat several times, detail C. This aids in conditioning the clay. Press both thumbs down in the center of the rotating mass to start a hollow, or depression. Widen this by inserting fingers of the left hand, D. Continue widening the hollow by using both hands, at the same time manipulating the rim with the fingers to bring it to the required thickness and height. Ridges are rubbed out with the fingers and a piece of wet felt, and the rim is smoothed with the square scraper, as in E. The knack of forming the clay into the various shapes is easily acquired after a little practice. Cutting the work from the throwing head is done as in detail F. When cutting work from the throwing head with the wire be sure to hold the wire taut as it may loop or kink and cause damage.

Throwing vases and jugs calls for much the same procedure, except that a larger ball of clay is used and the sides are drawn higher. Details G to L inclusive, Fig. 11, show the common technique quite clearly. For making the outward flare of a vase, simply exert greater pressure with the fingers of the left hand inside the rim than with the thumb of the same hand on the outside. The reverse movement shapes the curve in a jug, or teapot, as in G. The spout for a teapot is made by throwing a clay cone around a dowel and cutting it off at the required length with a knife while the

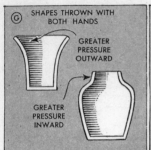

G SHAPES THROWN WITH BOTH HANDS

GREATER PRESSURE OUTWARD

GREATER PRESSURE INWARD

H THROWING A SPOUT — DOWEL

CUT WHILE TURNING

I ATTACHING SPOUT

SLIP CEMENT

SCORED

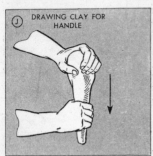

J DRAWING CLAY FOR HANDLE

K ATTACHING HANDLE

SCORED AND SLIP APPLIED

SLIP

L FORMING A LIP

work is in motion, as at H. A hole is then cut in the pot the size of the dowel. The clay around the hole is scored and slip is applied, which acts as a cement when the spout is gently pressed against the pot, as in detail I. To make handles, start with a pear-shaped ball of clay, as in detail J. Hold the clay in the left hand, wet the right hand and gradually draw a long, conical shape. Then, without using any pressure from the thumb, draw out the shape with the fingers to the size required. The handle is bent to shape and the ends are flattened as shown in detail K. It is then attached to the pot with slip in the same manner as the spout. To form a pouring lip on a jug or vase, work with the index finger of the left hand inside and thumb and index finger of the right hand on the outside, as in detail L. Procedures in coloring, firing and glazing are the same as used when processing castings.

Overlay decorations are applied by means of plaster dies, Fig. 12. A pat of clay is pressed into the die, the excess scraped flush with a straight-edge, and the die with the clay in it is pressed against the surface of the work.

Clay Modeling Tool From Handle Of Worn-Out Toothbrush

A plastic tool that will last indefinitely for modeling clay can be made from an old tooth-brush handle. Shear off the bristles with an old razor blade, and then saw off the opposite end of the handle at an angle. Sharpen this end and shape the handle to suit with a piece of sand-paper or a file.

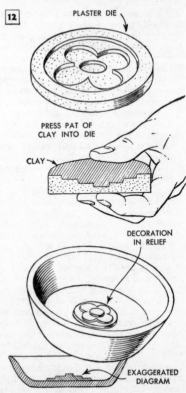

12

PLASTER DIE

PRESS PAT OF CLAY INTO DIE

CLAY

DECORATION IN RELIEF

EXAGGERATED DIAGRAM

ALSATIAN CHAIRS

THESE continental chairs with their widely splayed legs and attractive, carved backs are worthy projects for the home craftsman and provide distinctive pieces for a hall or dining room. Although each chair back appears difficult to make, actually it is fairly simple because the design first is cut through by scrollsawing. Either of the back designs is cut from a single panel, and the scrolled section finished in low relief with a chisel, veining tool and sandpaper. The seat is mounted on two cleats bored approximately 15 deg. from the vertical for insertion of the legs. The top ends of the legs are saw-cut to receive a wedge driven at right angles to the grain of the cleat. The top edges of the seat are rounded and, by using material 1⅝ in. thick, the seat can be hollowed to form a concave section for greater comfort. In assembling, the back is fastened to the cleats with angle brackets which are recessed flush. Either antique or natural finish, waxed and rubbed to a soft luster, is suitable for this type of chair.

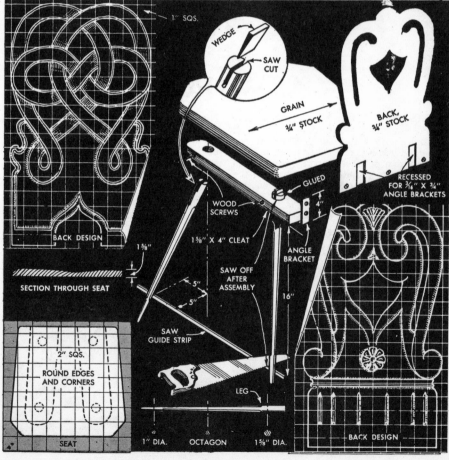

ARMCHAIR

THIS ARMCHAIR is a perfect companion piece for any knotty-pine room. Most parts are quite easy to make. The arm rest, however, involves fine jointing and shaping of a number of pieces to vary grain direction. You can simplify this by making the arms of only three pieces, joined on two sides near the back, or be content with a bandsawed plywood arm shaped from a single panel by following the squared pattern.

For the seat, which is 19 in. at the widest part, use two 1-in. pine boards, 12 in. wide and joined at the sides with glue. After sawing the shape desired, add the front piece, 2 in. wide, with the grain running across the edge of the seat, and fasten the

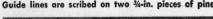

Guide lines are scribed on two ¾-in. pieces of pine

Scribed lengths are glued and held together by clamps

Reinforce seat with two boards, attached with glue and wood screws. Grain runs opposite direction to top

Dowel ends of legs, braces and rails are turned on a lathe. The ends may also be whittled with a knife

two reinforcing boards on the underside with glue and wood screws. Bevel the front edge of the seat slightly with a plane.

A 5-ft. length of 10-in.-wide stock is sufficient for the legs, back rest and side braces. Crosscut this board to give you two pieces, one 2 ft., the other 3 ft. long. Rip the 3-ft. length twice to get two 2-in.-wide strips for the four legs.

Now rip two or more full lengths, each 1½ in. wide, for the two sides and two crossrails, each of which will be planed to 1½ x 1½ in. Another two lengths, each 1½ in. wide, are cut from the 2-ft. length of stock to get the side braces. These end up as 1½ x 1½-in. squares, 20 in. long, and fit into notches cut into the sides of the seat.

The arm rest consists of a double layer of ¾-in. lumber. The sides comprise four glued-up pieces, arranged so the grain meets "on the bias" in alternating diagonals. However, if you lack a jointer that makes this work fast and pleasurable, you can fall back on a more simple assembly, building up the entire arc of the arms from three lengths, which meet at the center of the radius just under the back-rest ends. This will involve a minimum of waste stock. Make sure the grain runs the long way on the arms. The lower half of the arm assembly should overlap the point of the top joints so there will be added support.

The spindles between arm and seat, from 1¼ x 1¼-in. squares, can be turned on a lathe if desired to somewhat offset the square legs. It would be wise here to plane the spindles so they are not too uniform in appearance.

Sections for arms are cut from ¾-in. stock, with grain of alternating pieces planned for diagonal direction

Back rest is to be shaped with a rasp from a built-up block of 2-in. stock. Then smooth piece with sandpaper

Fit side braces into holes in leg rails. Holes must be drilled at angle, which you can determine as desired

Assemble chair by fitting spindles into seat. Finally, glue all joints and set chair aside to dry thoroughly

The ends of these spindles—as well as the legs, crossrail and arm braces—must be rounded into dowel shape, ¾-in. diameter, to fit into drilled holes for jointing. The result need not be critically perfect, as the parts widen out just beyond the dowel point and will partially cover any distortion resulting from inaccuracy.

Now you can go ahead with shaping the back rest. This is made from a built-up block consisting of three pieces of 2-in.-thick stock. Corners and back are trimmed to approximately the desired angle after the glue has set, then the front is shaped to its graceful curve with a rasp, plane and

sandpaper. You can decide on any contour, aiming for a gradual curve inward from the sides, and cutting down a taper from the bottom to the top.

The entire back rest, from arm to the top, is 5 in. high. The final thickness at the very top should be at least ½ in., but rounded and smoothed for a continuous line from end to end. Attach the back rest with at least four dowels in the base of the pyramid. Wood screws from underneath the arms will add support. For finishing the chair, sand it to remove any loose fibers, then coat with clear shellac (thinned half and half with alcohol).

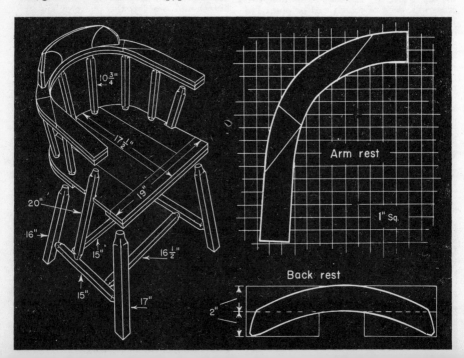

10 ¾"

17 ½"

19"

20"

16"

15"

16 ½"

15"

17"

Arm rest

1" Sq.

Back rest

2"

MODERN CHAIR
Of Cord and Plywood

ADD A DISTINCTLY modern touch to your room with this chair of plywood and parachute cord. In addition to plywood for the sides and legs, you will need the four pieces of pine shown in the material list below. The rail across the top of the back is beveled to a width of 2 in. to match the taper of the side-pieces. The front rail of the seat can be shaped either from a 2 x 4 or from a 1 x 4 and a 1 x 2 glued together. All joints are nailed and glued, using a plastic-resin glue. The chair is painted before the para-chute cord is put on, applying wood filler, then an enamel undercoating and two coats of satin-finish black enamel.

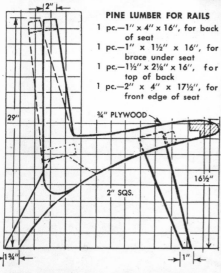

PINE LUMBER FOR RAILS

1 pc.—1″ x 4″ x 16″, for back of seat
1 pc.—1″ x 1½″ x 16″, for brace under seat
1 pc.—1½″ x 2⅛″ x 16″, for top of back
1 pc.—2″ x 4″ x 17½″, for front edge of seat

¾″ PLYWOOD

29″

2″ SQS.

16½″

1¾″   1″

Solid lines in pattern above show angle of back on original chair. Dotted lines show alternate angle

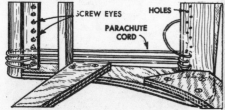

SCREW EYES   HOLES

PARACHUTE CORD

DOUBLE-DUTY LAWN CHAIR

Here's a novel trestle-table design adapted to lawn use either as a table or chair. Refinements include fitted seat and back cushions, and use of waterproof plywood instead of solid stock for the frame panels and top. The two front views below suggest modern and colonial-design treatment of the top and legs, but for hand-tool construction use the simple design shown in the perspective view. Assemble the parts which form the legs, seat and arms with screws and angle brackets. Detachable hair-filled cushions are box-type construction, the covers being made with welted seams

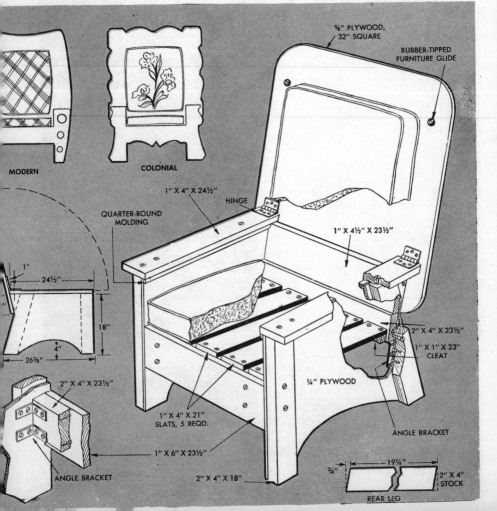

MODERN

COLONIAL

⅝" PLYWOOD, 32" SQUARE

RUBBER-TIPPED FURNITURE GLIDE

1" X 4" X 24½"

HINGE

QUARTER-ROUND MOLDING

1" X 4½" X 23½"

1"

24½"

18"

4"

26⅞"

2" X 4" X 23½"

2" X 4" X 23½"

1" X 1" X 23 CLEAT

¼" PLYWOOD

1" X 4" X 21" SLATS, 5 REQD.

1" X 6" X 23½"

2" X 4" X 18"

ANGLE BRACKET

ANGLE BRACKET

¾"

19¼"

2" X 4" STOCK

REAR LEG

CHAIR BOTTOM WEAVING

The completed seat is singed with the flame of a tightly rolled newspaper to remove the reed fibers

TO REPLACE an average-size reed chair seat, you'll need about one pound of oval-split reed, which can be purchased from a dealer in seating materials. The reeds must be soaked in water for at least a half hour before using. Tack two strips to the front rail as shown in Figs. 1 and 3. Go under the front rail, over the adjacent side rail,

and then across to the opposite side rail. Wrap both strips around this rail and make an extra turn around it before returning the warp underneath to the first side rail. Make an extra turn here and go across the top again, as in Fig. 4. Each time you come to a rail, wrap an extra turn of the warp around it firmly before returning to the other side of the seat.

When near the end of a warp strip, shorten it if necessary so that it will end on the underside of the chair. Notch the edges of the old and new strips as in Figs. 2 and 5, and tie with string. A temporary tie is

Warp is begun by tacking two reeds to front rail

Detail below at left shows how reed splice is made

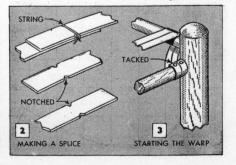

STRING

TACKED

NOTCHED

2 MAKING A SPLICE

3 STARTING THE WARP

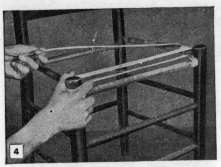

Warp strands are given one turn around side rails

Splicing warp strands is done on underside of seat

Woof strands are passed over and under warp strands

Woof is spliced by tucking end under warp strands

made around the rail at the last turn, as shown, to hold the strips while they are being spliced. Crowd the turns a bit wherever necessary so that the last warp on the upper side is back as far as possible. Start the woof across as a single strip at right angles to the front rail. This will leave a triangular space at the side. Weave under two, over two and around the rail, as in Fig. 6. Tuck the new piece in on top of the old one for a distance equal to two pairs of warp strips, as in Figs. 7 and 8.

When you have completed the square area, fill in remaining areas along the side rail as in Fig. 9. Start a short piece by pushing it into the smallest opening through which it will pass, and weave it around to the bottom, finishing by cutting off the strip and tucking in the end. Repeat with a shorter strip until the area is filled. Let the reeds dry overnight and then singe off the loose fibers. Be careful not to scorch the reeds. Singeing can be done with a newspaper torch.

Weaving woof is fun, just over two and under two

Fill-in areas at sides are woven with short strands

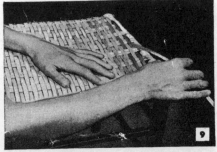

CHESSMEN

Chessmen in the Staunton pattern are familiar to all players and turning a set in the tournament size from fancy hardwood stock is wood turning at its best

FANCY hardwoods of natural contrast are the thing for turning this set in the larger tournament size where the king is 4 in. high. Black ebony for the dark-colored men and boxwood for those that are light colored make the best combination, Fig. 1. Walnut and maple also are suitable but compared to the finer woods they are only a compromise. Careful work with sharp tools on both ebony and boxwood produces a glass-smooth surface that needs no finishing or polishing whatever.

Begin by making a template from cardboard for each man, following the cross-hatched patterns in Fig. 9. You need only a half profile. Then, after turning the work

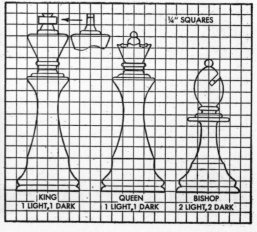

	¼" SQUARES
KING	QUEEN	BISHOP
1 LIGHT, 1 DARK	1 LIGHT, 1 DARK	2 LIGHT, 2 DARK

to round, use the template to lay off the exact location of shoulders, grooves and beads as in Fig. 2. After turning down the work to diameters which are near the finished dimensions, use the templates in conjunction with calipers to determine the accuracy of the profiles and diameters. If necessary you can make a screw center easily by turning an ordinary screw through a wood disk. Screw the disk to the lathe faceplate as in Fig. 3. Turn the knight to the shape shown in Fig. 4, then slot with a hacksaw—a hacksaw is best because of the fine teeth and stiff blade—and carefully cut away the waste on each side. Then, using a coping saw with a fine blade, saw the profile of the horse's head, Fig. 5. The rest is a handcarving job, but as you can see it's quite simple. Use a fine-tooth saw to slot the bishop and notice that this slot is made in two separate cuts, Fig. 9. To hollow the bases make a jig as in Fig. 6. Begin with the pawns and enlarge the hole in the jig as needed. Cut a recess in each base ½ in. in diameter by ¼ in., fill with lead wool and wood putty to hold the "ballast," Fig. 8. Finish by gluing felt disks to the bases.

If you use any contrasting woods other than ebony and boxwood, these will need sanding and finishing as you go along. Sand as in Fig. 7. On open-grained woods such as walnut follow sanding with a filler colored to suit. Then apply a coat of sealer and finish with several coats of wax. Aside from the carving on the knight, the only other hand work is squaring the cross on the king's crown, scalloping the edges of the queen's crown, notching the rim of the castle and carving the stonework on the column of the castle.

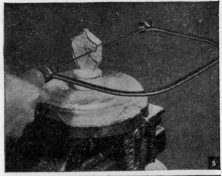

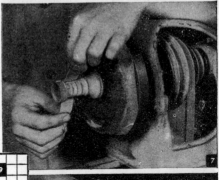

KNIGHT
2 LIGHT, 2 DARK

CASTLE
2 LIGHT, 2 DARK

PAWN
8 LIGHT, 8 DARK

CHEST DRAWERS

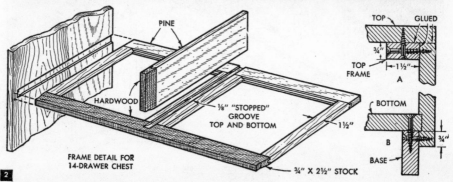

PINE

HARDWOOD

1/8" "STOPPED" GROOVE TOP AND BOTTOM

1½"

FRAME DETAIL FOR 14-DRAWER CHEST

¾" X 2½" STOCK

TOP   GLUED

¾"

TOP FRAME

1½"

A

BOTTOM

B

BASE

¾"

FOR the little girl in your home—or the small boy, for that matter —chests of drawers, such as the two shown here, will do much to improve the appearance of the bedroom and also serve as an incentive for the youngster to keep her clothes and possessions in a neat and orderly manner. Either chest may complement and serve to expand a suite that you have already. There is ample space in both for all your youngster's linen with possibly a drawer or so left over for a collection of childish treasures. The chest with two doors, Fig. 1, has a top drawer that is shallower and a bottom drawer that is deeper than the other five. All extend the full width of the chest. If you want to store blankets and bulky clothing, drawers like these are best. The other chest, Fig. 5, has fourteen drawers of equal size. Where many individual compartments are required, this chest would be the better choice. Selection of the one you prefer to build may be governed by these factors. The chests look best when made of hardwoods, such as walnut or maple, and stained. Or they can be made of the semi-hardwoods such as poplar or gum and then painted. The originals were made of maple and given a blond or bleached finish.

Construction of the closed chest is given in Fig. 3. The doors are glued up from solid stock and splined top and bottom as in Fig. 4 to prevent warping. Drawer construction is of the usual type. However, in this case narrow strips were nailed to the sides near the lower edge. The strips help avoid binding by preventing the entire side from coming in contact with the chest. Notice that the chest top overhangs an amount equal to the thickness of the doors so they are flush. If available, use long piano hinges to hang the doors. These will help prevent warping also. Friction catches are used in the top edge to hold the doors closed.

The sides, top and bottom are made of built-up sections joined as shown in Fig. 3. The back is plywood rabbeted to the sides. Blind grooves are cut in the sides for the frames which are

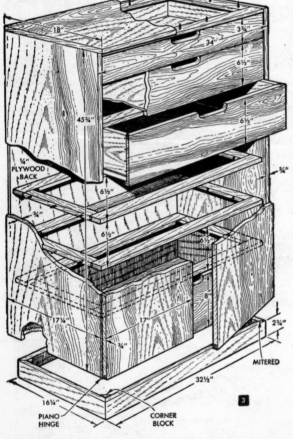

18"
34"
3¾"
6½"
6½"
45¾"
6½"
¾"
¼" PLYWOOD BACK
6½"
6½"
5½"
8"
17¼"
17"
¾"
2¾"
MITERED
16¼"
32½"
PIANO HINGE
CORNER BLOCK

3

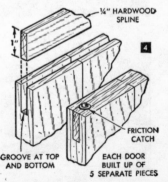

¼" HARDWOOD SPLINE
1"
4
GROOVE AT TOP AND BOTTOM
EACH DOOR BUILT UP OF 5 SEPARATE PIECES
FRICTION CATCH

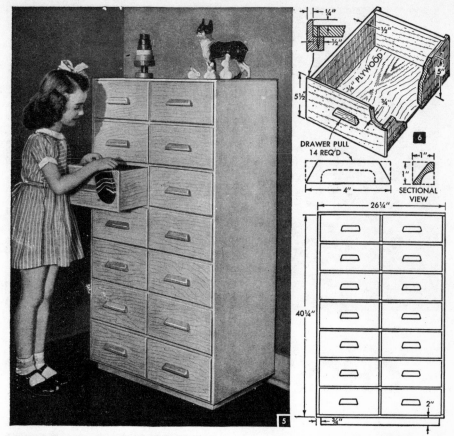

cut at the front corners to fit. Tongue-and-groove joints are used in assembling the frames. These are glued and screwed in place. The base has mitered joints reinforced with corner blocks and sets inside the cabinet. It is attached as indicated in detail B of Fig. 2. Detail A shows how the top is fastened to the sides and frame. After the cabinet is assembled, you may find that several thumbtacks in the frame where the drawers slide will make them work more smoothly. Also, the runners can be waxed occasionally. Although not shown, handles for the doors add to the beauty of the chest. These are round pieces planed to have one flat side and they are screwed to the doors.

In many ways, the construction of the 14-drawer chest is similar to that of the other chest. The sides, top, back and base are built in a similar manner. The overall dimensions vary, however. The spacing for the frames of the 14-drawer chest is equal since all drawers are the same size. Fig. 2 gives details of the frame assembly. Note that the front of the frame and the divider

can be hardwood while the remainder is pine or some other less expensive wood. This will reduce the cost of construction to some extent. The same type of construction can be used for the door chest. Fig. 6 gives the dimensions and method of assembly for the drawers. Plywood is used for the bottom, and the sides, front and back are made from solid stock. The front overlaps the frame on all sides. The drawer pulls are cut from 1-in.-square stock. In this chest the top is flush with the sides and does not overlap as in the previous case.

Many effects may be obtained in finishing the chests. If they are made of a semi-soft wood, spraying with a bone-white lacquer gives an excellent finish that is very popular. As a further touch, they may be decorated with decals. If hardwood is used, some light-toned finish is best. Maple can be bleached to a blond color that is almost white, while walnut will bleach to a russet or straw color. After the bleaching has been done and the bleach neutralized, spray with clear gloss lacquer. If the wood is maple a water-white lacquer is used.

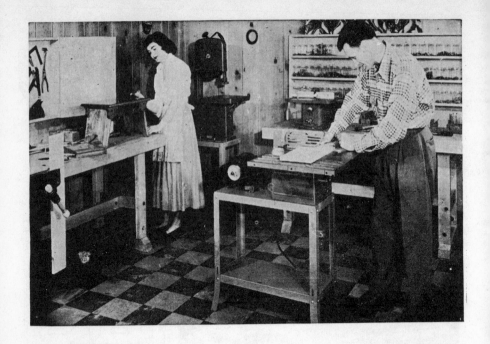

CHEST DRAWERS

Up to now we've been discussing the more common power woodworking machines in the small sizes suitable in both size and price for use in the homeshop. Now let's see what you can do with them on complete projects that are useful and attractive, for example the chest of drawers pictured at the right. Here's one, incidentally, that will delight the eye of the craftsman who likes modern design. But, you say, "That's too difficult for me to begin on. I'd have to start with a box and work up from there." But that's exactly what this project is, a box. Nothing more. Take the drawers out and what have you got left? A simple box, with rectangular frames equally spaced inside. Take a look at the details on the following page and see for yourself. Moreover, with the project standing on end as you see it at the right, the imaginary box doesn't even have a regular bottom in it! Without the drawers it consists only of a back, two sides and a top. Or, take that old grandfather clock you saw in some museum, and wished all the while you

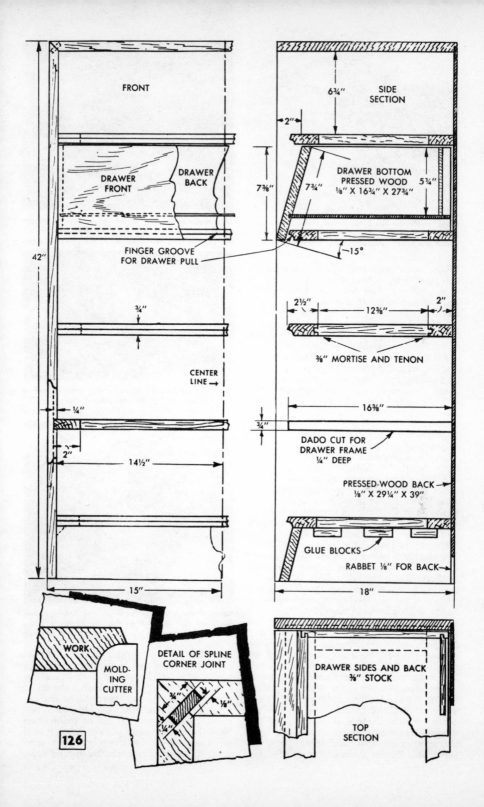

FRONT

DRAWER FRONT

DRAWER BACK

FINGER GROOVE
FOR DRAWER PULL

42"

¾"

CENTER
LINE →

¼"

2"

14½"

15"

SIDE
SECTION

6¾"

2"

DRAWER BOTTOM
PRESSED WOOD
⅛" X 16¾" X 27¾"

5¼"

7⅜"

7¾"

15°

2½"

12⅜"

2"

⅜" MORTISE AND TENON

16⅜"

¾"

DADO CUT FOR
DRAWER FRAME
¼" DEEP

PRESSED-WOOD BACK
⅛" X 29¼" X 39"

GLUE BLOCKS

RABBET ⅛" FOR BACK

18"

WORK

MOLD-
ING
CUTTER

DETAIL OF SPLINE
CORNER JOINT

¾"

⅛"

¼"

126

DRAWER SIDES AND BACK
⅜" STOCK

TOP
SECTION

Many craftsmen like this type of combination saw-jointer unit. Both machines are driven by one motor, which makes the combination suitable for small shops

This large table saw is set up to cut the finger groove on the edges of the drawer frames made for the chest of drawers detailed on the opposite page

The same machine set up to cut the spline groove in the mitered edge of the top piece for the chest of drawers pictured on page 85. Note special fixture

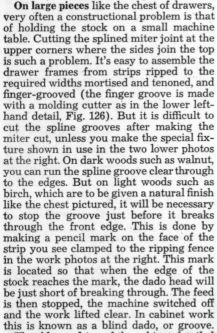

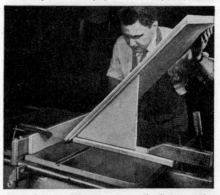

Here's the way the groove is cut. The fixture guides the piece and holds it at the correct angle while the guide clamped to rip fence keeps it in position

were looking at it that you had one like it. All right, why not build one? Of course, it looks difficult, but mentally take off the curved pediment at the top of the hood, the waist moldings and perhaps the fluted pilasters on the corners of the waist, and what's left? Only the base, the waist, and the hood, or movement compartment.

On large pieces like the chest of drawers, very often a constructional problem is that of holding the stock on a small machine table. Cutting the splined miter joint at the upper corners where the sides join the top is such a problem. It's easy to assemble the drawer frames from strips ripped to the required widths mortised and tenoned, and finger-grooved (the finger groove is made with a molding cutter as in the lower left-hand detail, Fig. 126). But it is difficult to cut the spline grooves after making the miter cut, unless you make the special fixture shown in use in the two lower photos at the right. On dark woods such as walnut, you can run the spline groove clear through to the edges. But on light woods such as birch, which are to be given a natural finish like the chest pictured, it will be necessary to stop the groove just before it breaks through the front edge. This is done by making a pencil mark on the face of the strip you see clamped to the ripping fence in the work photos at the right. This mark is located so that when the edge of the stock reaches the mark, the dado head will be just short of breaking through. The feed is then stopped, the machine switched off and the work lifted clear. In cabinet work this is known as a blind dado, or groove.

The sides and top of the cabinet detailed in Fig. 126 are built up from strips of solid stock edge-glued to build up to the required widths. Note that only one of the drawer-frame assemblies is detailed with the open-end mortise and tenon joint. On the others this detail has been omitted be-cause the end view of the cabinet is shown in section. Also, one of the drawer frames is made ½ in. longer so that it can be housed in a dado ¾ in. wide. All the other frames are butt-joined to the sides and reinforced with triangular glue blocks. If desired, the sides and top can be made from ¾-in. birch or walnut plywood, but it will be necessary to edge the pieces with solid stock in order to conceal the exposed edge.

CHILDREN'S CARS
Part One

LIVELY youngsters and craftsman fathers alike will get a thrill out of this tiny play car, which looks and drives like a real automobile except that it's scaled down to sidewalk-coaster size and travels at slow, safe speeds. It's driven by an auto starter motor of the type having a built-in reduction gear and is fitted with a foot brake, lever-operated clutch, pneumatic tires and a conventional steering gear. As pictured above, the original car measures 58 in. overall length, with a 42-in. wheelbase and 20-in. tread, but allowable variations in dimensions and the necessity of adapting certain parts according to availability, may change these dimensions slightly. For these reasons certain dimensions have been purposely omitted and adaptation or substitution of parts has been left to the discretion of the builder. An example is the length and type of the springs specified in the construction details. Obviously, these can be longer, or even slightly shorter than the lengths given. The side frames are of 2 x 2-in. oak and, in order to avoid waste in forming the curved ends, or lifts, the members are built up to the rough shape by gluing together strips of ¾-in. stock. Before gluing the strips together, be sure that there is ample allowance for bandsawing the curved sections at both ends of each piece. Use waterproof glue in the joints. After the glue is dry, bandsaw the curved ends and plane and sand the parts to the finished size. Apply a coat of shellac to prevent absorption of moisture. The side frames are joined near the ends with long studs, or draw bolts, and pipe spacers as shown on the blueprint on

a following page. Note that the front and rear-spring shackles are mounted on the draw bolts and that these must be left loose so that the shackles can move freely. Note also that the brake pedal is pivoted on the same draw bolt as the front-spring shackles. In this case two spacers are used to serve only as collars to position the pedal. Exact sizes of the draw bolts and spacers are not important.

Note especially the construction and

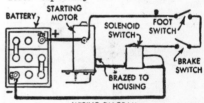

WIRING DIAGRAM

mounting of the front and rear axles on the springs. The front axle is fitted with drilled pads to which the underslung springs are bolted, but at the rear it will be noted that the axle bearings serve as spring pads. Shims of ⅛-in. flat steel are placed between the spring and the bearings, one shim being longer and having a drilled lug welded near the forward end to provide a bearing for the brake shaft when the band-type brake is used. When the shoe-type brake, shown in the detail below, is used, the brake-shaft bearing is attached to the car frame.

The front axle is of the conventional auto-type construction, the principal parts being made from pipe and flat steel, bent, welded and bolted together as in the blueprint. The drag link and tie rod can be taken from Ford Model-A steering linkage. Crosley or

American Austin parts may be substituted. Rods with ball joints also can be improvised. A Crosley or Austin steering gear can be used, the gear being mounted on a bracket under the hood. The steering shaft is approximately 22 in. long and ½ in. in diameter and is mounted on a generator bearing at the top end. The lower end of the shaft is fitted into an adapter sleeve, the size and length of the sleeve depending on the type of steering gear used. The steering wheel is 8 in. in diameter, the original being taken from a discarded toy.

Although details on the blueprint show the starter motor welded to a rocker shaft, which passes through a hole drilled in the flange of the reduction-gear housing to which it is welded, for best results weld a bracket to the gear housing and then weld the free end of the bracket to the rocker shaft. This construction will give a somewhat better clutch action when tightening and slackening the double V-belts with the clutch lever. The rocker shaft turns in bearings bolted to the side frames. The clutch shaft, with its tension spring, is mounted in the same manner. Use a 2-in. V-pulley on the reduction gear and a 5-in. pulley on the rear axle. Although double V-pulleys are shown, single-groove pulleys will serve the purpose quite satisfactorily. Only the right-rear ground wheel is fixed on the axle and serves as a driver. The left rear wheel turns free. This arrangement gives the necessary differential when turning.

Details on pages 136 and 137 give the wiring diagram, construction of the battery bracket and the position of the controls. Note the arrangement of the brake switch and how it works in the motor circuit. When it is desired to stop, the clutch lever is pushed forward and the brake pedal depressed. A small lug welded to the inner end of the clutch-lever shaft opens the brake switch and stops the starter motor. The motor cannot be started until the clutch lever is pulled part way back. This arrangement prevents undue idling of the starter motor. With the pulley sizes given and with the gear ratios of the average reduction-gear starter motor, the car travels at a speed of approximately five miles per hour. A 6-volt, 130-amp. battery will give about eight hours of service on one charge.

Construction of the sheet-metal body is quite simple. It is made in three sections which consist of the hinged rear deck, the driver's compartment and the hood, which includes the separate false grille. The pattern for the grille is first laid out on 2-in. squares and then cut to the form shown, before bending and soldering. Sides of the cockpit and the hood are attached to the side frames with screws uniformly spaced. The seat bottom, floor boards and dash are cut from ½-in. plywood. The seat can be upholstered if desired. Bumpers, dummy lights and other fittings are optional with the builder.

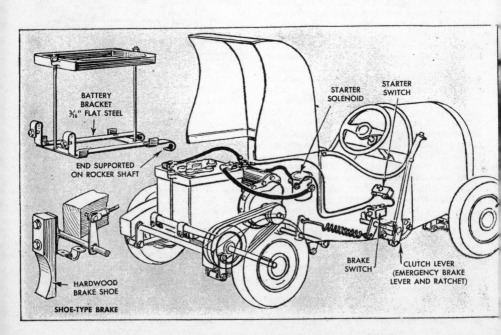

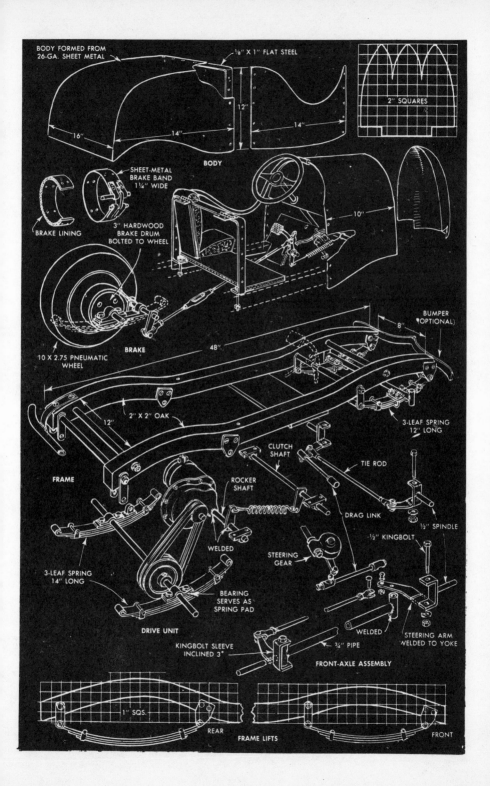

CHILDREN'S CARS

Part Two

COASTING along easily on velocipede ball bearings, this sidewalk Jeep will be the pride of any boy when he goes out on "reconnaissance patrols." Being assembled almost entirely of wood, the Jeep can be made with ordinary tools. White pine or other wood that does not warp easily will be satisfactory for the framework. However, the wheels and axle housings should be made of oak or maple or, for each wheel, you can glue together four pieces

① HALF OF GRILLE PATTERN

LAMP PAINTED ON
1" SQS.
2¼" R.
10¼"
½" HOLES
1¼"
1¼" 1¼" 1¼" 1½"
9¾"
8"
¢
NOTCHED TO FIT FRAME
DOWELED
1¼"

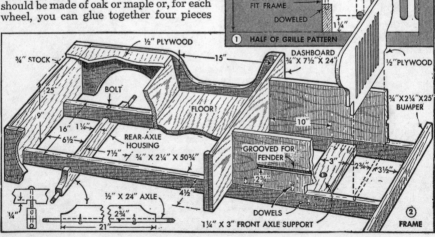

② FRAME

½" PLYWOOD
¾" STOCK
15"
DASHBOARD ¾" X 7½" X 24"
½" PLYWOOD
25"
BOLT
9"
16" 1¼"
6½"
FLOOR
REAR-AXLE HOUSING
7½" ¾" X 2¼" X 50¾"
10"
¾" X 2¼" X 25" BUMPER
GROOVED FOR FENDER
2¾"
3"
2¾" 3½"
¼"
½" X 24" AXLE
2¾"
21"
4½"
DOWELS
1¼" X 3" FRONT AXLE SUPPORT

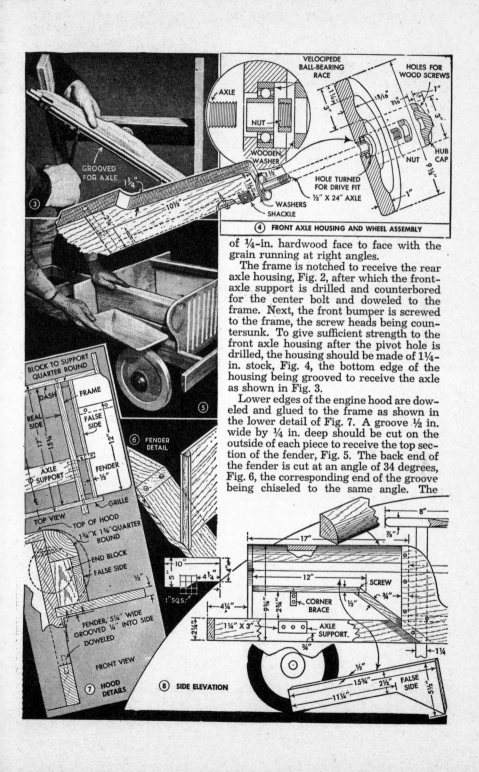

VELOCIPEDE BALL-BEARING RACE

AXLE

NUT

WOODEN WASHER

GROOVED FOR AXLE 1¼"

10½"

2¾"

WASHERS

SHACKLE

HOLE TURNED FOR DRIVE FIT ½" X 24" AXLE

HOLES FOR WOOD SCREWS

1¾"

3"

1½"

13/16"

7/16"

1"

3"

NUT

9½"

1"

HUB CAP

③

④ **FRONT AXLE HOUSING AND WHEEL ASSEMBLY**

of ¼-in. hardwood face to face with the grain running at right angles.

The frame is notched to receive the rear axle housing, Fig. 2, after which the front-axle support is drilled and counterbored for the center bolt and doweled to the frame. Next, the front bumper is screwed to the frame, the screw heads being countersunk. To give sufficient strength to the front axle housing after the pivot hole is drilled, the housing should be made of 1¼-in. stock, Fig. 4, the bottom edge of the housing being grooved to receive the axle as shown in Fig. 3.

Lower edges of the engine hood are doweled and glued to the frame as shown in the lower detail of Fig. 7. A groove ½ in. wide by ¼ in. deep should be cut on the outside of each piece to receive the top section of the fender, Fig. 5. The back end of the fender is cut at an angle of 34 degrees, Fig. 6, the corresponding end of the groove being chiseled to the same angle. The

⑤

BLOCK TO SUPPORT QUARTER ROUND

DASH

FRAME

REAL SIDE

FALSE SIDE

17"

15¾"

12"

AXLE SUPPORT

FENDER ½"

GRILLE

TOP VIEW

⑥ **FENDER DETAIL**

TOP OF HOOD

1¾" X 1¾" QUARTER ROUND

END BLOCK

FALSE SIDE

½"

FENDER, 5¼" WIDE GROOVED ¼" INTO SIDE

DOWELED

FRONT VIEW

1"

⑦ **HOOD DETAILS**

10"

5"

4¼"

1" SQS.

4¼"

2¼"

1¼" X 3"

8"

⅞"

17"

12"

SCREW

¾"

½"

9¾"

2¾"

CORNER BRACE

AXLE SUPPORT

¾"

½"

15¾"

2½"

11¼"

FALSE SIDE

5½"

1¼

⑧ **SIDE ELEVATION**

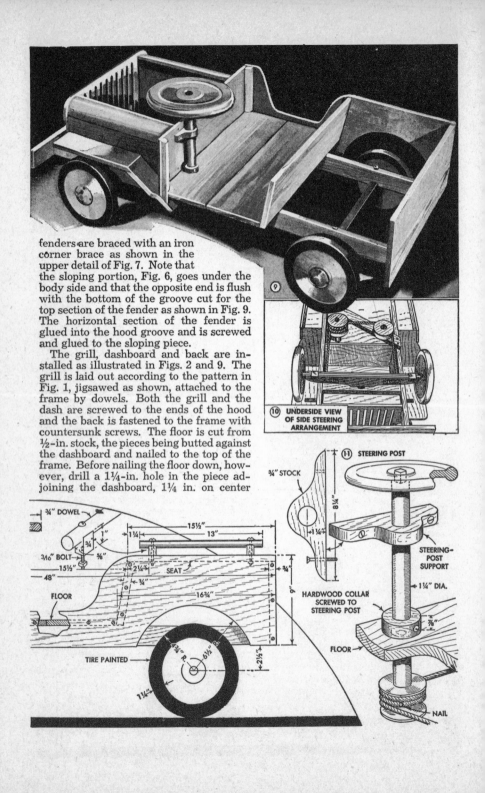

fenders are braced with an iron corner brace as shown in the upper detail of Fig. 7. Note that the sloping portion, Fig. 6, goes under the body side and that the opposite end is flush with the bottom of the groove cut for the top section of the fender as shown in Fig. 9. The horizontal section of the fender is glued into the hood groove and is screwed and glued to the sloping piece.

The grill, dashboard and back are installed as illustrated in Figs. 2 and 9. The grill is laid out according to the pattern in Fig. 1, jigsawed as shown, attached to the frame by dowels. Both the grill and the dash are screwed to the ends of the hood and the back is fastened to the frame with countersunk screws. The floor is cut from ½-in. stock, the pieces being butted against the dashboard and nailed to the top of the frame. Before nailing the floor down, however, drill a 1¼-in. hole in the piece adjoining the dashboard, 1¼ in. on center

⑨

⑩ UNDERSIDE VIEW OF SIDE STEERING ARRANGEMENT

⑪ STEERING POST

¾" STOCK

8¾"

1¼"

STEERING-POST SUPPORT

1¼" DIA.

HARDWOOD COLLAR SCREWED TO STEERING POST

⅞"

FLOOR

NAIL

¾" DOWEL

3/16" BOLT

15½"

15½"

48"

13"

1¼"

1"

¾

⅝"

2¼"

¾"

SEAT

16¾"

¾"

9"

FLOOR

TIRE PAINTED

3½" R.

6½"

2½"

1¼"

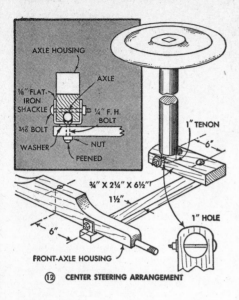

AXLE HOUSING

AXLE

1/8" FLAT-IRON SHACKLE

1/4" F. H. BOLT

3/16 BOLT

WASHER

NUT

PEENED

1" TENON

6"

3/4" X 2 1/4" X 6 1/2" T

1 1/2"

1" HOLE

6"

FRONT-AXLE HOUSING

⑫ CENTER STEERING ARRANGEMENT

from the front edge, for the steering post.

The body sides are 9¾ in. high at the front and 9 in. high at the back, Fig. 8, with the lower front corner cut off at an angle flush with the fender. The two sides should be tacked together and the curves band-sawed in one operation to assure identical pieces. They are screwed to the back, dashboard, floor and back rest. The back rest fits behind the floor and extends at an angle to within ½ in. of the top of the sides, both edges being beveled to fit the floor and seat respectively. To make the quarter round used on the sides of the hood, glue four pieces of 2 by 2 by 17-in. wood together, using paper between all joints. Turn this unit to a diameter of 3½ in. and then split into four quarter-rounds with a chisel. Cut the false engine sides and end blocks shown in Fig. 7. Making and installing the seat rails will complete the body.

In turning the wheels, a circle 3 in. in diameter should be marked on the wheel with pencil to locate the hub which will be turned separately. Note that the hole for the bearing is cut part way through the wheel to a point which will allow the bearing to run in the center, as shown in the circular detail, Fig. 4. Be sure the hole is cut in straight so that the bearing will be tight when it is driven to the center. After the bearing is driven in, it is followed by a tight-fitting wooden collar, glued on. If, however, velocipede bearings are not available, you can turn 1-in. spindles on

the ends of an oak axle and drill the wheels to rotate with a snug rather than a binding fit. With this arrangement, spindles must be kept thoroughly lubricated with graphite. To avoid any season cracks, it is well to give the wheel a coat of shellac or sanding sealer immediately after it is finished and sanded. The tire is then painted on with slate-gray porch or deck paint.

A wooden chuck is necessary for turning the hubs. It is merely a 5-in. wooden disk screwed to a 3-in. faceplate. The work is fastened to the chuck with wood screws inserted through the chuck into the work outside the area to be turned.

The steering wheel and cross arm are glued to their respective ends of the steering post after the support and collar are slipped on and the post is inserted through the floor as in Fig. 11. The support is bolted through the dashboard, all bolts being bradded to prevent their working loose. If an all-wood front axle is used, the flat-iron shackles shown in Fig. 4 may be eliminated and the steering rods bolted through both axle and housing as in Fig. 12. It is necessary that the steering rods pivot at a point directly beneath the front axle and that they be an equal distance from the center on both the housing and the steering cross-arm, otherwise the mechanism will bind when the wheels are turned. It is better to locate these pivot points when the parts are being assembled to avoid any discrepancies. If two or more youngsters are to ride on the Jeep, the steering wheel may be placed on the left side to allow more than one to ride at the same time. In this case, the steering mechanism will consist of one pulley wide enough to take three turns of sash cord with a nail through the second turn, and a second pulley over which the cord runs to connect to the axle, as shown in Figs. 10 and 11. The cord should form perfect right angles when the front axle is square with the frame.

Four sash lifts make the steps on the side of the seat. A floor mat, electric horn, and spare wheel are suitable accessories. Paint the body a dull green, and use aluminum paint for the headlamps and the star in the middle of the hood.

CHILDREN'S CARS
Part Three

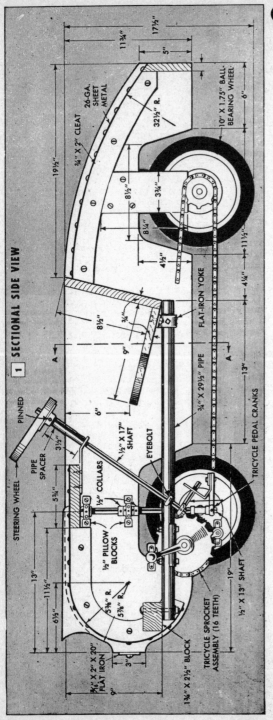

1 SECTIONAL SIDE VIEW

Labels in figure: STEERING WHEEL · PINNED · PIPE SPACER · ½" COLLARS · ½" PILLOW BLOCKS · ½" x 17" SHAFT · EYEBOLT · ¾" x 29½" PIPE · TRICYCLE PEDAL CRANKS · FLAT-IRON YOKE · 10" x 1.75" BALL-BEARING WHEEL · 26-GA. SHEET METAL · ¾" X 2" CLEAT · TRICYCLE SPROCKET ASSEMBLY (16 TEETH) · ½" x 13" SHAFT · 1¾" x 2½" BLOCK · ⅜" x 2" X 20" FLAT IRON

Dimensions: 17½" · 11¾" · 5" · 6" · 32½" R. · 19½" · 8½" · 3¾" · 8¼" · 8¼" · 4½" · 11½" · 4¼" · 4¾" · 8½" · ¾" · 9" · 13" · 6" · 3½" · 5¾" · 13" · 11½" · 6½" · 5¾" R. · 5¾" R. · 1" · 1¾" x 2½" · 3" · 9"

D AD WILL have little trouble "selling" the family small fry on the features of this sporty, pedal-driven auto—one look will be enough. They'll be quick to see the real headlights, plastic windshield, rubber tires and airplane-type steering wheel. Built from common parts and stock lumber, the car features a chain drive, using a standard tricycle sprocket bolted to a pipe support.

Fig. 1 gives the dimensions for laying out the sides on 1 x 12-in. pine stock. Cleats for supporting the sheet-metal hood and rear deck are screwed and glued to the inner faces of the sides ½ in. down from the top edge. Mounting cleats for the pillow blocks which carry the rear axle are centered in the wheel openings. Remember to make a right and left-hand assembly. The sides are joined together at the front with a heavy cross member, to which the pipe support is bolted, and at the back with a 1 x 6 board. Long flat-headed screws are used to fasten these cross members, the rear member being 16 in. long, and the front one 14½ in. long. The seat board and back are also screwed in place at this time. The final wooden piece to be added is the 1 x 6-in. board that supports the windshield and steering-column bracket. However, you may find it more convenient to fasten this in place after the pillow blocks for the steering assembly are installed.

Fig. 2 shows the chassis assembly at a glance. The ¾-in. pipe support for the car is drilled at the points indicated for mounting the tricycle sprocket, the eyebolt for the steering column and the bolts which anchor the pipe to the body. A U-shaped yoke, bent from flat iron, is used to fasten the rear end of the pipe to the bottom of the seat.

Lengths of ½-in. cold-rolled shafting are used for the steering assembly, the steering column and the front and rear axles. Details in Figs. 2 and 3 show how "knuckles" for the front wheels are improvised from ¼-in. pipe tees. These are drilled or reamed out and then cross-pinned to lengths of ½-in.

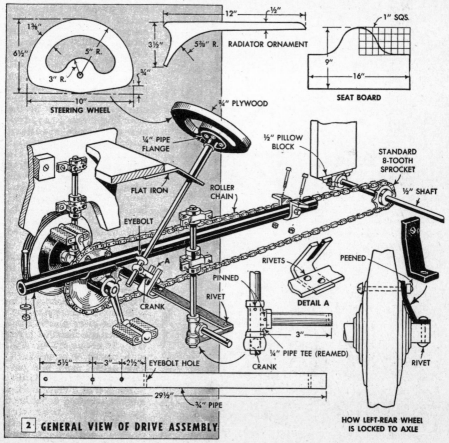

1 3/8"
6 1/2"
5" R.
3" R.
10"
STEERING WHEEL

12"   1/2"
3 1/2"
5 3/8" R.
RADIATOR ORNAMENT
3/4"

1" SQS.
9"
16"
SEAT BOARD

3/4" PLYWOOD
1/4" PIPE FLANGE
1/2" PILLOW BLOCK
STANDARD 8-TOOTH SPROCKET
1/2" SHAFT
FLAT IRON
ROLLER CHAIN
EYEBOLT
A
RIVETS
PEENED
PINNED
RIVET
CRANK
DETAIL A
RIVET
3"
1/4" PIPE TEE (REAMED)
CRANK

5 1/2"   3"   2 1/2"   EYEBOLT HOLE
29 1/2"
3/4" PIPE

2 GENERAL VIEW OF DRIVE ASSEMBLY

HOW LEFT-REAR WHEEL IS LOCKED TO AXLE

The wooden radiator ornament is screwed to the hood from the underside, while two roundheaded screws hold the flat-iron bumper in place

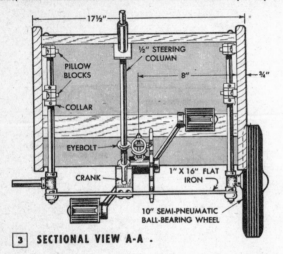

3 **SECTIONAL VIEW A-A .**

Like a tricycle, braking is done with the pedals, and if the driver has difficulty reaching the pedals, a back cushion can be provided

rod, 3-in. lengths being provided for the wheel axles. Note that the tees are pinned about ¾ in. from the ends of the vertical lengths to permit attaching radius arms to the lower ends. Cranks taken from tricycle pedals were used for these on the original car, although you can make them from bar stock, drilling and tapping each one for a setscrew. Note that a third crank is used on the steering column to engage a slotted bracket riveted to a flat-iron radius rod. Two collars, one above and one below the lower pillow block on each side of the car, hold the steering assembly in place. The lower end of the steering column is supported by an eyebolt, while the upper end is held by a flat-iron bracket. A pipe spacer placed over the upper end of the shaft holds the column in place. The pipe flange, to which the steering wheel is fastened, is drilled out and pinned to the column. Pillow blocks, which provide bearings for the rear wheels, are screwed securely to the ends of the mounting cleats provided, and an 8-tooth standard sprocket is fitted to the axle in line with the tricycle sprocket. Slotted mounting holes in the latter provide takeup of the roller chain. Any 10-in. semi-pneumatic, ball-bearing wheels can be used. Details in Fig. 2 show how the left wheel is locked to the rear axle.

The sheet-metal hood and deck covering are attached to the cleats with oval-headed screws and cup washers, spaced about 2 in. apart. The windshield consists of two pieces of clear plastic 5 x 8 in. which are fastened to the body at about a 2-in. slant with pieces of metal angle. The lights used are battery-operated headlights purchased at a bicycle shop, and are attached to the hood by driving the mounting screws into wooden blocks fitted under the sheet metal.

CHILDREN'S CLOTHES RACK

THIS child's-room costumer makes it easier for youngsters to hang hats and coats neatly on a rack. Pony heads in cut-out design, which serve as braces for the column, and a pint-sized Scotty sitting at attention on the top effectively match the usual decorations of a child's room. The whole thing's easy to make, too. All you need are hand tools and a few pieces of suitable hardwood. Birch is especially recommended because it is so easy to finish with either colored enamels or varnish to match the other furnishings. Parts are joined with screws and all edges are sanded smooth before finishing.

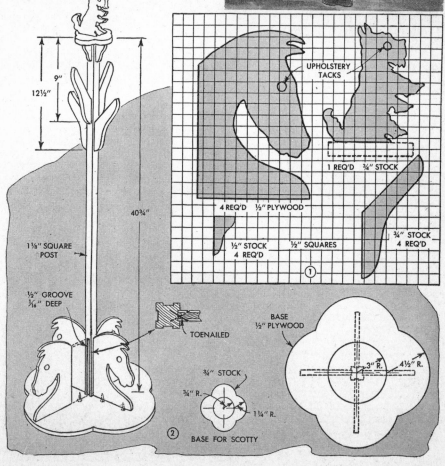

9"

12½"

40¾"

1⅛" SQUARE POST

½" GROOVE 1/16" DEEP

TOENAILED

UPHOLSTERY TACKS

1 REQ'D ¾" STOCK

4 REQ'D ½" PLYWOOD

½" STOCK 4 REQ'D

½" SQUARES

¾" STOCK 4 REQ'D

①

¾" STOCK

¾" R.

1¼" R.

② BASE FOR SCOTTY

BASE ½" PLYWOOD

3" R.

4½" R.

CHILD'S FOLDING TABLE AND

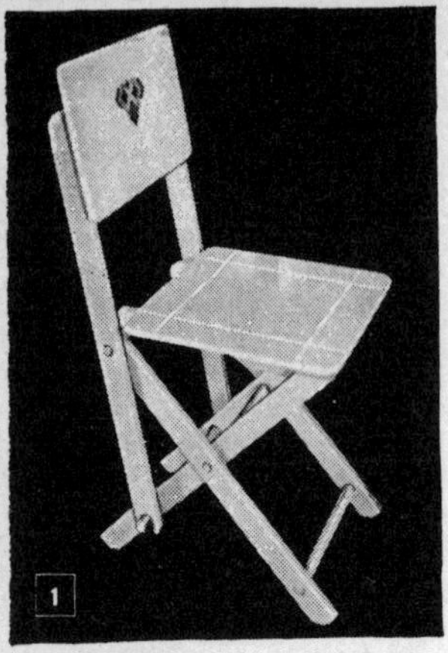

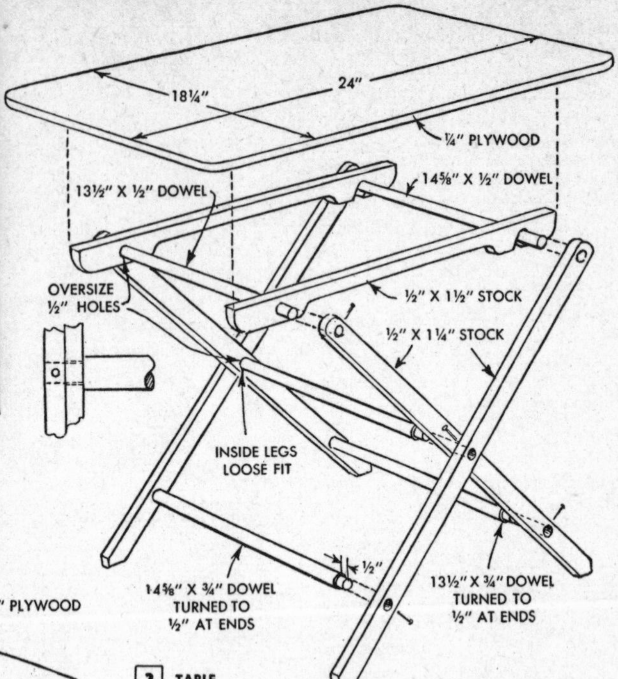
24"
18¼"
¼" PLYWOOD
14⅝" X ½" DOWEL
13½" X ½" DOWEL
OVERSIZE ½" HOLES
½" X 1½" STOCK
½" X 1¼" STOCK
INSIDE LEGS LOOSE FIT
½"
14⅝" X ¾" DOWEL TURNED TO ½" AT ENDS
13½" X ¾" DOWEL TURNED TO ½" AT ENDS

3 TABLE

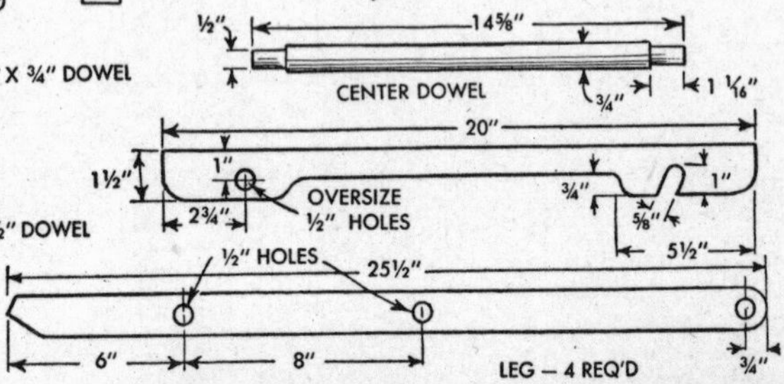
½"
14⅝"
CENTER DOWEL
¾"
1 1/16"
20"
1½"
1"
OVERSIZE ½" HOLES
2¾"
¾"
⅝"
1"
5½"
½" HOLES
25½"
6"
8"
¾"
LEG — 4 REQ'D

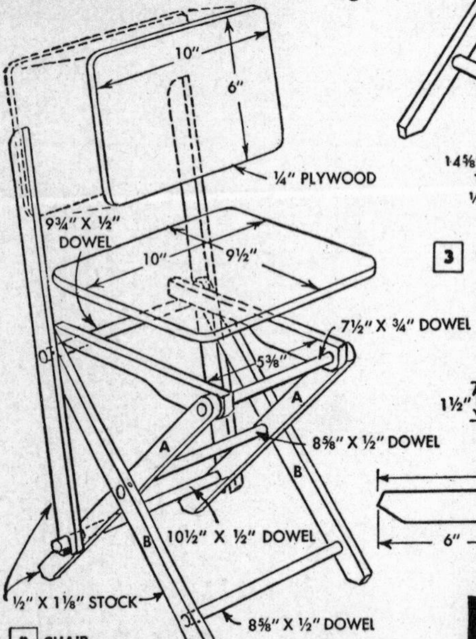
10"
6"
¼" PLYWOOD
9¾" X ½" DOWEL
10"
9½"
7½" X ¾" DOWEL
5⅜"
A
A
8⅝" X ½" DOWEL
B
B
10½" X ½" DOWEL
½" X 1⅛" STOCK
8⅝" X ½" DOWEL

2 CHAIR

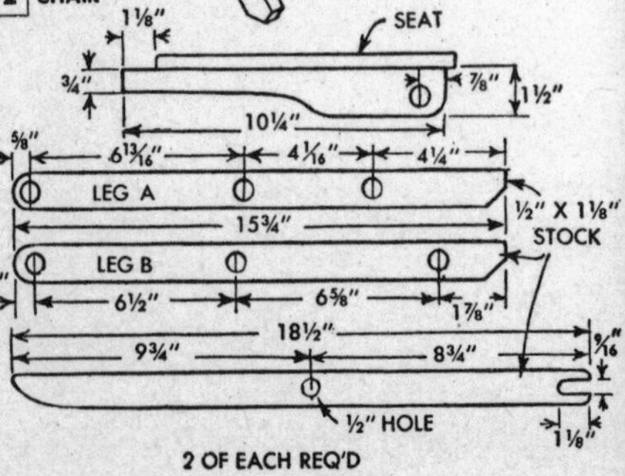
1⅛"
SEAT
¾"
⅞"
1½"
10¼"
⅝"
6 13/16"
4 1/16"
4¼"
LEG A
½" X 1⅛" STOCK
15¾"
LEG B
¾"
6½"
6⅝"
1⅞"
18½"
9¾"
8¾"
9/16"
½" HOLE
1⅛"
2 OF EACH REQ'D

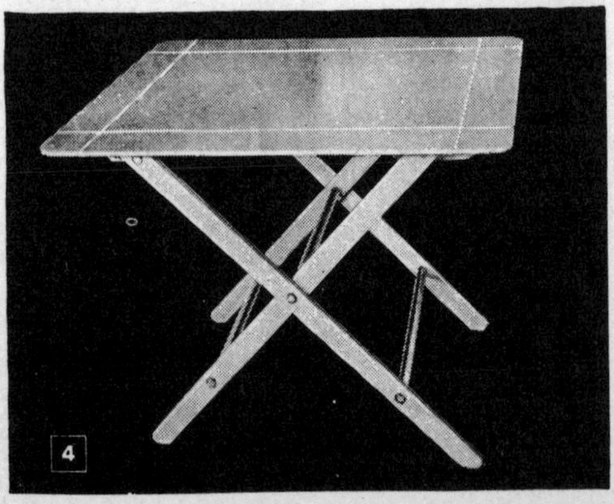

CHAIRS

Just the thing to make her Christmas set of dishes complete. Table and chairs fold compactly for storing

TEA PARTIES galore are in store for the little hostess of your family when she can entertain with this novel table-and-chair set. It is lightweight and folds as in Fig. 5, so that little tots can carry it easily. Very little material is required to make it.

The chairs: Any number of chairs can be made. Several duplicate parts can be cut and drilled at one time, Fig. 6, and if power tools are available, a setup can be used to mass-produce the parts quickly and uniformly. Fig. 2 details the assembly of the chair and the plan below it gives the size of the members comprising the framework. Note that the stretchers are standard dowel stock and are purchased ready-made. With the exception of the seat board and back rest, which are plywood, all parts are of ½-in. stock. Leg and back members are 1⅛ in. wide, while the seat supports are shaped from stock 1½ in. wide. Notice that the ends of the stretchers fit flush with the outside faces of the legs and that the lower rear one extends through the back legs about ⅞ in. at each end, over which the notched back members hook. Except where the parts pivot, all stretcher holes should be bored for a light press fit, the others being made slightly oversize. In the latter case, the holes can be enlarged for a sliding fit with a round file or sandpaper wrapped around a smaller dowel. In assembling the parts, allow sufficient clearance between the joints. It's a good idea to use a metal or cardboard washer to prevent rubbing of the painted surfaces. Nails are driven crosswise through the legs and into the stretchers where indicated.

The table: Construction of the table is similar to the chairs. Fig. 3 shows how it goes together, and also gives the size of the parts required. Note that the stretchers are turned down at the ends to fit ½-in. holes in the legs. This adds rigidity, but, if desired, you can simply drive them into undersize holes and pin them. The top and its underframing must be ready for assembly at the same time as the other parts. The holes in which the top pivots are made

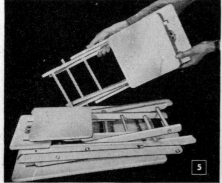

Here's how compactly the table and chairs fold. This is a welcome advantage in the home where storage space is limited. Set can include two or more chairs

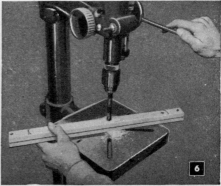

Where a number of chairs or several complete sets are to be made, cut and bore duplicate parts by mass-production methods, using simple jigs made of wood

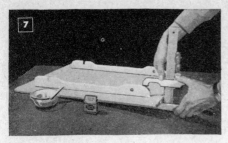

Above, clamping the underframing to plywood table top. Left, testing workability of chair before dismantling it for finishing. Spray gun speeds painting

oversize, and the notches at the opposite end are formed by first drilling ⅝-in. holes and then sawing in from the edge at an angle to meet the holes.

Finishing: The parts can be painted easily if done before assembly. Check to see that the chairs and table fold freely and then dismantle for finishing. Spray equipment turns the job into play and permits use of quick-drying lacquer. Give all the parts a coat of lacquer sealer first and when dry sand them lightly. Then finish with a couple coats of lacquer. Brushing lacquer is available but it requires considerable experience to apply. Very little brushing can be done and the lacquer must be applied with full brush loads in a sweeping motion to avoid lap marks. Enamel, perhaps, is the best to use with a brush. The original set was done in light blue and striped in white as shown in Figs. 1 and 4. Decals can be added to the chair backs.

Children's Picnic Table Has Adjustable Seats

26"

19"

13"

18½"

30"

HEIGHT ADJUSTMENT HOLES

Durable, good looking and light enough to be moved about easily, this picnic table for children can be used indoors or out. It is built of lengths of scrap hardwood flooring and is assembled with bolts through the legs and framing, the tongue-and-grooved top being attached with screws. Holes drilled in the legs permit the seats to be adjusted for the height. The table can be stained or left natural, but spar varnish should be applied to protect it from moisture if it is to be used outdoors.

CHILDREN'S PLAYHOUSES

A DAUGHTER'S HERO is in the making when Dad sets to work building this little "dream home" for the No. 2 boss of the family. A home of her own in which to copy Mommie will make her the proudest little housekeeper in the neighborhood. True, this pint-sized cottage is apt to cost more than Dad would be willing to invest if he were to order all of the material from a lumberyard. But by rounding up a number of good-sized wooden packing boxes, which usually can be had for little or nothing from local merchants, building costs will barely dent the pocketbook.

The one-room floor plan measures approximately 4 x 6½ ft., and the house is so designed that it can be taken apart in sections for storing or moving. You'll note in the drawings that the various members specified for the wall framing are common lumberyard sizes, being 1 x 2, 2 x 2, etc. Although it is possible to build up these sizes from random widths and lengths of box lumber, as was done by the Rev. Mr. Shedd, those unable to obtain scrap wood suitable for the framing members will have a minimum of cutting if the stock sizes given are used. Common No. 2 grade lumber will be satisfactory for these pieces and considerably less expensive than select stock. As you may know, 1 x 2 material actually measures ¾ in. x 1⅝ in. This holds true with all lumberyard sizes, 2 x 2 being 1⅝ in. x 1⅝ in. square, etc. The thin material taken from lettuce crates is used as

siding, the ends of the pieces being butted against 1 x 2 battens which are nailed to the face of 2 x 2 studs.

Both ends of the house are made exactly alike, a 16 x 16-in. window being framed in each one. The back and front walls are of the same over-all size and differ only in that a door and a window are framed in the front wall. While the front and back walls are shown in two separate sections bolted together at the center to further aid in storing the dismantled house, they can be made in one section where the storage problem is of no concern. Totaling 80 in. over all, the front-wall framework pictured in following illustrations includes the thickness of the end walls. The sectional detail above the same drawing shows how flat-headed bolts are installed to lock the four walls together at the corners. Note that 1 x 2 strips are nailed to the studs wherever indicated to provide nailing surfaces for the ends of the siding. Note also how 1 x 2 corner boards are nailed only to the corners of the end walls. Each wall can be finished complete and then all four bolted together, or the skeleton framework of each wall may be bolted to the other wall frames first, and then the siding applied. In the latter case, the floor of the house should be made ready for bolting the walls to it. As the detail shows, the floor is simply a 2 x 6 frame set on edge and floored over. Holes are made in the lower members of the wall-section frames to slip over bolts protruding through sides of the floor platform. It might be well to creosote the underside of the floor platform to preserve it against rot. Regardless, the house should be elevated off the ground by erecting it on bricks placed at the corners.

Door and window frames are built up in the manner indicated, a frame being made in each case to fit the particular opening and then faced with a ¾-in. casing. Window sash are made by framing a pane of ¼-in. crystal glass with wooden strips grooved to fit over the edge of the glass. Two small hinges at the bottom of each sash will permit opening. If desired, small screens can be made for the windows. The door is sided with slats taken from lettuce crates so it will match the rest of the house and is hinged to swing inward and fitted

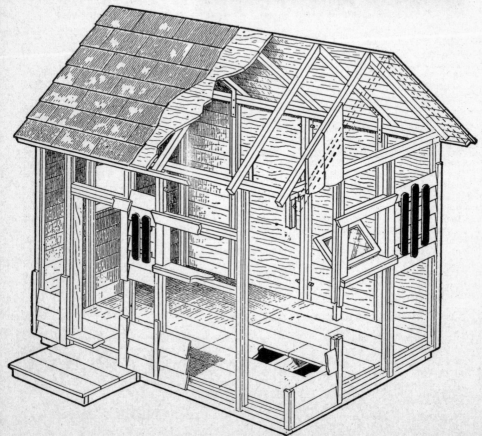

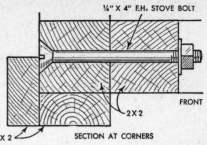

¼" X 4" F.H₂ STOVE BOLT

FRONT

2 X 2

1 X 2

SECTION AT CORNERS

witn a knob and lock. Final treatment of the outside includes the addition of shutters to the windows and a stoop in the front of the door.

The removable roof of the house is made in one piece and is attached by means of steel straps and screws. Roof framing requires fourteen 2 x 2 rafters, four being used at the ends of the overhang. Note that the rafters at the gables are joined together with a 2 x 2 plate to provide nailing surfaces for the vertical batten boards. Rounding the lower ends of these boards adds a decorative touch to the gable ends. The roof boards overhang the gables about 6 in. and are first applied, then sawed off

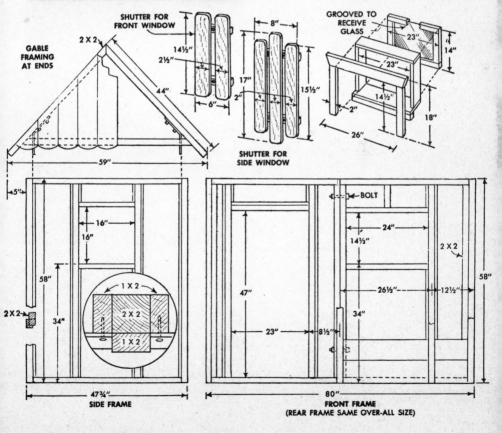

GABLE FRAMING AT ENDS

2 X 2

44"

59"

SHUTTER FOR FRONT WINDOW

14½"

2½"

6"

8"

17"

2"

15½"

SHUTTER FOR SIDE WINDOW

GROOVED TO RECEIVE GLASS

23"

23"

14"

14½"

2"

26"

18"

5"

16"

16"

58"

34"

1 X 2

2 X 2

2 X 2

1 X 2

47¾"

SIDE FRAME

BOLT

24"

14½"

2 X 2

47"

26½"

12½"

34"

23"

8½"

58"

80"

FRONT FRAME
(REAR FRAME SAME OVER-ALL SIZE)

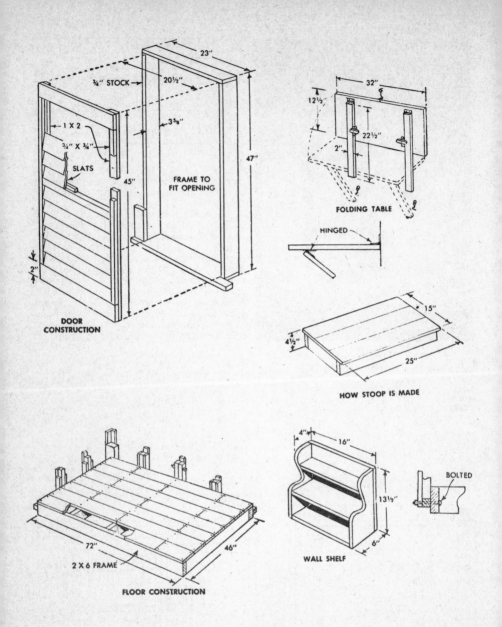

23"

¾" STOCK → 20½"

1 X 2

¾" X ¾"

SLATS

45"

3⅝"

FRAME TO
FIT OPENING

47"

2"

**DOOR
CONSTRUCTION**

32"

12½"

22½"

2"

FOLDING TABLE

HINGED

15"

4½"

25"

HOW STOOP IS MADE

4"

16"

13½"

6"

WALL SHELF

BOLTED

72"

46"

2 X 6 FRAME

FLOOR CONSTRUCTION

evenly at the ends and finally nailed to
2 x 2 rafters fitted flush with the ends.
Regular roll roofing or asphalt shingles are
used on the roof. The details show how a
little shelf and folding table can be made to
supplement regular play furniture. The
top of the table is hinged along the back
edge in a manner that will allow it to fold
upward and flat against the wall when not
in use. Two wooden turn buttons attached
to the underside of the table are provided
for holding the hinged supports in place,
and hooks and screw eyes are used to lock
the table in the folded position as well as in
a setup position. A scrap of linoleum may
be added to the table top. A long extension cord plugged into a garage outlet will
permit the house to be lighted.   ★ ★ ★

There are few toys that delight a little girl like a walk-in playhouse. This plywood cottage is a yard toy that will bring many hours of pleasure and it is small enough for indoor use in rainy weather or during the cold months

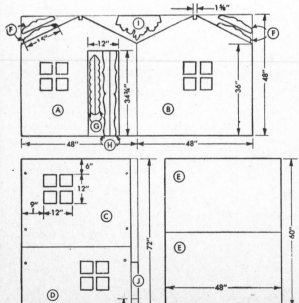

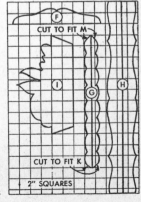

2" SQUARES

CUT TO FIT M

CUT TO FIT K

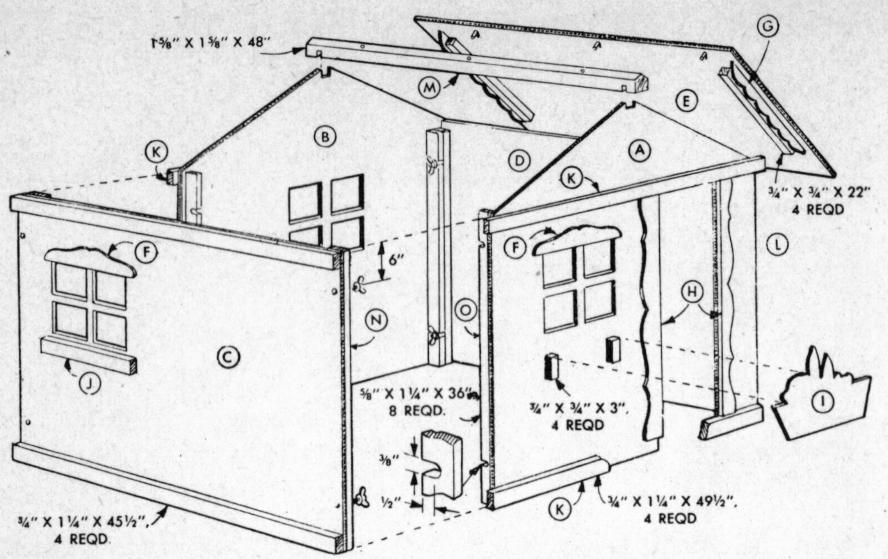
1⅝" X 1⅝" X 48"
G
M
E
B
K
A
D
¾" X ¾" X 22"
4 REQD
F
L
6"
N
O
H
C
J
⅝" X 1¼" X 36"
8 REQD.
¾" X ¾" X 3".
4 REQD
I
⅜"
½"
¾" X 1¼" X 49½".
4 REQD
K
¾" X 1¼" X 45½".
4 REQD.

DESIGNED to be set up or taken down in just a few minutes, this quaint little play cottage collapses to form a compact unit that can be stored under a bed or in a closet. The sides, roof and trim are cut from three 4 x 8-ft. sheets of plywood, and a few lengths of solid stock are required for uprights, plates, cleats and ridge board. Although ⅜-in. plywood was used on the original house, ¼-in. plywood or hardboard will serve the purpose. If the house is to remain outdoors during the summer months, be sure to use weatherproof

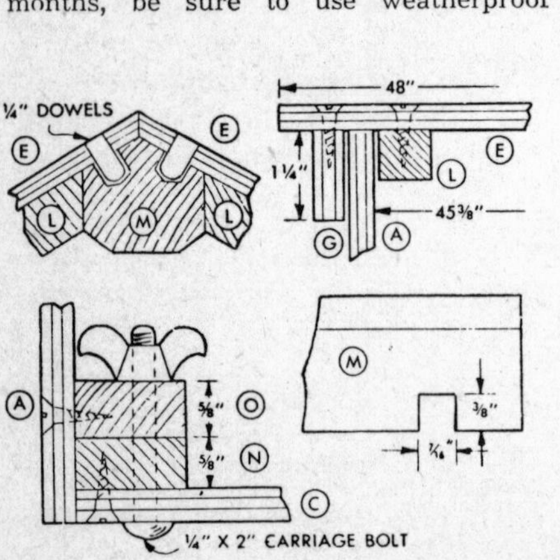
¼" DOWELS
E
E
L
M
L
48"
1¼"
E
L
45⅜"
G
A
A
⅝"
O
⅝"
N
C
¼" X 2" CARRIAGE BOLT
M
⅜"

(marine-type) plywood for the walls and roof. Note in the details how the corner uprights of the sidepieces are fitted with bolts which engage notches cut in the corner uprights of the end panels. Wing nuts lock the uprights together for quick assembly. The ridge board is notched to fit over the gables and drilled to receive dowels inserted near the upper edge of each roof panel. Valances and cleats form channels near ends of the roof panels. The channels engage the edges of the gables. Sills, lintels and doorway trim are glued and screwed directly to the plywood panels, but the window boxes are given the effect of depth by mounting them on ¾-in.-sq. spacer blocks fastened to the plywood. If the house is intended primarily for outdoor use, it will be worth-while to include a raised floor to keep the children off the damp ground. The floor can be made by screwing a sheet of plywood or hardboard to 1 x 2-in. joists set on edge. The joists should be spaced not more than 12 in. apart. To facilitate storage, make the floor in two parts, hinging them together if desired. Notch the corners of the floor to clear the uprights when the walls are set up around it. The floor can be painted with porch enamel or marine varnish, and made even more attractive by covering it with a remnant of linoleum. Paint the walls, roof and trim of the house in bright colors and, if you wish, hang plastic or oilcloth curtains at the windows. Although a door is not necessary, a simple one can be made by hinging a plywood panel to the doorway, fitting the panel with a knob-type drawer pull on each side.

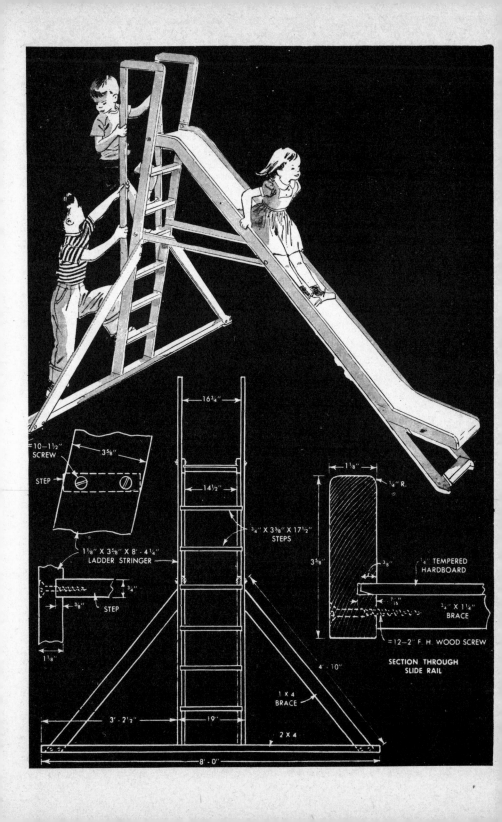

#10-1½"
SCREW

3⅝"

STEP

1⅛" X 3⅝" X 8' - 4¼"
LADDER STRINGER

¾"

⅜"

STEP

1⅛"

16¾"

14½"

¾" X 3⅝" X 17½"
STEPS

3' - 2½"

19"

8' - 0"

1 X 4
BRACE

2 X 4

4' - 10"

1⅛"

¼" R.

3⅝"

⅜"

7⁄16"

¼" TEMPERED
HARDBOARD

¾" X 1¼"
BRACE

=12-2" F. H. WOOD SCREW

SECTION THROUGH
SLIDE RAIL

Children's Slide

MATERIAL LIST

Tempered hardboard

1 pc. ¼" x 15¼" x 12' — Slide bed

Clear pine, redwood or cedar

2 pcs. — 1⅛" x 3⅝" x 14" — Top slide rails
2 pcs. — 1⅛" x 3⅝" x 10' - 4" — Side slide rails
2 pcs. — 1⅛" x 3⅝" x 25" — Bottom slide rails
2 pcs.—1⅛" x 3⅝" x 8' - 4¼"—Ladder stringers
2 pcs.—1⅛" x 3⅝" x 6' - ⅜"—Ladder handrails
2 pcs.—1⅛" x 3⅝" x 24"—Ladder handrails
2 pcs.—¾" x 3⅝" x 4' - 10"—Braces
2 pcs.—¾" x 1⅝" x 4' - 10"—Stay braces
1 pc.—1⅝" x 3⅝" x 14½"—Slide base
1 pc.—1⅝" x 3⅝" x 8'—Ladder base
2 pcs.—¾" x 3⅝" x 14½"—Slide cleats
7 pcs.—¾" x 1¼" x 14½"—Slide cleats
6—⅜" x 2½" carriage bolts
36—#10-1½" flat-head wood screws
30—#12-2" flat-head wood screws

Shrieks of delight from your youngsters will well repay you for the few hours it takes to build this junior-size back-yard slide. It is designed to be made from stock lumberyard material to eliminate unnecessary cutting, and ¼-in. tempered hardboard is used for the bed of the slide. The sectional detail through the rail of the slide shows how the hardboard is held in grooves and supported at intervals by 1 x 2 cross members. Where it is necessary to curve the hardboard at the top and bottom of the slide, the material must first be dampened for about 24 hr. to make the hardboard somewhat pliable. This is accomplished by placing wet cloths over the points of bend and keeping them wet for the required period. An application of varnish followed by wax will protect the bed of the slide and make it as slick as ice. Note that ladder assembly and braces are attached to the slide with bolts for dismantling when storing the slide during the winter

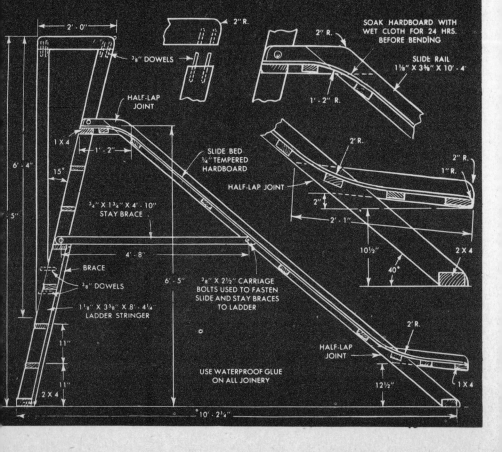

CHILDREN'S WARDROBE

YOU won't have to coax your children to hang up their clothes if they have a wardrobe house like this one. Complete with cedar-shingled roof and lapped siding, it can be placed anywhere against a wall. Besides the space inside the house for hanging clothes there's an "attic" for storing blankets and other extras. Drawers fitted into the side of the house take the place of a dresser or chest for slippers, sweaters and other small garments. Notice that the house is floored. This detail can be omitted and a threshold substituted for the doorstep if the house is made as an extension to an already existing closet. A small mirror attached to the outside surface of the door will give the entrance a realistic appearance as well as reflect the little owner's features. Or you can hang a mirror on the inside of the door, reserving the outside for a miniature knocker, house number or name plate. A toggle switch that controls interior lighting occupies the place of a bell button beside the door.

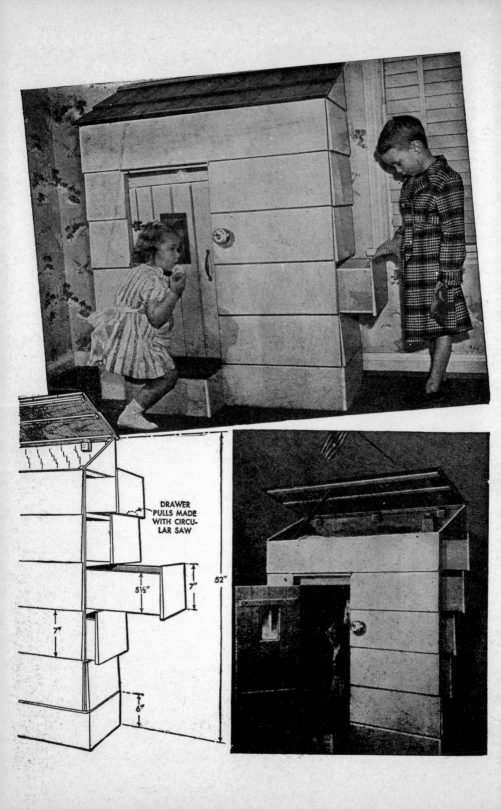

DRAWER PULLS MADE WITH CIRCULAR SAW

52"

7"

5½"

7"

6"

CHILD'S CHIFFOROBE

DESIGNED to complete the furnishings of a child's room, this attractive chifforobe offers generous wardrobe space, a chest of drawers with a full-width storage drawer and a special compartment for toys or linens. It looks its best when made from a close-grained wood such as poplar or birch, and finished in ivory enamel with the interior drawer fronts finished in the natural color of the wood. As the first step in the construction, build up the top to the required width by edge-gluing four to six strips of selected stock. Allow ½ in. all around for trimming to finish size. Although on the detail following shows the edge of the top molded, this can be omitted if no shaper is available. While the glued-up top is drying, cut selected stock for the drawer fronts, corner posts and the scrolled front and back aprons. Bandsaw the edges of the drawer fronts and the aprons, laying out the curves full size from the patterns given below. Round the bandsawed edges and sand smooth. Groove and rabbet the front and back posts. Frame the ends by fitting top and bottom rails and then glue and clamp the parts together. Note that the front posts are cut off square at the lower ends, flush with the scrolled edge of the apron, and are fitted with turned feet. Drill a hole in the lower end of each front post to take a ½ x 1¼-in. tenon. After turning out the feet, glue the parts together.

Note the assembly of parts in sections A-A and B-B, then build up the top and bottom frames, using grooved stretchers

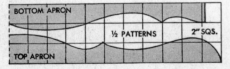

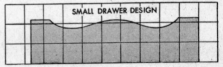

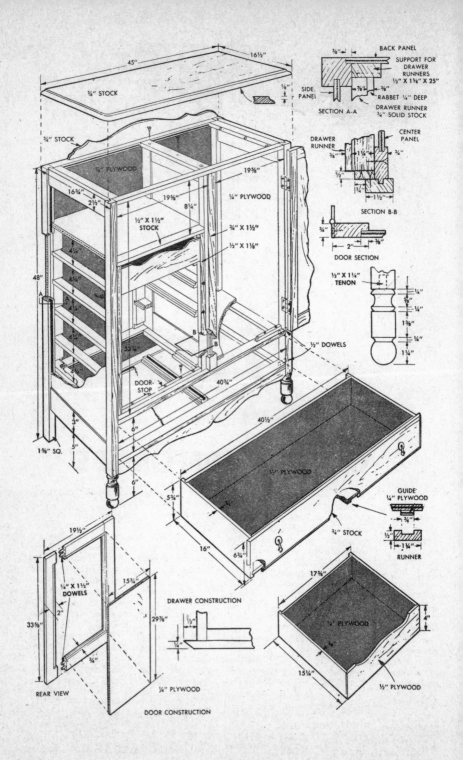

45"
16½"
¾" STOCK
⅛"
¾" STOCK
¼" PLYWOOD
19⅜"
¼" PLYWOOD
16¾"
2½"
19⅜"
8¼"
½" X 1½" STOCK
¾" X 1½"
½" X 1⅛"
48"
4½"
4⅛"
4⅛"
4¼"
32¼"
B
B
B
A
DOOR-STOP
40¾"
½" DOWELS
2⅝"
2"
6"
6"
1⅝" SQ.
5"
40½"
½" PLYWOOD
¾" STOCK
5¾"
¼"
16"
6¾"

BACK PANEL
⅜"
SUPPORT FOR DRAWER RUNNERS ½" X 1⅜" X 25"
SIDE PANEL
⅞"
RABBET ¼" DEEP
DRAWER RUNNER ¾" SOLID STOCK
SECTION A-A

DRAWER RUNNER
CENTER PANEL
⅜"
1¼"
¾"
½"
¼"
1½"
SECTION B-B

¾"
2"
⅜"
DOOR SECTION

½" X 1¼" TENON
¼"
⅞"
¼"
1⅜"
¼"
1¼"

GUIDE ¼" PLYWOOD
¾"
½"
1¼"
RUNNER

19½"
¼" X 1½" DOWELS
2"
15¾"
33⅜"
29⅞"
¾"
REAR VIEW
¼" PLYWOOD
DOOR CONSTRUCTION

DRAWER CONSTRUCTION
½"
¼"

17⅝"
¼" PLYWOOD
4"
15¼"
½" PLYWOOD

and the tenoned rails. Note that the bottom frame is paneled to provide dustproof construction, and that the back stretchers are rabbeted to take the back panel. Build up the intermediate frame, then drill blind holes for ½ or ¼-in. dowels which join the frames to the posts. After making a trial assembly of the parts to check the fit, apply glue to the doweled joints and clamp the parts together. Check the assembly for square corners before the glue dries, and cut and fit the back panel while the assembly is in the clamps. Attach the panel with screws, but do not use glue in the joints. Now, note that the back ends of the inside drawer runners are housed in grooves cut in uprights fitted into the corners of the drawer compartment, and that this compartment and the special storage space above are formed by a paneled partition supported on the intermediate frame. Make up this paneled partition first and join to the top and intermediate frames with screws and glue. Now, groove the back drawer-runner supports and screw them in place. The front-runner supports are ripped to the same width but are not grooved, the front ends of the runners being attached with screws as in the detail and section B-B. Rabbet the runners and glue and screw them in place. Attach the top, then fit plywood bottoms in the storage and wardrobe compartments. Now all that remains is the making and fitting of the drawers and doors. Construction of the drawers is clearly shown in the details, but note that the large drawer is fitted with a ½-in.-plywood bottom for added rigidity and also is fitted with a center guide. Doors can be paneled in the manner shown or the panels can be housed in grooves cut in the stiles and rails. The doors are hinged to close flush, but the lower drawer front is rabbeted all around and the outer edges are beveled to give a raised-panel effect. After the cabinet has been completely assembled, sand all exposed surfaces and apply a coat of sanding sealer. When this is dry, sand lightly and finish with two coats of ivory enamel. Apply a sanding sealer to the inside drawer fronts, sand lightly when dry, and finish in the natural color with two coats of varnish or one coat of water-white lacquer. The exposed center upright and the front drawer-runner supports also can be finished in the natural color if desired. Attach two pulls to the lower drawer.

CHIMNEYS

Repairing Damaged Chimney

When the bricks near the base of a chimney have begun to crumble due to an accumulation of moisture, repairs can be made easily by replacing two or three bricks at a time. Use a hammer and cold chisel to chip away the defective bricks and mortar and, after replacing the bricks, allow the mortar to set for a day or two before removing more bricks. Repeat this operation until all the damaged bricks have been replaced. Use a mortar of quick-setting cement and sand, adding very little lime. If the chimney does not have a cleanout door, leave out a couple of bricks and fit the opening with a metal cover.

Arthur N. Nelson, Kansas City, Mo.

Cleaning Soot From Chimney

A soot-filled chimney can be cleaned quickly by filling a burlap bag with excelsior and weighing it down with a couple of bricks. Then tie a length of rope to the top of the bag and drop it down the chimney, working it up and down against the sides to loosen the soot. If no excelsior is available, stuff the bag with crumpled newspaper, or wadded pieces of burlap. If you have sufficient quantities of steel wool on hand, however, use it in preference to the paper or burlap.

Insulation Packed Around Chimney Keeps Fire From Spreading

A source of danger frequently overlooked when fire-proofing a home is the space between a brick chimney and the adjoining floor or ceiling. Fire originating in the basement or first floor will travel through this vent and soon become difficult to control. A good preventive for this is to pack the space with a fill-type insulation. Not only will this stop the draft action of a fire, but it will seal off each floor during the winter and aid in conserving heat.

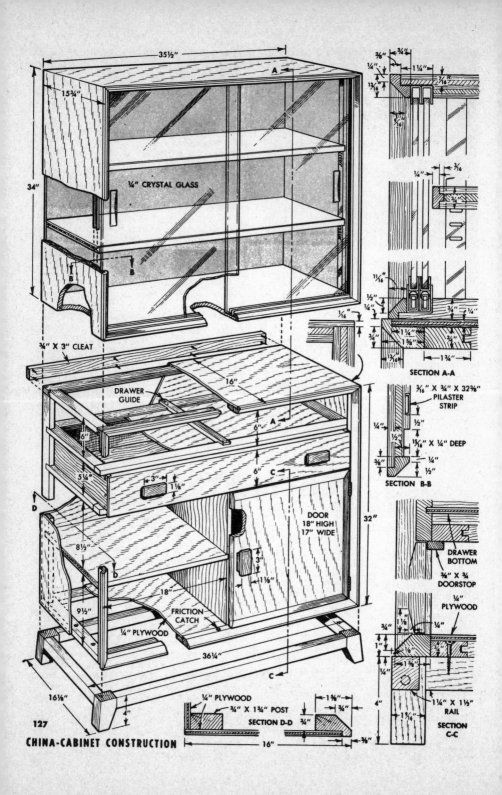

A

15¾"

35½"

¼" CRYSTAL GLASS

34"

B

B

¾" X 3" CLEAT

DRAWER GUIDE

16"

A

6"

6"

6"

5¼"

C

3"   1⅛"

D

DOOR
18" HIGH
17" WIDE

32"

8½"

D

3"

18"

11½"

9½"

FRICTION CATCH

¼" PLYWOOD

36¼"

C

16½"

4"

127

CHINA-CABINET CONSTRUCTION

¼" PLYWOOD

¾" X 1¾" POST

SECTION D-D   ¾"

1⅝"   ¾"

16"

⅜"

SECTION A-A

¾"   ¾"
¼"   1¼"   ⅛"
1¾"

⁵⁄₁₆"

¼"   ³⁄₁₆"

¾"

11¼"
½"   ¼"
1¼"   ¾"   ¼"
1⅝"   ¾"
1³⁄₁₆"   1¾"

⅛"

¾"

SECTION B-B

³⁄₁₆" X ¾" X 32⅜"
PILASTER STRIP
½"
¼"
½"   1¾" X ¼" DEEP
⅜"   ¼"
½"

DRAWER BOTTOM

⅜" X ¾
DOORSTOP
¼"
PLYWOOD

¾"   1⅛"   ¼"
1"   ⅛"
1⅝"

¼"

1¼" X 1½"
RAIL
4"
1¾"

SECTION C-C

CHINA CABINET

MADE FROM FINE cabinet woods, this project is a decorator's piece. It has sliding crystal-glass doors and the lower cabinet doors are made in a raised-panel design that gives the raised-panel effect without the enclosing frame. This is accomplished simply by beveling the edges of the panels which form the doors. Note, however, that only three edges are beveled on each door. Also, the front edges of the sides and top and the bottom stretcher are beveled. This has the pleasing effect of relieving the front of the cabinet, thus emphasizing detail in the same way as does a picture frame on a fine old painting.

Can you picture this china cabinet in your dining room? It's a modern version of the old-fashioned sideboard. It has raised panel doors in a recessed front below, and sliding crystal-glass doors above

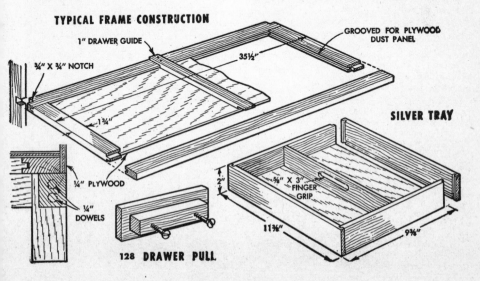

TYPICAL FRAME CONSTRUCTION

1" DRAWER GUIDE

GROOVED FOR PLYWOOD DUST PANEL

¾" X ¾" NOTCH

35½"

1¾"

¼" PLYWOOD

¼" DOWELS

SILVER TRAY

2"

⅝" X 3" FINGER GRIP

11¾"

9¾"

128 DRAWER PULL

Chip Carving Is Easy

Notch carving is another name for it and its beauty is in the characteristic precision and repetition of the detail

CHIP CARVING that equals the work of the old masters sounds like a big order, but study the step-by-step procedure beginning with Fig. 1 and you'll see that it's just as the title of the story says—easy. There are reasons, too. In the first place, to do simple chip carving you need only two knives with blades shaped as shown above. Just the shape of the blades alone is of the greatest aid in doing the work for no matter how you hold the knives the cutting edges are designed to give clean, shearing cuts. Another reason why chip carving is easy is the layout of the pattern full size directly on the wood. Because of this you don't have to depend on accuracy of eye alone, you have a line to follow, and, as most of the beauty of chip carving is in its geometric symmetry of arrangement, about all that's left in the way of requirements is care in handling the knife and in following the lines of the pattern. Fig. 8, A to F inclusive, suggests some of the basic patterns of chip-carved decoration.

In addition, Figs. 7 and 13 show a six-pointed star and a spiral design that work in well with other patterns laid out by means of straight lines on flat surfaces. In a gen-

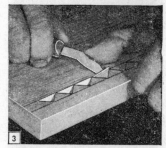

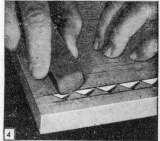

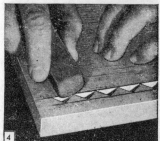

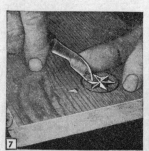

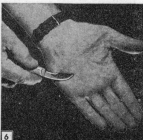

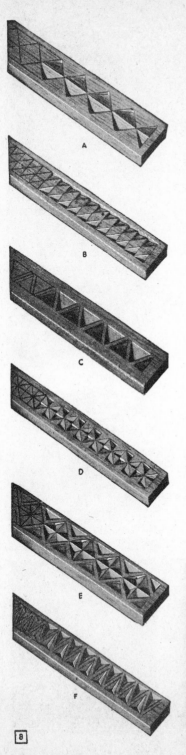

A

B

C

D

E

F

8

eral way, the whole ornamentation of any object by means of chip carving consists of an arrangement of small triangular shapes, squares and diamonds cut into the surface of the wood either in an allover pattern or as centerpieces and borders. No matter what degree or extent of ornamentation you decide on, the procedure is very much the same. It begins with the layout of the pattern, Fig. 1. Then, with the design shown, the next step is the two vertical cuts with the bevel-edged knife blade. These are quite generally called "stabbing" cuts and special care is taken to see that the cutting edge follows the pattern line as it enters the wood. The next and final cut with the slitting knife is shown in Fig. 3. This merely lifts out the chip and, of course, must be done with care so that the wood is not torn or splintered. The pattern pictured is merely a repetition of these three cuts. To finish up, you erase those parts of the pattern lines that remain after the cuts are made over the whole area.

Figs. 5 and 6 show how to sharpen the knife on an oilstone and whet the edge on the palm of your hand. In sharpening, use a fine oilstone and if you should nick the edge grind out the nick on a wet grindstone. Avoid a short bevel as this causes the blade to lift the chip too quickly, splintering the wood ahead of the cutting edge. It's almost impossible to control a blade sharpened with a short bevel because the cutting edge acts as a wedge. Rather, the bevel of a blade used in carving should extend from the back of the blade to the cutting edge and should be flat, not curved. The best procedure in renewing the cutting edge when there are no nicks is to sharpen on the oilstone, hone the edge lightly on a hard slipstone, then finish on the palm of your hand or on a piece of full-grain leather.

Figs. 9 to 12 inclusive show the layout and carving of a design essentially the same as that already described except that there are three stabbing cuts instead of two. If you study the six suggested designs in Fig. 8 you will see that there is a basic similarity between all of them although no two of them appear alike in over-all pattern. One of the best and simplest ways to finish chip carving is to apply successive coats of furniture wax and polish with a soft bristle brush. Don't use shellac or varnish because such finish would destroy the beauty of the carving.

9

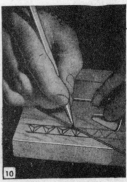

10

Picture Frame

You won't find this picture frame on every store counter. It's different because it has a hand-carved base. First there's the selection of wood, then a little sawing, grooving and sanding to do. Of the soft, close-grained woods choose white pine, basswood, poplar or red gum, the latter being the choicest of all. Maple, birch and cherry are perhaps the choice among the hardwoods suitable for chip carving

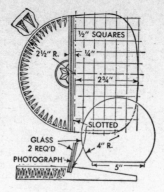

Book Ends

Book ends always show skillful handcraft to the best advantage. Everybody sees them at some time or other and you can always be casual about mentioning that you made them. That's usually enough, that is, if you did a good job. One thing about chip carving, especially on curved surfaces such as you have here: The layout should be exact, for the beauty of chip carving is in its precision of detail and design

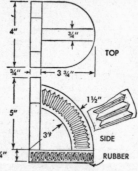

Pipe Rack

A chip-carved pipe rack is really something but practice a little on simpler work before you tackle this one. Choose a finer wood such as cherry or red gum and make the pattern layout with the greatest care because it really pays off in the finished job. Complete all hole drilling and sanding on the separate parts before assembling the rack. Finish with several coats of wax and polish lightly with a soft bristle brush

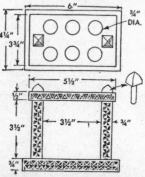

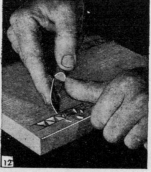

CHRISTMAS CARDS

WHEN CHRISTMAS draws near, many take care of the greeting-card problem by simply going out and buying them. But the card that bears a really personal and sincere greeting is one that represents the handiwork of the sender. Today, most of the personalized cards are limited to the photographic type, largely because they can be mass-produced with a minimum of effort. While photo cards offer a variation from commercial cards, in most cases they lack color. However, there are several other types of greeting cards that can be duplicated in quantity, as well as color.

TRACING PAPER — SHELLAC **3**

COPY — GREETINGS **4**

TRACING PAPER **5** — WAXED COPY — ETINGS

PRESSING CLOTH **6**

1⅛" SQ. STOCK — HARDBOARD

12" X 18" FRAME — LEG **1**

GUIDES

CORD — STENCIL SILK **2**

UNDERSIDE OF FRAME

MERRY CHRISTMAS **7**

Silk-screen process: Printing by silk screen requires a frame such as the one detailed in Fig. 1. This can be purchased as part of a kit including paints, or you can easily make one yourself. The underside of the frame is covered with No. 6 or 8 stencil silk. The silk is stretched taut as a drumhead and held by a length of cord which is wedged into a groove running completely around the frame, Fig. 2. The use of loose-pin hinges in hinging the frame to its base makes it convenient to remove the printing frame for cleaning and when applying the design.

Two different methods of printing may be used. In the direct method, the design to be printed is first drawn on paper, then placed under the silk and traced onto the screen with a fine pencil. When this is done, a medium, called resist (tempera show-card colors), is applied to the screen to block out portions of the design not to be printed. Areas of the screen surrounding the actual card size are masked off with paper and tape to save paint and keep the unused portion of the screen clean.

The design is reproduced by forcing paint through the open meshes of the silk screen, using a rubber squeegee as shown in the photo on this page. In the indirect method,

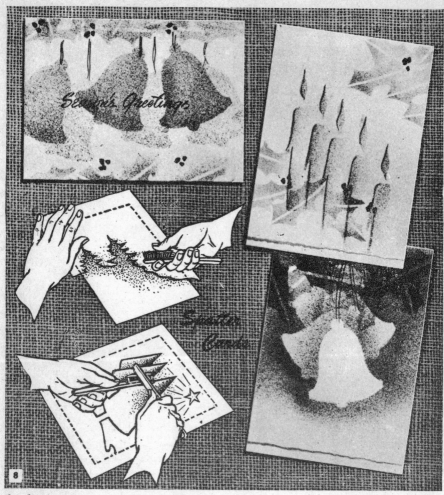

the design is made into a stencil which is attached to the underside of the screen, and the paint is transferred to the card through the stencil. Figs. 3 to 6 inclusive show the steps in preparing a stencil. First, a piece of tracing paper large enough to cover the entire screen is coated with shellac. Then the card design is coated with a thin film of wax with the fingers. Next, the tracing paper, shellac side up, is rolled over the waxed copy. Now all portions of the design that you want to print are cut out with a razor blade and finally the stencil is attached to the underside of the screen by pressing with a medium-hot iron. A quantity of thick silk-screen paint is poured onto the screen and wiped across the open portions of the stencil with the squeegee. Duplicate work is held in register under the screen by cardboard guides which are fastened to the base of the unit. By using colored paper for your cards, a two-color job can be produced with one printing.

Fig. 7 shows an example of four-color silk-screen work. Here, the tree branches, greeting and border of the card are drawn directly onto the screen and a seperate tracing-paper stencil is made for each ball. The screen pattern is run off first and then, when the cards are dry, the screen is cleaned and each colored ball is printed in turn, registering the stencil of each in the proper position on the underside of the screen. Printing can be done on almost any material, wood, cloth, metal or paper.

Spatter technique: A toothbrush is the main item you need for producing spatter cards. Several sample cards are shown above, consisting of a single fold, the lower edge of the front flap having a torn, or deckled, edge. The card design is produced by means of paper masks or stencils which

Cellophane Cards

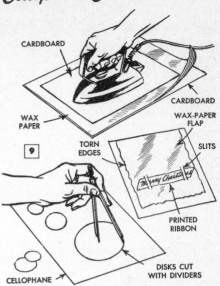

CARDBOARD

WAX PAPER

CARDBOARD

WAX-PAPER FLAP

TORN EDGES

SLITS

9

PRINTED RIBBON

CELLOPHANE

DISKS CUT WITH DIVIDERS

10

are placed over the areas that are not to be spattered. Fig. 8 shows two methods that can be used to flick the paint from the toothbrush, and another good method is to hold a tea strainer over the card and rub the brush over the wire mesh. Using show-card paints, dip the brush in the paint and hold it about 4 in. from the work.

Novelty Cards

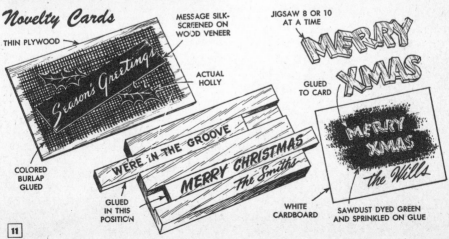

THIN PLYWOOD

MESSAGE SILK-SCREENED ON WOOD VENEER

ACTUAL HOLLY

JIGSAW 8 OR 10 AT A TIME

GLUED TO CARD

COLORED BURLAP GLUED

GLUED IN THIS POSITION

WHITE CARDBOARD

SAWDUST DYED GREEN AND SPRINKLED ON GLUE

11

Folding Photo Cards

12

RULED TO
REPRESENT
WINDOW

3½" X 10"
PHOTO PAPER

FOLDED

ENTIRE CARD PRINTED
FROM ONE NEGATIVE

Season's Greetings

13

8" X 10"
PHOTO PAPER

GROUP
PHOTO

TAPE

FOLD ON
DOTTED
LINES

COLORED
CELLOPHANE

HOLES CUT
IN CARD

Wax paper and cellophane. This is, perhaps, the quickest and most inexpensive type of card to produce. Here, balls, trees, candles, etc., are cut from colored cellophane and fastened to the back side of a wax-paper flap which adds a "frosty" effect to a twig or other design painted on the card itself. A household iron is used to stick the cellophane to the waxed paper as shown in Fig. 9, and Fig. 10 gives two examples of what can be done. Note in the lower card that spatter work is used also.

Photo and novelty cards: Figs. 11, 12 and 13 offer suggestions for several unusual cards. Fig. 13 shows how color can be introduced in the case of a photo card by using a cellophane insert between the folds.

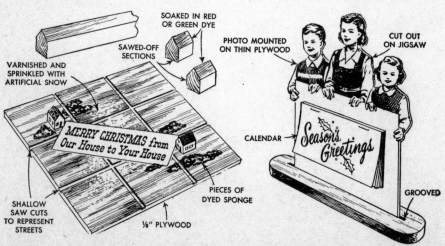

SAWED-OFF
SECTIONS

SOAKED IN RED
OR GREEN DYE

PHOTO MOUNTED
ON THIN PLYWOOD

CUT OUT
ON JIGSAW

VARNISHED AND
SPRINKLED WITH
ARTIFICIAL SNOW

*MERRY CHRISTMAS from
Our House to Your House*

CALENDAR

Season's Greetings

SHALLOW
SAW CUTS
TO REPRESENT
STREETS

⅛" PLYWOOD

PIECES OF
DYED SPONGE

GROOVED

Make Your Own
TREE ORNAMENTS

IF YOU'RE TIRED of trimming the Christmas tree with the same ornaments year after year, you will find these Tide-covered novelties a refreshing change. The ornaments are made by coating a variety of common items with a mixture of Tide and plastic starch as described in the sequence A to D, below. Best results are had by applying the mixture when the humidity is low so the ornaments will dry quickly. The icing will keep for several days in a covered container. Use such items as clothespins, pipe cleaners, drinking straws, cardboard cutouts, pretzels and nuts for basic props and cover the icing with sign-maker's glitter or paint with fingernail polish. Various types of trim, such as silver or gold dust, sequins, beads, ribbons and rhinestones should be collected before icing the props.

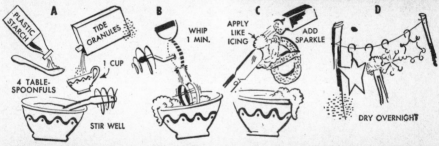

A — PLASTIC STARCH — 4 TABLESPOONFULS — TIDE GRANULES 1 CUP — STIR WELL

B — WHIP 1 MIN.

C — APPLY LIKE ICING — ADD SPARKLE

D — DRY OVERNIGHT

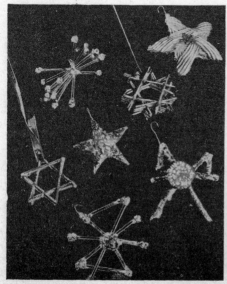

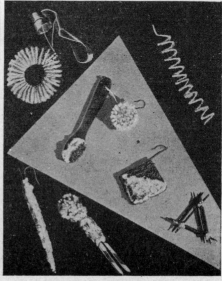

..Christmas Tree Stands

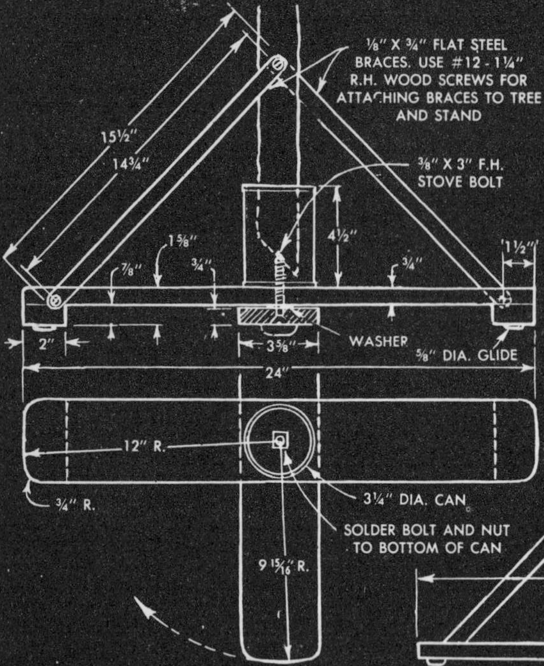

1/8" X 3/4" FLAT STEEL BRACES. USE #12 - 1 1/4" R.H. WOOD SCREWS FOR ATTACHING BRACES TO TREE AND STAND
15 1/2"
14 3/4"
3/8" X 3" F.H. STOVE BOLT
4 1/2"
1 5/8"
7/8"
3/4"
3/4"
1 1/2"
2"
3 5/8"
WASHER
5/8" DIA. GLIDE
24"
12" R.
3/4" R.
3 1/4" DIA. CAN
SOLDER BOLT AND NUT TO BOTTOM OF CAN
9 15/16" R.

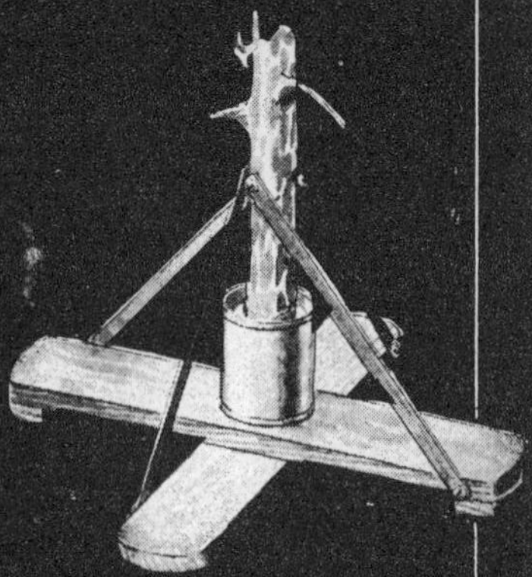

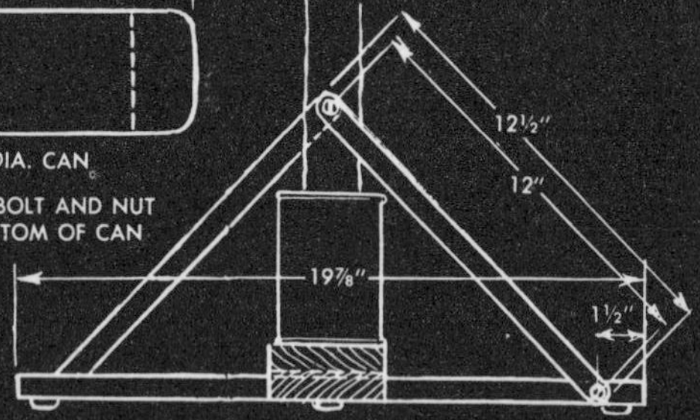

12 1/2"
12"
19 7/8"
1 1/2"

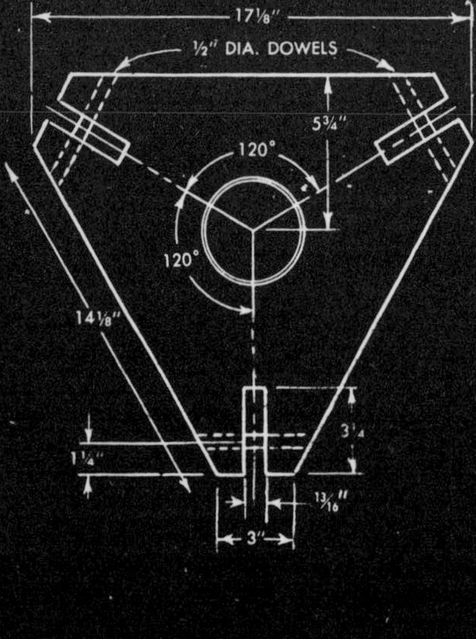

17 1/8"
1/2" DIA. DOWELS
5 3/4"
120°
120°
14 1/8"
3 1/4
1 1/4"
13/16"
3"

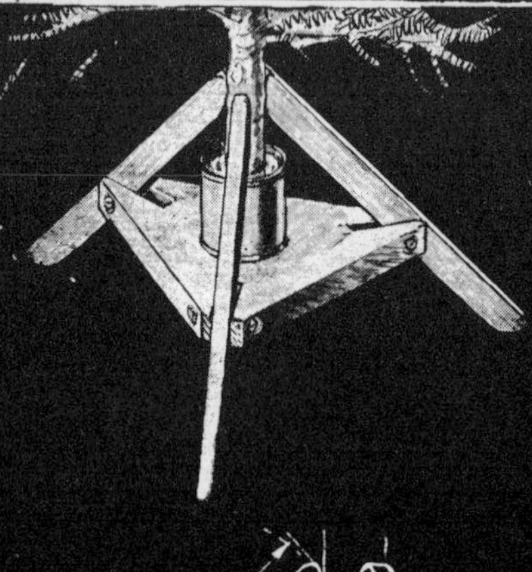

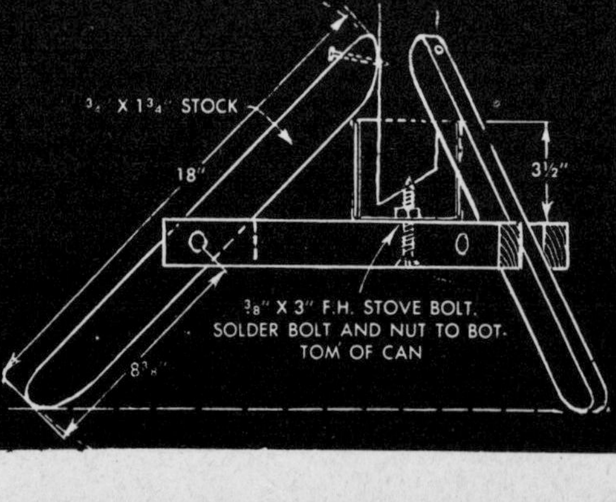

3/4 X 1 3/4 STOCK
18"
3 1/2"
3/8" X 3" F.H. STOVE BOLT. SOLDER BOLT AND NUT TO BOTTOM OF CAN

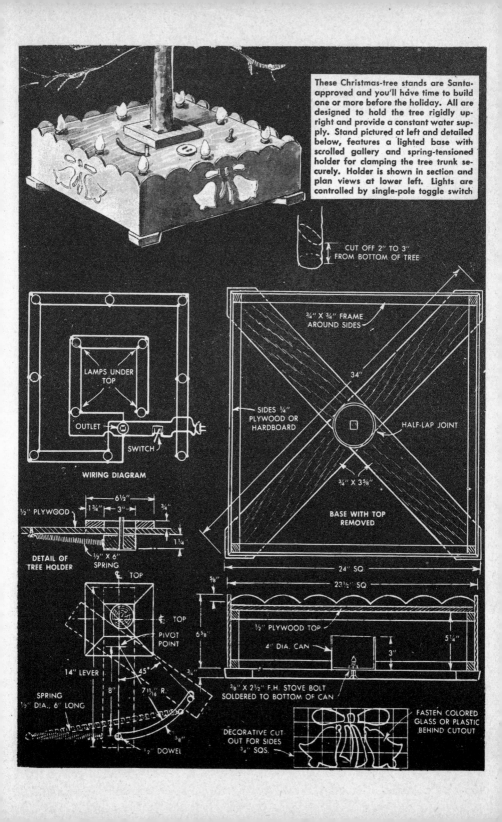

These Christmas-tree stands are Santa-approved and you'll have time to build one or more before the holiday. All are designed to hold the tree rigidly upright and provide a constant water supply. Stand pictured at left and detailed below, features a lighted base with scrolled gallery and spring-tensioned holder for clamping the tree trunk securely. Holder is shown in section and plan views at lower left. Lights are controlled by single-pole toggle switch

CUT OFF 2" TO 3" FROM BOTTOM OF TREE

LAMPS UNDER TOP

OUTLET

SWITCH

WIRING DIAGRAM

¾" X ¾" FRAME AROUND SIDES

34"

SIDES ¼" PLYWOOD OR HARDBOARD

HALF-LAP JOINT

¾" X 3⅜"

BASE WITH TOP REMOVED

24" SQ

6½"

1¾"   3"   ¾"

½" PLYWOOD

1¼"

DETAIL OF TREE HOLDER

½" X 6" SPRING

⅝"

23½" SQ

½" PLYWOOD TOP

4" DIA. CAN

5¼"

3"

TOP

⅊ TOP

PIVOT POINT

6⅜"

14" LEVER

45°

8"

7¹¹⁄₁₆" R.

¾"

SPRING ½" DIA., 6" LONG

⅝"

½" DOWEL

⅜" X 2½" F.H. STOVE BOLT SOLDERED TO BOTTOM OF CAN

DECORATIVE CUT-OUT FOR SIDES ¾" SQS.

FASTEN COLORED GLASS OR PLASTIC BEHIND CUTOUT

CHRISTMAS TREES

FOIL STARS WIRED TO DOWEL

CREPE PAPER

SMALL ORNAMENT

CREPE PAPER

WIRED

BEAD

END OF WRAPPING GLUED

1/8" DOWEL

PIPE CLEANER

SPOOL WRAPPED WITH YARN

MINIATURE Christmas trees that add a novel touch to gay holiday decorations can be assembled from such common items as pipe cleaners, crepe paper, beads, etc. Typical trees suitable for table decoration are pictured and detailed above at the right. A spool wrapped with colored yarn forms the base and a length of 1/8-in. dowel serves as a tree trunk. On one of the trees shown a small bell is used as a base. Pipe cleaners are wired to the trunk to form branches, the outer ends of the cleaners being bent up or down, depending on the type of tree desired. By turning the ends up and forcing small colored beads over the upturned ends, a remarkably realistic simulation of candles is achieved. When the ends of the branches are turned down and curved inward they form hangers for bells or other miniature ornaments. After the branches are wired in position on the trunk, both the trunk and branches are wrapped with narrow strips of colored crepe paper. Colored balls or foil stars form effective top ornaments. Stars are wired to the top of the trunk and ball ornaments can be at-tached with a drop of liquid glue. Another type of tree, pictured above at the left, forms a secondary shade over a reading lamp. Make a tall cone of heavy colored paper, the open end of the cone being of the same diameter as the lamp shade. Cut round, diamond, or star-shaped holes in the cone and glue squares of colored tissue or cellophane paper over them to simulate tree ornaments. Decorate with a fringe and spiral wrapping of tinsel as shown. When the lamp is lighted the effect is attractively realistic. Utilizing the same idea, larger decorative trees can be made by gluing or tacking paper cones in graduated sizes to a length of dowel or a broomstick. The cones should overlap, the largest one being placed at the bottom.

CHUCK FITTING ON YOUR LATHE

A chuck that is fitted properly and handled carefully will give many years of satisfactory service

ONE OF THE MOST interesting turning jobs you'll want to do after buying your own metal-turning lathe, and one that will save you money, is machining the chuck back when fitting the new chuck to the lathe. As supplied by the manufacturer, the chuck back is a rough casting and must be machined all over and internally threaded to fit the spindle nose. Most lathe chucks of professional quality are recessed to take the chuck back in a light, press fit and this calls for some accurate machine work.

For mounting a small, light chuck, the back can be turned from a tool-steel round. But for the larger, heavier chucks, it is best to use the cast back supplied by the manufacturer or make your own by turning a wooden pattern, as in Fig. 1, and having the back cast at a local foundry. The dimensions given are for a spindle having a diameter of 1½ in. with 8 threads to the inch, and may be varied to suit your particular spindle. To allow for machining, the casting pattern is made ⅛ in. oversize, and sufficient draft is provided so the pattern can be easily withdrawn from the molding sand. Note, also, that the center hole is tapered sharply. After turning the pattern, sand it smooth and apply two or three coats of shellac, sanding between coats.

To machine the rough casting, center it, hub outward, on the lathe faceplate and clamp it in place. Machine the flange and outer surface of the hub to size, and bore the hole for the threads, remembering that the hole must be 1½ in. in diameter less the depth of the threads. Then, grind an internal threading tool to the proper shape, checking it with a thread gauge as in Fig. 2, detail A. Give this tool slightly more front clearance than an external threading tool to prevent the heel of the tool from rubbing against the work. Insert the tool in a heavy boring bar, setting the tool exactly on the horizontal lathe center line as in detail B. Unscrew the faceplate from the spindle, and adjust the threading tool

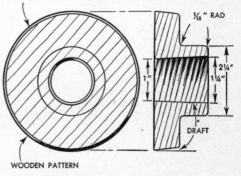

DIA. TO SUIT CHUCK RECESS PLUS SHRINKAGE

1/16" RAD

2¼"
1¼"
1"

DRAFT

WOODEN PATTERN

CASTING TURNED TO PUSH FIT IN CHUCK RECESS

120°

9/16"

1½" X 8 THREAD

2⅛"

SHOULDER

1 CHUCK BACK, CAST IRON

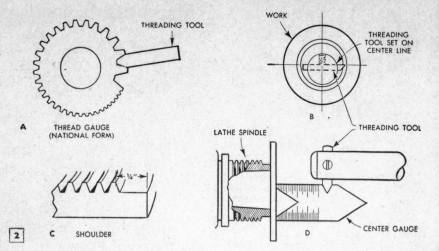

A THREAD GAUGE (NATIONAL FORM)

2 **C** SHOULDER

B

D CENTER GAUGE

square with the work by fitting the point into a center gauge. The gauge is positioned on a disk held against the end of the spindle as in detail D. Adjust the boring bar in its holder with as little overhang as possible to prevent springing, and then replace the faceplate on the spindle.

When the threads are nearly completed, unscrew the faceplate from the spindle, with the work attached, and test the threaded hub of the chuck back for fit on the lathe spindle. If the threads are too tight, replace the faceplate on the spindle and take several finishing cuts with the thread-cutting tool. Repeat until a perfect fit is obtained.

Note in detail C that a ¼-in. shoulder must be cut on the inside of the newly threaded hub. This allows the chuck back to be turned firmly against the shoulder on the spindle nose. The inside edge of the hole in the hub should be beveled slightly and the machined surfaces polished smooth with fine emery cloth.

Now, the work can be removed from the faceplate and the hub of the chuck back screwed onto the lathe spindle. The chuck back is faced square and the flange is turned to a firm push fit in the chuck recess. Take light finishing cuts, and frequently press the chuck over the flange to check the fit.

When the chuck back fits perfectly, remove it from the spindle. Chalk the face of the flange heavily and insert it in the chuck recess. Then tap the flange with a soft hammer to transfer the location of the bolt holes in the chuck to the chalked surface of the flange. Drill the bolt holes in the chuck-back flange ¹⁄₁₆ in. larger than the diameter of the bolts used to fasten the back to the chuck. This is important, as binding of the bolts against the sides of the holes will impair the accuracy of the chuck.

After bolting the back to the chuck, mount the chuck on the lathe spindle, and use a dial indicator on the outer diameter of the chuck to check the alignment.

To insure long life and satisfactory results from your chuck, keep it clean. Be sure that no chips or dirt become embedded in the seating surfaces of the spindle, chuck or threads. The shoulder, face and pilot of the headstock spindle determine the accuracy of the chuck, so be careful not to nick or bump the shoulder and pilot.

When mounting the chuck, oil the threads of the spindle and chuck back. To turn the chuck onto the spindle, hold the chuck in the hand and turn the spindle pulley with the left hand until the chuck is just tight enough to hold securely. Do not switch on the lathe motor to screw the chuck onto the spindle and don't spin the chuck up to the shoulder, as doing this is likely to make the chuck difficult to remove. Lubricate your chuck frequently with No. 10 oil.

Overloading the chuck by mounting work that has a diameter larger than that of the chuck body extends the jaws to the point where undue strain is exerted on the screws or scroll. In addition, always use a wrench of the size provided with the chuck. Using a larger wrench for greater leverage will result in permanent damage to the scroll or screws, and also to the chuck jaws. If the jaws seem to be jammed, do not force them. Instead, disassemble the chuck and find the cause of the obstruction.

The chuck probably will need cleaning. When doing this, be sure to remove any chips that have worked into the jaw slots, screws or scroll. Oil all moving parts before reassembling. When the chuck is not in use, store it in a cabinet or on a shelf where it will be protected from dirt, chips and accidental damage.

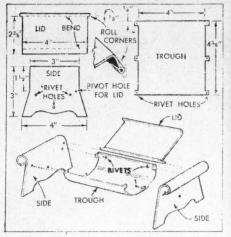

CIGARETTE BOX

Made of sheet aluminum or copper, this novel cigarette box resembles a miniature chair when open. It consists of four pieces: two sides, a semicylindrical trough, and a pivoted lid. Although the box illustrated was designed for extra-long cigarettes, it can be made smaller for standard-length cigarettes by changing the 4-in. dimension of the lid and trough to 3 in. First, lay out the pieces on 16 or 18-ga. sheet metal and cut them to size with tinner's snips. Round the sharp edges with a file or emery cloth and drill rivet holes through the six tabs on the trough. The trough and sides are formed around a wooden dowel or a piece of pipe wrapped with heavy paper. To avoid hammer marks when bending, use a wooden or rawhide mallet. Bend the tabs on the trough at right angles and use the trough as a template for drilling the rivet holes in the sides of the box. Two additional holes, one in each of the sidepieces, must be located and drilled for the hinge prongs of the lid. When assembling, insert the prongs in these holes before riveting the sides to the trough. The box is finished by buffing to a high luster or rubbing with fine emery cloth to a satin finish. The buffing can be done with a soft wheel charged with polishing rouge. A coat of clear lacquer will prevent the metal from tarnishing and thus eliminate frequent polishing.

Plastic Cigarette Box Has Novel Tilting Cover

Made from transparent plastic, this cigarette box consists of a tilting compartment or tray pivoted in a frame formed by two ends and a base as shown. The tray is of sufficient size to hold twenty or more cigarettes, either regular or "king" size. The cover also is pivoted between the ends. Pressing the knob tilts the tray and lifts the cover simultaneously. When the tray is released it swings back to the horizontal position and the cover automatically closes. All parts are shown in the cross-hatched diagram above, the two end pieces of the frame, part No. 3, and those of the tray, part No. 4, being duplicates. Parts Nos. 1 and 2 are the bottom and top. Pivot pins for the tray are cut from 3/16-in. plastic rod and the lifting knob is cut from the same material, 1/2 in. in diameter and 3/4 in. long. A flat is filed on one side of the knob as shown so that it can be cemented to the tray easily. All other parts are cut from 3/16-in. sheet plastic to the sizes indicated in the cross-hatched details, except the curved portion of the tray, which is 1/8 in. thick. Material can be cut with a bandsaw or jigsaw if slow-speed attachments and metal-cutting blades are available, otherwise by hand with a hacksaw or coping saw. Finish the edges of the plastic with fine wet-or-dry sandpaper and be sure the joining edges of bottom and ends are square. The entire assembly is joined with plastic cement.

CIGARETTE LIGHTER

Needle and Thread Guide Wick Through Cigarette Lighter

The usual difficult job of getting a new wick into a cigarette lighter can be simplified if a threaded needle is used as a guide. Sew through the new wick, loop the thread around the end, and secure it tightly. After removing the old wick from the lighter, insert the needle and thread in the wick opening and pull the new wick through, then trim with a pair of scissors.

Cleaning Cigarette-Lighter Wheel To Assure Quick Ignition

Cigarette lighters often fail to work because soft material from the flint clogs the file wheel. When this occurs, clean out the wheel with a "file card," a strip of heavy canvas material having short lengths of wire projecting through it, about 30 to the inch. This is available at most hardware stores.

CIRCLE CUTTERS
for sheet-metal shops

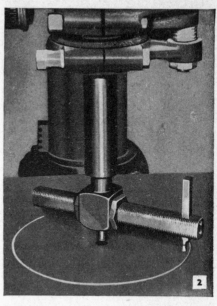

SMALL SHOPS that do a variety of work in sheet metals have frequent use for circle cutters of the type that can be driven by a drill press. Home craftsmen also find use for these cutters in toymaking and ornamental metalwork. Pictured are two approved designs, one made from aluminum alloy especially for light work in wood, hardboard, plastics and soft metals, the other for the heavy-duty jobs in metals. The latter type, shown in Fig. 1 and pictured in use in Fig. 2, is fully detailed in Fig. 6. The shank is machined with a No. 2 Morse taper to fit a drill-press spindle, or sleeve, and it also is turned with an integral pilot. The lightweight job detailed in Figs. 3 and 5 and pictured in operation in Fig. 4, clamps directly to the taper spindle of the drill press into which the pilot drill, of the tapered-shank type, is fitted.

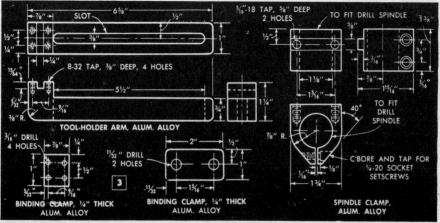

TOOL-HOLDER ARM, ALUM. ALLOY

BINDING CLAMP, 1/4" THICK ALUM. ALLOY

BINDING CLAMP, 1/4" THICK ALUM. ALLOY

SPINDLE CLAMP, ALUM. ALLOY

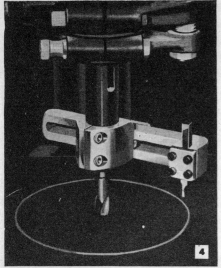

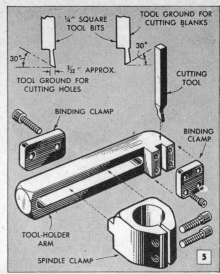

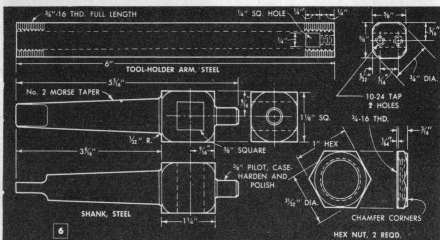

Although the best workmanship would require that the square holes in the shank and tool-holder arm, Fig. 6, be broached, it is possible to drill holes and square them with a file with sufficient accuracy. However, the tool-holder arm must be a smooth, sliding fit in the squared hole in the shank to prevent chattering in heavy cuts. The tool-holder arm, Figs. 1 and 6, is threaded its full length and flats are milled on the four sides, bringing the dimension across the flats to ⅝ in. The length of the arm gives a maximum radius adjustment of approximately 5 in.

The lightweight cutter, Figs. 3, 4 and 5, does an exceptionally smooth, clean job on a variety of materials. When carefully made, it is practically chatterproof. Both the cutting tool and the tool-holder arm are held in place with binding clamps of special design and these two parts are attached to the taper sleeve with a binding clamp of sufficient length to hold the parts in exact alignment. Note that the cutting bit is supported in a groove milled across the face of the binding-clamp seat and that the groove is slightly less than ¼ in. deep, Fig. 3. This allowance is necessary to permit the clamp to seat the bit firmly. The upper details in Fig. 5 show how to grind the bit for cutting holes and blanks in thin material. When ground for hole cutting, the bit leaves the outer edge smooth. When ground for blank cutting, the inner edge of the cut is smooth. For work in metals, the speed of the cutter should not exceed 100 r.p.m.

CIRCULAR SAW

CONVERTED FROM LATHE

YOUR woodturning lathe is quickly converted to a bench saw when equipped with this setup. All you do is mount an arbor and saw between the lathe centers as in Fig. 1, lower the table over the blade and you're ready to start sawing. When not in use, the table swings back out of the way against the wall as in Fig. 8. Such a setup naturally requires that the lathe be mounted on a stand or bench which can be pulled out into the center of the room to permit ripping long stock.

The original saw was made for a lathe having a 9-in. swing, although with a few changes in dimensions the idea is adaptable to any size lathe. The first step in construction is to make the saw arbor detailed in Fig. 2. This is machined from a length of 1⅜-in. cold-rolled steel to accommodate the bore of the saw blade. One end of the arbor is bored and threaded internally to screw onto the threaded lathe spindle, and the other end is fitted with a bronze bushing which is pressed in place to receive the tailstock center. In use, the hole in the bushing is filled with grease before the center is engaged. If you wish, a ball-bearing "live" center in the tailstock can be substituted for the bronze bushing. For best results, the lathe speed should be approximately 4000 to 5000 r.p.m. for an 8-in. blade and pro-

Hinged table that lowers over saw blade mounted between centers will convert a lathe into an efficient bench saw

portionately faster or slower for a smaller or larger one. The saw blade should be mounted near the tailstock end of the arbor to reduce whipping and vibration to a minimum.

Fig. 3 shows the rear support to which the saw table is hinged. The support consists of two angle-iron brackets, of a size to suit the lathe at hand, bolted to a 1-in. hardwood strip, the brackets being bolted permanently to the bench top. The saw table is built up from three hardwood boards ¾ by 10 by 30 in., which are doweled and glued together edgewise as shown in Fig. 5. Several bar clamps are used to draw the pieces together tightly. Cleats 3 in. wide are screwed to the underside of the top at the front and rear edges to keep the surface flat. If you are able to obtain ¾-in. plywood, the table can be from a

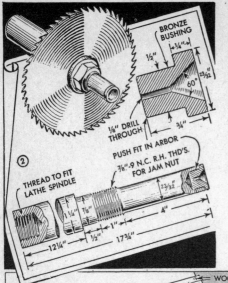

single piece, 30 in. square, or a stock drawing board or a breadboard of a suitable size can be purchased and used for the table. Still another method, in some respects the best, is to rip 30 1-in.-wide strips from 1-in. hardwood and glue these together with waterproof glue. A top made in this way is exceptionally rigid and will not warp. Where it is desired to use the saw to make shoulder cuts, grooves, etc., the depth of cut is regulated by two flat-iron legs as in Fig. 7. These extend through holes in the bench top and are made adjustable by a clamping device which consists of a section of angle iron fastened to the bench top and tapped to receive short cap screws and a plate. Tightening the screws locks the table at any set position and loosening them allows the legs to be withdrawn and moved with the table when not in use. The legs are pivoted to the front edge of the table with brackets of angle iron in the manner shown in Fig. 7.

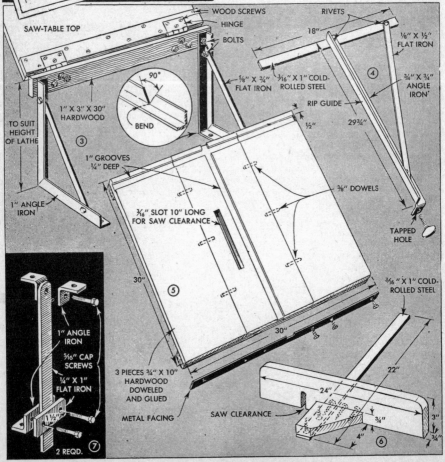

The rip fence, Fig. 4, operates in a groove across the rear of the table, and is locked in position with a setscrew which bears against a metal facing strip attached to the front edge of the table. A groove for the crosscut guide is run parallel to the saw slot and on the right-hand side of it. If you wish, the slot can be enlarged and provided with an insert so that a dado head can be mounted on the arbor. Both grooves should be cut about ¼ in. deep so that the guide bars are slightly below the table surface. The fence on the rip guide is a length of angle iron braced as shown. The crosscut guide is made according to Fig. 6, and it is important that the head be attached to the metal bar at 90 degrees. While its use is restricted to crosscutting only, miter cuts can be made with it by using a template block of the desired angle inserted between the work and the guide. Or a trunnion of metal or wood, patterned after a commercial guide, can be attached to make the head adjustable for angle cutting. You even may be able to

Two tools in one—simply mount the arbor between lathe centers, lower the table and, presto!—you have an excellent circular saw

purchase a regular cutoff gauge and cut the groove in the table to fit it. Complete the job by sanding the table and applying a coat of thinned shellac. Then sand lightly and wax.

ONE OF THE KNOTTIEST problems you will encounter in planning the power-tool equipment for your homeshop is what tools to buy. In the first place one should keep in mind that it is not possible to cost-account the equipment and the returns from it on a year-to-year basis in dollars and cents. When you purchase a set of golf clubs you don't bother with such details and that's exactly the way to classify the purchase of your homeshop power tools. If you like to work with your hands, either in wood or metals, then there is no way to calculate or measure profit and loss on initial investment. The "profit" takes the form of hours, then years, of recreation. Fitting out a home workshop is just another way of providing recreational facilities for yourself and your family.

If you're planning the workshop from scratch and have only a few household hand tools to serve as a nucleus around which to build a well-equipped shop, then the question of what power tool to purchase first becomes important. Its selection will be determined by what you want to do first in the list of shop projects you have planned. That brings the proposal to the point where it is necessary to

CIRCULAR SAW
A BASIC POWER TOOL

SIZES OF HOMESHOP TOOLS				
TOOL	BASIS FOR NAME SIZE	SMALL	MEDIUM	LARGE
CIRCULAR SAW	DIAMETER OF SAW BLADE	7"	8"	10"
DRILL PRESS	MAXIMUM DIAMETER CENTER-DRILLED CIRCULAR WORK	11-12"	13-15"	15-18"
WOOD LATHE	DIAMETER OF TURNED FACEPLATE WORK	8-9"	10"	12"
JIGSAW	DISTANCE FROM BLADE TO FRAME (THROAT CAPACITY)	12-16"	16-18"	24"
BANDSAW	DISTANCE FROM BLADE TO FRAME (THROAT CAPACITY)	10-12"	12-14"	14-18"
JOINTER	LENGTH OF KNIVES IN CUTTER HEAD	4"	4¼-4½"	6"
DISK SANDER	DIAMETER OF SANDING DISK	8-9"	10"	12"
BELT SANDER	WIDTH OF BELT	3"	4"	6"

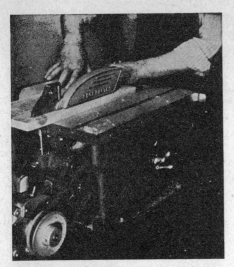

Best safety practice requires that the circular saw be operated with a guard whenever possible. In all photos in this book where the saw guard is not shown it has been purposely omitted to show the operation

among all the common power tools suited to woodworking. It is true that the list under "drill press" contains more affirmative answers, but it should be remembered also that the "yes" answers under circular saw include more than 75 percent of all woodworking operations required in cabinetmaking. Neither does the chart include all operations possible on the machines listed, as all of these tools are capable of working metals as well as wood.

To produce a neat workmanlike job on the simplest project in wood, straight, squarely cut edges and exact widths are essential. In the more intricate projects, angle cuts, grooves, dadoes (stopped grooves) and rabbets will be necessary in the joinery plan. Nearly all cabinet work of even the simplest design requires straight moldings as a decorative feature. All these diversified operations can be done on a circular saw fitted with the proper accessories. After ripping the stock to the required widths and lengths you can assemble a dado head on the circular-saw arbor and run all the grooves and rabbets necessary for assembling a cabinet drawer in a few minutes. And if you are careful to make the correct measurements the parts will fit together like a factory job. For the practical applications such as making shelving, bookcases, kitchen cabinets and outdoor woodwork such as trellises and ornamental fences, you can save money by doing the work yourself, and in the majority of cases all the work can be done on the circular saw.

For these reasons most experienced crafters agree that the circular saw is first choice in power-tool equipment for the homeshop. However, there is another way for the prospective purchaser to approach

consider the versatility of each of the common power woodworking tools.

Although there is no all-around power tool to be had, perhaps the circular saw comes the nearest to earning this classification. However, it does have some limitations. For example, it would not be possible to produce a wall or corner cabinet with scrolled decorations on a circular saw. Intricate curved work cannot be done on this machine. But if you take a moment to study the chart below and note the list of operations under "circular saw" you will see that it rates first in versatility

JOB AND MACHINE CHART OF STANDARD OPERATIONS

JOB	CIRCULAR SAW	DRILL PRESS	BANDSAW	JOINTER	JIGSAW	WOOD LATHE
STRAIGHT SAWING	YES	NO	YES	NO	YES	NO
DRILLING A HOLE	NO	YES	NO	NO	NO	YES
CUTTING A CURVE	NO	NO	YES	NO	YES	NO
CUTTING A MORTISE	NO	YES	NO	NO	NO	NO
CUTTING A GROOVE	YES	YES	NO	NO	NO	NO
CUTTING A TENON	YES	YES	YES	YES	NO	NO
PLANING A BOARD	YES (With Molding Head)	YES (With Planer Head)	NO	YES	NO	NO
INTERNAL CUTTING	NO	YES (By Routing)	NO	NO	YES	NO
MAKING A TURNING	NO	NO	NO	NO	NO	YES
SHAPING AN EDGE	YES	YES	NO	NO	NO	NO
SANDING AN EDGE	YES (With Disk)	YES (With Drum)	YES (With Belt)	NO	YES (With Sleeve)	YES (With Drum or Disk)
SANDING A SURFACE	NO	NO	NO	NO	NO	NO

"YES" in bold-face type indicates the job is done particularly well

Looking at the picture above you can see right away the advantage of the circular saw with tilting arbor. The stock always is worked on a level table. This is a big help when it is necessary to cut long pieces or bevel-rip a large panel of plywood. Pictured below at the left is disadvantage of tilting-table saw

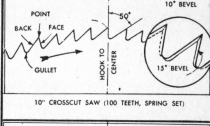

POINT

BACK FACE

GULLET

HOOK TO CENTER

50°

10° BEVEL

15° BEVEL

10" CROSSCUT SAW (100 TEETH, SPRING SET)

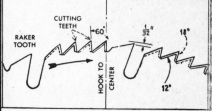

CUTTING TEETH

RAKER TOOTH

HOOK TO CENTER

60°

1/32"

18°

12°

10" PLANER BLADE (HOLLOW-GROUND)

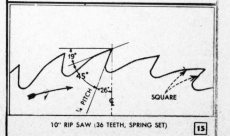

19°

45°

1/4 PITCH

26°

SQUARE

10" RIP SAW (36 TEETH, SPRING SET)

15

the problem of what machine to buy first. If, for example, turned projects predominate in your first-project plans, then a lathe is the logical first choice. Let the purchase of other machines follow as the need for each one arises. Using the same rule-of-thumb, if you plan a number of scroll-sawed projects, then buy a jigsaw and build a shop around it. Or, for less intricate scrollwork where the design is cut through from edge to edge or is continuous along one edge of the stock, a bandsaw will fill

the bill. If it is fitted with a ripping fence, either the standard accessory supplied for most small machines, or with a piece of square stock clamped to the table, the bandsaw is capable of ripping stock with the same accuracy as the circular saw. The larger jigsaws will do the same thing, although not nearly as fast. Most jigsaws, even the small machines, are fitted with movable blade chucks which can be turned 45 deg. This provision enables the operator to feed the stock to the blade from the side of the machine and makes it possible to handle either straight or curved cuts on long stock without interference of the machine frame.

There's still another angle that influences the choice of that first machine. No matter how you figure it, it is not possible or practical to eliminate hand work in the home hobby shop. In fact, it is not essential or

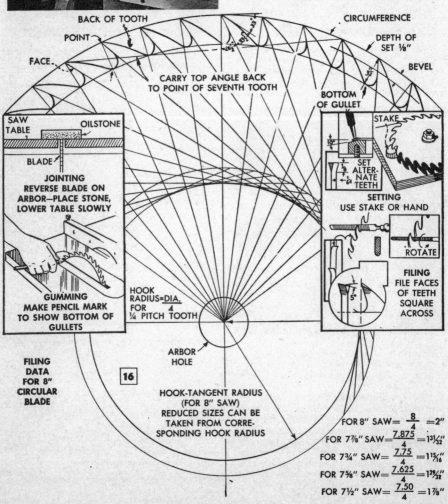

BACK OF TOOTH

POINT

FACE

CIRCUMFERENCE

DEPTH OF SET ⅛"

BEVEL

CARRY TOP ANGLE BACK TO POINT OF SEVENTH TOOTH

BOTTOM OF GULLET

SAW TABLE — OILSTONE

BLADE

JOINTING
REVERSE BLADE ON ARBOR—PLACE STONE, LOWER TABLE SLOWLY

GUMMING
MAKE PENCIL MARK TO SHOW BOTTOM OF GULLETS

STAKE

SET ALTER-NATE TEETH

SETTING
USE STAKE OR HAND

ROTATE

FILING
FILE FACES OF TEETH SQUARE ACROSS

HOOK RADIUS=DIA.
FOR ¼ PITCH TOOTH

ARBOR HOLE

FILING DATA FOR 8" CIRCULAR BLADE

16

HOOK-TANGENT RADIUS
(FOR 8" SAW)
REDUCED SIZES CAN BE TAKEN FROM CORRE-SPONDING HOOK RADIUS

$$\text{FOR 8" SAW} = \frac{8}{4} = 2"$$

$$\text{FOR 7⅞" SAW} = \frac{7.875}{4} = 1^{31}/_{32}"$$

$$\text{FOR 7¾" SAW} = \frac{7.75}{4} = 1^{15}/_{16}"$$

$$\text{FOR 7⅝" SAW} = \frac{7.625}{4} = 1^{29}/_{32}"$$

$$\text{FOR 7½" SAW} = \frac{7.50}{4} = 1⅞"$$

The circular saw does bevel ripping at any angle up to 45 deg. This machine is a tilting-arbor type

Making a miter cut, using the miter-gauge stop. The stop assures that duplicate pieces will be same length

Whenever necessary to rip or resaw narrow stock, use a push stick. Don't take unnecessary chances!

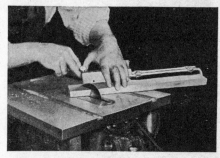

Here's the tilting-arbor saw set up to make a compound miter cut. Note use of the miter-gauge stop

A straight bevel cut across the grain with the arbor tilted to 45 deg. Note how miter-gauge stop is used

Here's another application—cutting short blocks to exact length. Note stop block clamped to rip fence

With a dado head you can cut grooves of exact width and depth. This accessory is essential in cabinet work

Here's the dado head again, cutting a tenon. It makes both the cheek and shoulder cut in one operation

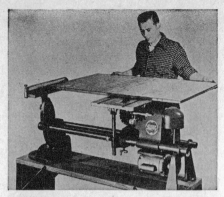

A combination machine of this type, with special circular-saw attachment, is just the thing for cutting plywood panels or stock glued up to wide widths

A tilting-arbor circular saw having wide table extensions of the open-grid type is a favorite with building contractors and experienced home craftsmen. Machine is self-contained and readily portable to job

Beside the basic circular saw, here are three other basic power shop tools, the bandsaw, drill press and grinder, none of which you can very well do without in a shop equipped for both wood and metal working

desirable to mechanize all the diversified operations necessary in building even the more simple projects. You can drill or bore holes in wood with hand tools and plane or joint the edges of boards with a hand jointer plane. A lot of the curved work can be done satisfactorily with a coping saw. But you won't find it easy or practical to rip stock to exact widths, run accurate grooves, make moldings, cut close-fitting angle joints or make tight-fitting tenons with hand tools. This brings us back where we started—to that very nearly all-around power tool, the circular saw. So, we'll make this machine first choice for home hobby shops and discuss the various kinds available.

In the relative blade and table sizes the 7-in. circular saw—meaning one taking a maximum blade diameter of 7 in.—rates small, while the 10-in. machine rates large for the average home shop. Probably the best choice, everything considered, is the 8-in. machine. These machines are offered in both the tilting-table and the tilting-arbor types. As a rule, the tilting-arbor comes higher in initial cost but in the long run it's usually worth the difference. Take a good look at the two types pictured in the photos earlier pg. and you'll see why. In the upper photo the operator is making an angle cut on long stock. Note that the blade is tilted to the required angle but the table remains level. In the lower photo the operator is cutting a compound angle with the table tilted and the blade remaining stationary in the vertical position. The difference between the two types of machines is merely that of convenience. So far as accuracy goes, one machine is as good as the other. Due to the simplification of the design, the tilting-table machine sells for considerably less money, size for size.

Several makes of the smaller machines also are fitted with ripping-fence extensions so that the ripping fence can be adjusted to points beyond the edge of the machine table. This permits ripping cuts on wide panels. Photos on the preceding page show methods of using stops when crosscutting parts to length. Several ways of holding the stock when cutting straight miters are shown.

CIRCULAR SAW SANDER-UNIT

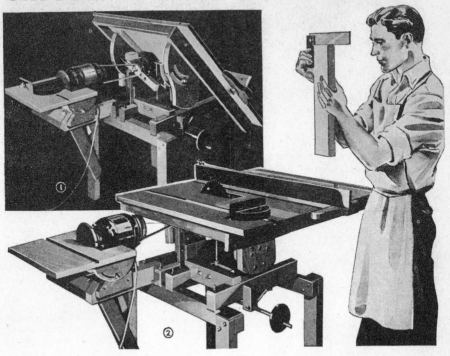

THIS combination workshop unit features an 8-in. saw having a 30 by 36-in. table that will tilt 45 deg., Fig. 1, a swinging saw mandrel, and a direct-drive disk sander. A ⅓-hp. motor operates both machines as shown in Fig. 2.

Construction begins with the stand. From Fig. 7 you can see clearly how it is put together with ¼-in. carriage bolts. All stock measures 2 by 3 in., and note that the upper ends of the legs are notched for rigidity. The position of the two-piece front and rear trunnion supports can be marked at this time, and the holes drilled, but it is best not to bolt them to the stand until after the complete trunnion assembly has been attached. The saw hinge support, detailed in Fig. 5, is set 4⅜ in. in from the end of the rails between which it is bolted. Now for the trunnions and their slides. Make these of ¾-in. birch or maple and take pains in laying them out from the pattern given in Fig. 8. The concave edge of the slide must make a perfect rubbing fit with the trunnion, and the curved bolt slot

should equal the curve of the trunnion so that the latter will not bind. To the back side of each trunnion and its slide, guides of ⅛-in. hard-pressed board are fitted as shown in Fig. 6. These are cut as indicated to overhang the edge of the trunnions 1 in., forming a lip which overlaps the slide. Use flathead screws for attaching the guides, countersinking the heads flush with the surface. The trunnion-bolt holes through the supports are bored 3⁵⁄₁₆ in. down from the top. Holes for bolting the slides to the trunnion supports are located by placing the trunnion on its bolt and then with a thin cardboard shim between the slide and the support, center the slide beneath it and clamp the latter temporarily to the support. When you have the slide adjusted so that the trunnion works smoothly, drill four holes through both pieces for ¼-in. bolts. A semi-hard brass strap attached to the edge of each slide to bear against the edge of the trunnion (see side view Fig. 8) takes up the thrust of the table when tilted. In place of the cardboard, thin washers are

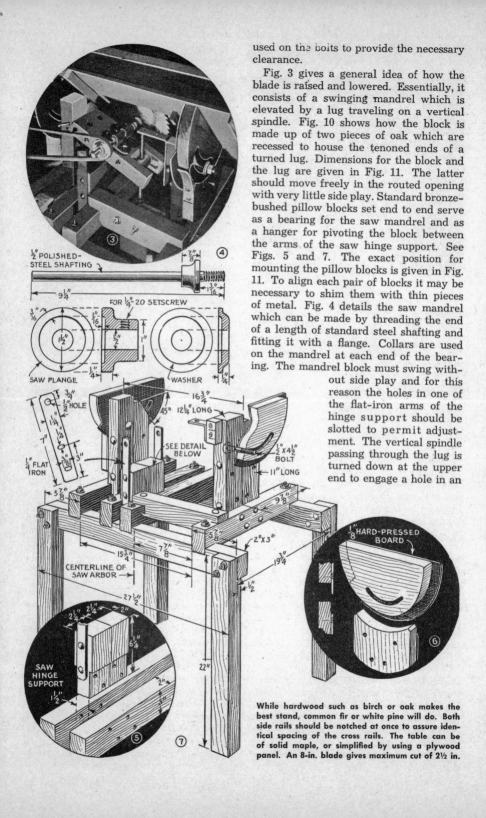

used on the bolts to provide the necessary clearance.

Fig. 3 gives a general idea of how the blade is raised and lowered. Essentially, it consists of a swinging mandrel which is elevated by a lug traveling on a vertical spindle. Fig. 10 shows how the block is made up of two pieces of oak which are recessed to house the tenoned ends of a turned lug. Dimensions for the block and the lug are given in Fig. 11. The latter should move freely in the routed opening with very little side play. Standard bronze-bushed pillow blocks set end to end serve as a bearing for the saw mandrel and as a hanger for pivoting the block between the arms of the saw hinge support. See Figs. 5 and 7. The exact position for mounting the pillow blocks is given in Fig. 11. To align each pair of blocks it may be necessary to shim them with thin pieces of metal. Fig. 4 details the saw mandrel which can be made by threading the end of a length of standard steel shafting and fitting it with a flange. Collars are used on the mandrel at each end of the bearing. The mandrel block must swing without side play and for this reason the holes in one of the flat-iron arms of the hinge support should be slotted to permit adjustment. The vertical spindle passing through the lug is turned down at the upper end to engage a hole in an

While hardwood such as birch or oak makes the best stand, common fir or white pine will do. Both side rails should be notched at once to assure identical spacing of the cross rails. The table can be of solid maple, or simplified by using a plywood panel. An 8-in. blade gives maximum cut of 2½ in.

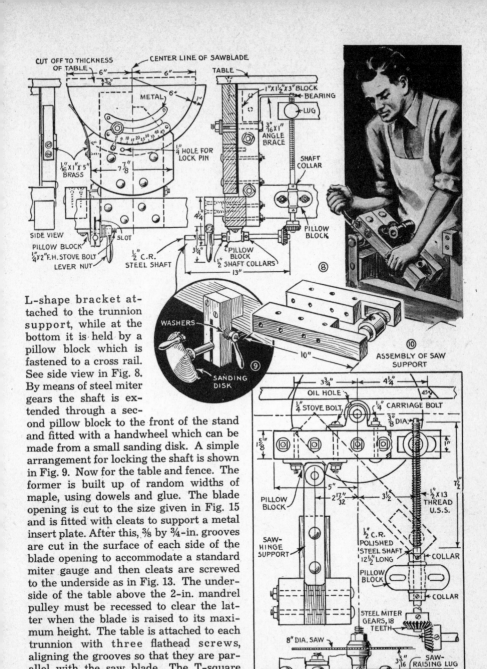

Diagram labels (Fig. 8): CUT OFF TO THICKNESS OF TABLE · CENTER LINE OF SAWBLADE · TABLE · 6" · 6" · ¾" · 6" · 1" · METAL · 1"×1½"×3" BLOCK · BEARING · LUG · ³⁄₁₆×1" ANGLE BRACE · SHAFT COLLAR · ¼" HOLE FOR LOCK PIN · 7⅞" · ¹⁄₁₆"×1"×5" BRASS · 4¼" · PILLOW BLOCK · SIDE VIEW · PILLOW BLOCK · ¼" F.H. STOVE BOLT · LEVER NUT · SLOT · ½" C.R. STEEL SHAFT · 3¼" · PILLOW BLOCK · 2 SHAFT COLLARS · 13" · (8)

Fig. 9: WASHERS · SANDING DISK · (9)

Fig. 10: 10" · ASSEMBLY OF SAW SUPPORT · (10)

Fig. 11 labels: OIL HOLE · 3¾" · 4¼" · 45° · ¼" STOVE BOLT · ¼" CARRIAGE BOLT · ⅜" DIA. · 1⅜" · PILLOW BLOCK · 5" · 2¹⁷⁄₃₂" · 3½" · ½"×13 THREAD U.S.S. · 7½" · SAW-HINGE SUPPORT · ½" C.R. POLISHED STEEL SHAFT 12½" LONG · COLLAR · PILLOW BLOCK · COLLAR · STEEL MITER GEARS, 18 TEETH · 8" DIA. SAW · 3³⁄₁₆" · SAW-RAISING LUG · 4" · TOP VIEW · 1½" · ½" · 2" · 1" · 2¹¹⁄₁₆" · 3⅛" · (11)

L-shape bracket attached to the trunnion support, while at the bottom it is held by a pillow block which is fastened to a cross rail. See side view in Fig. 8. By means of steel miter gears the shaft is extended through a second pillow block to the front of the stand and fitted with a handwheel which can be made from a small sanding disk. A simple arrangement for locking the shaft is shown in Fig. 9. Now for the table and fence. The former is built up of random widths of maple, using dowels and glue. The blade opening is cut to the size given in Fig. 15 and is fitted with cleats to support a metal insert plate. After this, ⅜ by ¾-in. grooves are cut in the surface of each side of the blade opening to accommodate a standard miter gauge and then cleats are screwed to the underside as in Fig. 13. The underside of the table above the 2-in. mandrel pulley must be recessed to clear the latter when the blade is raised to its maximum height. The table is attached to each trunnion with three flathead screws, aligning the grooves so that they are parallel with the saw blade. The T-square fence is undercut to ride the table at three points. Figs. 12 and 14 show how bolts and wing nuts are fitted at the front and rear to clamp it in position. With a T-bevel set at known angles, the scale on the front trunnion can be marked for degrees by holding the bevel in contact with the table

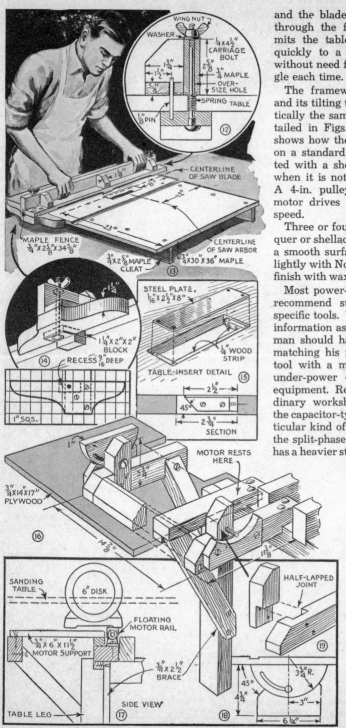

WING NUT
WASHER
1/4 x 4 1/2" CARRIAGE BOLT
1 3/4"
5/8"
3/4" MAPLE OVER-SIZE HOLE
1 1/2"
5/8"
SPRING TABLE
1/8" PIN
(12)

CENTERLINE OF SAW BLADE
1 1/2"
2"
23"
MAPLE FENCE 3/4" x 2 5/8" x 34 5/8"
3/4" x 2 5/8" MAPLE CLEAT
CENTERLINE OF SAW ARBOR
3/4" x 30" x 36" MAPLE
(13)

1 1/4"
1 1/4" x 2" x 2" BLOCK
RECESS 9/16" DEEP
(14)
1" SQS.

STEEL PLATE, 1/16" x 2 1/2" x 8"
1/4" WOOD STRIP
TABLE-INSERT DETAIL
(15)
2 1/2"
45°
2 3/4"
SECTION

1"
5 1/4"
MOTOR RESTS HERE
3/4" x 14" x 17" PLYWOOD
(16)
14 7/8"
1 1/8"

SANDING TABLE
6" DISK
HALF-LAPPED JOINT
FLOATING MOTOR RAIL
3/4" x 6" x 11 1/2" MOTOR SUPPORT
3/4" x 2 1/2" BRACE
(19)
TABLE LEG
SIDE VIEW
(17)
(18)
45°
4 3/4"
3 3/4" R.
3"
6 1/4"

and the blade. A lock pin fitted through the front trunnion permits the table to be returned quickly to a horizontal position without need for checking the angle each time.

The framework of the sander and its tilting table, which is practically the same as the saw, is detailed in Figs. 16 to 19. Fig. 17 shows how the motor is mounted on a standard motor rail and fitted with a shelf on which to set when it is not belted to the saw. A 4-in. pulley on a 1750-r.p.m. motor drives the saw at correct speed.

Three or four coats of clear lacquer or shellac will give the tables a smooth surface. Rub each coat lightly with No. 5-0 sandpaper and finish with wax.

Most power-tool manufacturers recommend suitable motors for specific tools. Using this source of information as a guide, the craftsman should have no difficulty in matching his newly made power tool with a motor that does not under-power or over-power the equipment. Recommended for ordinary workshop power tools is the capacitor-type motor. This particular kind of motor is similar to the split-phase type except that it has a heavier starting winding connected in series with a condenser. The capacitor-type motor is easily recognized by the extra case on the top or the side. Repulsion-induction motors are excellent for heavy-duty work. Avoid long, light-extension cords in wiring the power tool in its permanent location. The flimsy light cord is not only unsafe, but it robs your motor of as much as 25 percent of the motor's rated power.

1

ROLLER SUPPORT
FOR INFEED

ONE MAN EASILY
HANDLES STOCK
12 TO 16 FT. LONG

ROLLER SUPPORT
FOR THE OUTFEED

INFEED AND OUTFEED ROLLER SUPPORTS ARE A
PRACTICAL SOLUTION TO HANDLING BIG WORK
ON SMALL SAW TABLES. A TYPICAL SETUP IS
SHOWN ABOVE, AND A UNIT EASY TO MAKE IS
SHOWN BELOW. SAME SUPPORT CAN BE USED WITH
A SIDE ROLLER FOR CUTOFF WORK AS IN FIG. 11

HANDLING BIG

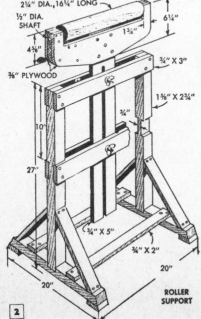

HARDWOOD ROLLER
2¼" DIA., 16¼" LONG

½" DIA.
SHAFT

6¼"

1¾"

4⅝"

¾" X 3"

⅜" PLYWOOD

1⅝" X 2¾"

¾"

10"

27"

¾" X 5"

¾" X 2"

20"

20"

ROLLER
SUPPORT

2

WHILE the small table on the average circular saw provides adequate support for most of the work done in the basement workshop, occasionally there are times when an extra-large panel or long board must be ripped or crosscut. Trying to do this singlehandedly in cramped quarters is not only difficult but hazardous. However, there are improvised setups which give big-saw capacity to home-shop machines with the added features of convenience and safety for the operator.

Along with these setups, however, there are a few important points to remember when handling oversized work in either crosscutting or ripping. First, use a blade with standard ripping or combination teeth which have been correctly sharpened and set. Never use a hollow-ground (planer) blade because of the danger of a kickback should the blade suddenly bind in the cut. Also, wherever possible, use both the guard and the splitter with which the machine is equipped. Finally, it is important to adjust the blade so that it projects no more than ½ in. above the top of the stock. This helps to hold the cut open and prevent binding, and aids in steadying the blade in heavy cuts.

Ripping long boards: Fig. 1 shows how

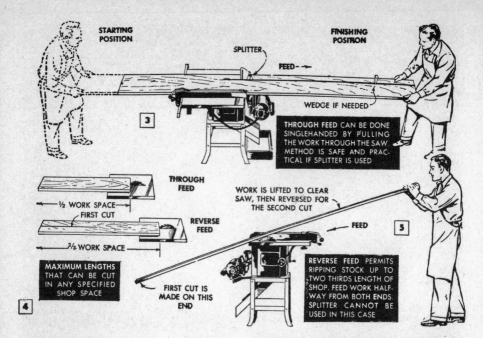

STARTING POSITION

FINISHING POSITION

SPLITTER

FEED

WEDGE IF NEEDED

3

THROUGH FEED CAN BE DONE SINGLEHANDED BY PULLING THE WORK THROUGH THE SAW. METHOD IS SAFE AND PRACTICAL IF SPLITTER IS USED

THROUGH FEED

WORK IS LIFTED TO CLEAR SAW, THEN REVERSED FOR THE SECOND CUT

½ WORK SPACE

FIRST CUT

REVERSE FEED

FEED

5

⅔ WORK SPACE

4 MAXIMUM LENGTHS THAT CAN BE CUT IN ANY SPECIFIED SHOP SPACE

FIRST CUT IS MADE ON THIS END

REVERSE FEED PERMITS RIPPING STOCK UP TO TWO THIRDS LENGTH OF SHOP. FEED WORK HALFWAY FROM BOTH ENDS. SPLITTER CANNOT BE USED IN THIS CASE

WORK ON YOUR CIRCULAR SAW

two simple roller supports build big-saw capacity into the small machine. Although the infeed and outfeed supports in this setup are made from pipe and fittings, adjustable supports to serve the same purpose can be made from stock lumber as in Fig. 2. Ripping long stock without any supports can be done in two ways. One is the infeed-and-pull-through method detailed in Fig. 3. The other method is the reverse feed, Fig. 5, where the ripping cut is run half the length from both ends of the stock. Fig. 4 shows the maximum lengths which can be cut with these methods. When accurate work is desirable or necessary, a straight-through feed with both the infeed and out-

feed ends of the board supported, as in Figs. 1 and 6, is the most practical, especially when it is necessary to rip duplicate pieces in long lengths. When making a support such as that in Fig. 2, it's a good idea to make allowance for sufficient range of adjustment to accommodate long work on the bandsaw and jointer as well. A short outfeed table, or a roller, attached directly to the saw table, as in Figs. 7, 8 and 9, is helpful not only for ripping long stock but for dadoing and molding operations. On

TABLE-EXTENSION ROLLERS ARE MOST PRACTICAL WHEN RIPPING DUPLICATE PIECES IN LONG LENGTHS

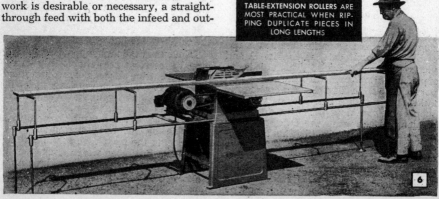

6

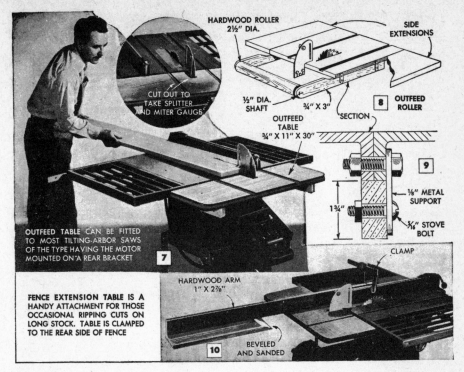

HARDWOOD ROLLER 2½" DIA.

SIDE EXTENSIONS

CUT OUT TO TAKE SPLITTER AND MITER GAUGE

½" DIA. SHAFT

¾" X 3"

SECTION

OUTFEED TABLE ¾" X 11" X 30"

8 OUTFEED ROLLER

9

⅛" METAL SUPPORT

1¾"

5/16" STOVE BOLT

OUTFEED TABLE CAN BE FITTED TO MOST TILTING-ARBOR SAWS OF THE TYPE HAVING THE MOTOR MOUNTED ON A REAR BRACKET

7

CLAMP

HARDWOOD ARM 1" X 2⅞"

FENCE EXTENSION TABLE IS A HANDY ATTACHMENT FOR THOSE OCCASIONAL RIPPING CUTS ON LONG STOCK. TABLE IS CLAMPED TO THE REAR SIDE OF FENCE

BEVELED AND SANDED

10

tilting-arbor saws having the splitter support back of the table, it will be necessary to cut an opening in the auxiliary table to permit the splitter to swing with the blade through the tilt range. Both the table and roller can be mounted in various ways, depending to some extent on the type of saw table. Another type of outfeed support, which is especially useful for ripping an occasional piece of long stock, is pictured in Fig. 10. It is clamped to the ripping fence in the manner shown.

Crosscutting long stock: This is somewhat more difficult, especially where the cutoff must be made near the end of wide stock. Clamping a supporting strip to the drill-press table as in Fig. 12 offers a simple solution to the problem of cutting an occasional long piece. A better method is use of the roller unit detailed in Fig. 11 and pictured in use in Fig. 13. This unit is designed to interchange with the roller support detailed in Fig. 2. An extra-long miter gauge with a ball-bearing roller to support the overhang makes it easy to handle long pieces when the cutoff is made near the end as in Fig. 15. This unit consists of a long guide board fitted with two miter gauges and an outboard roller that rides on the under edge of the saw-table extension as in Fig. 14. Of course, the length and construction of the unit must be

adapted to the machine on which it is to be used. Care should be taken to position the miter gauges with the guide bars exactly the same distance apart so that they do not bind in the table grooves. Another adaptation which will work out satisfactorily on some small saw tables is providing an outboard miter-gauge groove, or slot, by attaching a rabbeted strip to the outer edge of the table, or the table extension, as in Fig. 16. Screw a long guide board to the miter gauge and you have the setup pictured in Fig. 17, which enables the operator to stand well to the left of the saw table and crosscut long boards without any additional support. If the edge of the saw table is not machined, then cut a full-width groove in the center of the strip for the miter-gauge bar.

Trim cuts: Ordinary supports of the type already described are suitable only for ripping and cutting off stock of medium standard widths. On bench-type saw tables the length of the miter-gauge grooves will permit cutting off stock up to 12 in. wide. In some cases you can cut off stock up to 18 in. wide by reversing the miter gauge and placing the back edge of the material against it. But when wider stock, such as plywood panels or solid stock glued up to wide widths, must be trimmed, the miter gauge cannot be used. Figs. 18, 19 and 20

Outboard Support Is Needed For Long Cutoffs

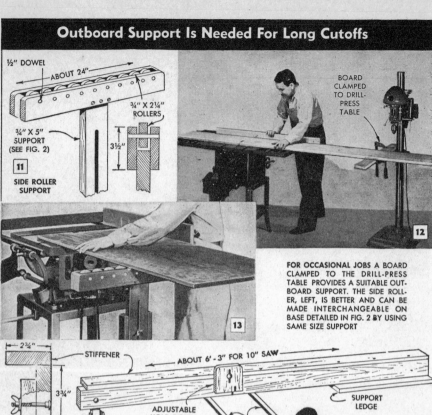

½" DOWEL

ABOUT 24"

¾" X 2¼" ROLLERS

¾" X 5" SUPPORT (SEE FIG. 2)

3½"

11 SIDE ROLLER SUPPORT

BOARD CLAMPED TO DRILL-PRESS TABLE

12

13

FOR OCCASIONAL JOBS A BOARD CLAMPED TO THE DRILL-PRESS TABLE PROVIDES A SUITABLE OUTBOARD SUPPORT. THE SIDE ROLLER, LEFT, IS BETTER AND CAN BE MADE INTERCHANGEABLE ON BASE DETAILED IN FIG. 2 BY USING SAME SIZE SUPPORT

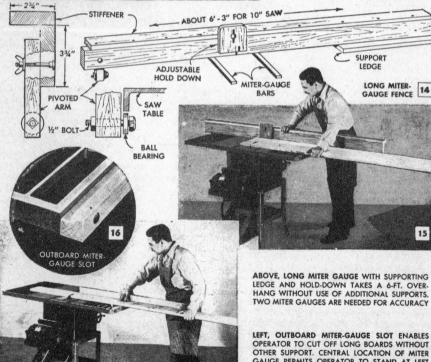

2¾"

STIFFENER

ABOUT 6'-3" FOR 10" SAW

3¾"

ADJUSTABLE HOLD DOWN

MITER-GAUGE BARS

SUPPORT LEDGE

LONG MITER-GAUGE FENCE **14**

PIVOTED ARM

½" BOLT

SAW TABLE

BALL BEARING

16

OUTBOARD MITER-GAUGE SLOT

15

17

ABOVE, LONG MITER GAUGE WITH SUPPORTING LEDGE AND HOLD-DOWN TAKES A 6-FT. OVERHANG WITHOUT USE OF ADDITIONAL SUPPORTS. TWO MITER GAUGES ARE NEEDED FOR ACCURACY

LEFT, OUTBOARD MITER-GAUGE SLOT ENABLES OPERATOR TO CUT OFF LONG BOARDS WITHOUT OTHER SUPPORT. CENTRAL LOCATION OF MITER GAUGE PERMITS OPERATOR TO STAND AT LEFT OF SAW TABLE TO GUIDE WORK WITH EASE

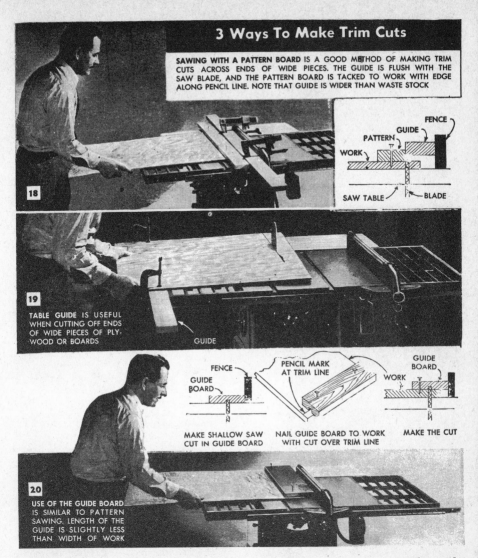

3 Ways To Make Trim Cuts

SAWING WITH A PATTERN BOARD IS A GOOD METHOD OF MAKING TRIM CUTS ACROSS ENDS OF WIDE PIECES. THE GUIDE IS FLUSH WITH THE SAW BLADE, AND THE PATTERN BOARD IS TACKED TO WORK WITH EDGE ALONG PENCIL LINE. NOTE THAT GUIDE IS WIDER THAN WASTE STOCK

18

FENCE
GUIDE
PATTERN
WORK
SAW TABLE — BLADE

19

TABLE GUIDE IS USEFUL WHEN CUTTING OFF ENDS OF WIDE PIECES OF PLY-WOOD OR BOARDS

GUIDE

FENCE
GUIDE BOARD
PENCIL MARK AT TRIM LINE
WORK
GUIDE BOARD

MAKE SHALLOW SAW CUT IN GUIDE BOARD   NAIL GUIDE BOARD TO WORK WITH CUT OVER TRIM LINE   MAKE THE CUT

20

USE OF THE GUIDE BOARD IS SIMILAR TO PATTERN SAWING. LENGTH OF THE GUIDE IS SLIGHTLY LESS THAN WIDTH OF WORK

show three ways to solve this problem. The procedure is similar to pattern sawing in that a pattern or guide board is used on top of the stock. This is guided either by a strip clamped to the ripping fence, Fig. 18, or by a strip clamped to the work which rides along the left-hand edge of the saw table as in Fig. 19, or simply by a strip attached to the work as in Fig. 20. Of the three methods, the first is the most commonly used as it produces the most accurate work and is best for duplicating a number of pieces. Of course, the limited width of the guide, Fig. 18, makes it possible to trim only narrow widths from the ends of the stock. For making cuts across

the ends or near the center of wide panels, the table guide, Fig. 19, generally gives the best results. Always use the splitter with the table guide, and hold the work firmly against the edge of the table to prevent it from twisting or being thrown upward by the saw blade. The splitter cannot be used with either of the other methods, so make sure that the teeth are sharp and have a medium-wide set. The procedure in Fig. 20 requires a separate guide board for each piece of varying width. A shallow groove, or a saw cut, is made lengthwise on one face of the guide. Then the guide is attached to the work with one edge of the groove flush with the trim line at both ends.

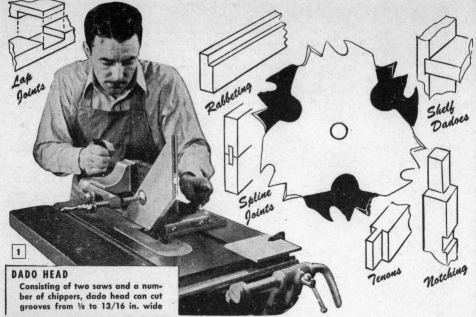

Lap Joints

Rabbeting

Spline Joints

Shelf Dadoes

Tenons

Notching

1

DADO HEAD
Consisting of two saws and a number of chippers, dado head can cut grooves from ⅛ to 13/16 in. wide

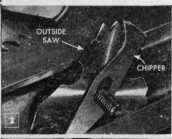

OUTSIDE SAW

CHIPPER

2

STRIP OF PAPER

3

GUMMED-PAPER WASHER

4

CIRCULAR SAW

DADO HEAD

WHEN PURCHASING a dado head for your power saw, you can select from several styles. The spring-set head, shown in the photos at the left, has the advantage of low cost and easy maintenance. If you have an 8 or 10-in. saw, a 6-in. dado head is the proper size to use. Each blade of a dado saw commonly cuts a ⅛-in. kerf, while the addition of chippers increases the width of cut to 13⁄16 in. by sixteenths. One saw plus one 1⁄16-in. chipper can be used to make a 3⁄16-in. groove. In any combination, the chippers next to the saws should be arranged to fall in saw gullets, Fig. 2. When mounting a dado head put the saws and chippers on the arbor one at a time, keeping the chippers evenly distributed around the circle. To remove the head, take off the outside saw, spin the chippers together and remove in one group. Two saws together will cut a ¼-in. groove. This can be increased slightly by inserting paper between the saws, Fig. 3. Gummed paper washers, Fig. 4, also can be used.

Cutting duplicate dadoes: Fig. 6 shows the best method of duplicating dadoes when the cuts are not regularly spaced. Make the first piece by cutting the dadoes to pencil marks. Use this piece as a pattern and nail it to a second piece. Now, with a nail

DUPLICATE DADOES

By using first piece as a pattern, duplicate dadoes can be cut. This pattern is nailed over other pieces to be dadoed and cuts are located with a guide pin. Left, equally spaced dadoes are worked by fitting nail guide in first of two cuts made to pencil marks. By setting each cut in turn to this guide pin, as many evenly spaced cuts as needed may be made

or wooden guide pin to engage the pattern, the second piece can be cut to duplicate the first. When cuts are spaced regularly, the first two cuts on the first piece are made to pencil marks. Then, with the dado head engaged in the second cut, a nail is placed along the edge of the first cut and driven into the miter-gauge facing, Fig. 7. By setting each cut to this guide pin, as many evenly spaced cuts can be made as desired, Fig. 5.

Blind dadoes: Accurate work on blind dadoes requires the use of stops, Fig. 8. These are located, as in Fig. 9, with the work placed alongside the saw which is set at the required cutting depth. A back stop, Fig. 10, is useful as it locates the cut and prevents any kickback when the work is lowered over the saw. When dadoing one

or two pieces, it is practical to work to pencil marks instead of using positive stops.

Corner joints: The dado head is used to make several kinds of corner joints, the most popular being the simple rabbet joint shown in Figs. 11 to 13. The dado-head setup should be a little wider than the thickness of the work, Fig. 11. For short-run work a narrower setup can be used, making the rabbet in two passes. The dado-and-rabbet joint, Fig. 14, is popular for drawer backs. In short-run work, piece B is cut with the work flat on the table, using the same setup as for part A but changing the depth. This has a disadvantage in that any variation in work thickness will affect the thickness of the tenon. To assure a constant tenon width, the cut should be made with the tenon side against the fence,

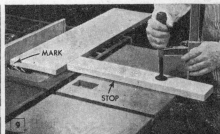

BLIND DADOES

Grooves stopped short of one or both ends of the work are called blind dadoes or gains. Stops assure accuracy and the starting stop also prevents kickback when work is lowered onto the dado blade. For offhand work it is more practical to work to pencil marks instead of using positive stops

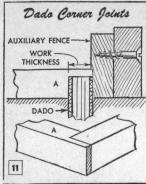

Dado Corner Joints

AUXILIARY FENCE
WORK THICKNESS
A
DADO
A

11

AUXILIARY FENCE
WORK FLUSH WITH OUTSIDE SAW

12

A

13

RABBET JOINT

Rabbet joint is useful and easy to make. Only part A is cut. Fig. 12 shows fence, used as stop, being set to work thickness. A faster setup is made with stop clamped to miter-gauge facing or saw table

A
B

14

STOP
A

15

B
B
¼" PLYWOOD TABLE

16

ABOUT ⅓ WORK THICKNESS
WORK THICKNESS
A
B

DADO AND RABBET

Dado and rabbet uses ¼-in. dado for ¾-in. stock. Part A should be cut first. For one or two joints, Part B is worked flat on the table. For production runs, an end cut, Fig. 16, is more accurate

TENON JIG USED AS STOP
A

17

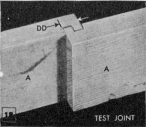

DD
A

18   TEST JOINT

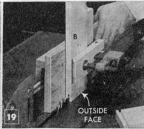

B
OUTSIDE FACE

19

DOUBLE DADO

EQUAL
DD
UNEQUAL
A
B
A
B

Double dado with equal dadoes is easiest to set up but unequal construction is stronger. Double-dado spacing is maintained by using tenon jig as stop for piece A and as work-holding device for piece B

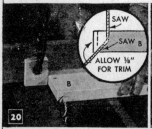

SAW
SAW B
ALLOW ⅛" FOR TRIM
B

20

STOP

21

A

22

A
B

½ WORK THICKNESS
A
B

RABBET AND MITER

To get a clean miter, rabbet and miter should allow ⅛ in. per joint overlength. Part B is cut entirely by sawing. Part A is sawed at 45 deg., after which dado head is used to cut rabbet, Fig. 22

STRIP CUTTING OF RABBET JOINT

Strip cutting of rabbet joint is useful timesaving technique for mass cutting. Combined saw and dado cut work to length and make rabbet in one pass. Rabbet at opposite end of piece is cut by using saw blade as stop

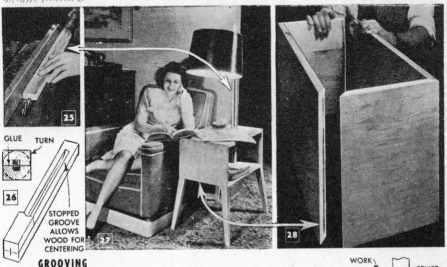

GROOVING

Lamp-table construction features grooving with ⅜-in. dado for wiring groove and single saw for splined miters. In grooving for spline keep the cut well to inside for maximum strength

Fig. 16. If an auxiliary table or insert is used, cuts of this kind can be made freehand. *Caution:* Never freehand narrow work over the regular dado insert because the large opening may let the work drop through to the table. The double-dado and rabbet-and-miter joints shown in Figs. 17 to 22 are useful dado joints, but are subject to variations both in proportions and working methods. Methods of cutting them are learned more readily by practice than by reading, and working methods often depend on the number of pieces to be cut. Time can be saved by combining a saw with the dado head, Figs. 23 and 24, to cut the work to length and make the rabbet in one pass.

Grooving: Grooving is just another name for dadoing, although it is used specifically

for narrow cuts or cuts with the wood grain. A typical application is the wiring groove for a lamp, Figs. 25 to 27. When turning the work after gluing, many workers prefer a blind groove, Fig. 26, so that the ends of the work will present solid stock for lathe centering. After the piece is turned, it is a simple matter to drill in an inch to connect with the grooves. The splined miter joint, Fig. 28, is commonly grooved with a single dado saw, keeping the cut well to the inside for maximum strength, as shown in the diagram. The cut usually is stopped at both ends, using stops as previously described for square cutting.

Angular notching: The angular notch provides a simple means of fitting table legs, Fig. 29. It is poor practice to attempt this freehand or with makeshift support

ANGULAR NOTCHING

Simple jig holds work at required 45-deg. position for angular notching. It is poor practice to attempt this cut freehand or with makeshift support blocks jammed under the work

TONGUE-AND-GROOVE

Tenons and tongue-and-groove joints can be cut with dado saws spaced by suitable hardwood collar

blocks jammed under the work. Take time to do the job right by ripping a piece of ¾ x 4-in. stock at a 45-deg. angle and nailing the two parts over a plywood base, Figs. 32, to provide a rigid holding device for the work.

Tenons: A quick way to make tenons is to work the stock flat on the saw table and cut away the waste wood from either side by turning the work over. Like all work using this reversal method, the thickness of the tenon will vary with the work thickness; hence this method is practical only when using wood of uniform thickness. For tenoning a number of pieces, a setup with a spacing collar between the saw blades does an excellent job independent of work thickness. This reverses the usual dado setup, since the saws are on the inside and the chippers outside, Fig. 31. The tenoning operation is shown in Fig. 33. Obviously, the same arrangement will work for the tongue of the tongue-and-groove joint, Fig. 34. The spacing collar can be metal or hardwood and should be thicker than the desired tenon by the amount of set on the saws. ★ ★ ★

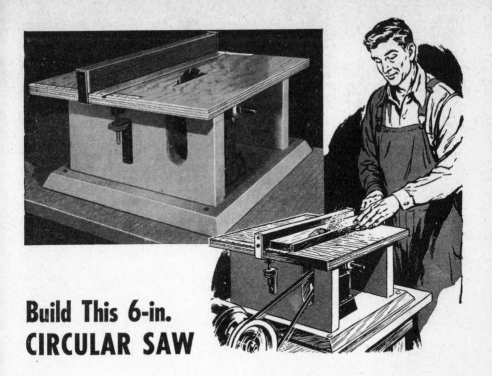
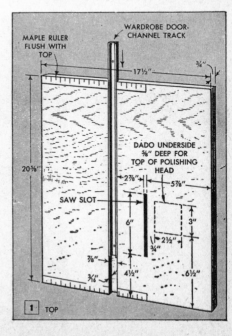

Build This 6-in.
CIRCULAR SAW

HOME CRAFTSMEN, hobbyists and others who have only occasional need for a small circular saw can easily build a serviceable one from a few pieces of hardwood, assorted bolts, flat iron and a polishing head of the type having a straight spindle fitted with two machined collars. A light polishing head of this type makes a suitable arbor for a 6-in. saw blade. The top, or saw table, Fig. 1, is made from ¾-in. hardwood plywood, such as oak or birch. Have your lumber dealer cut the piece to size, run the ³⁄₁₆ x ⁷⁄₈-in. groove and also cut the saw slot in the position indicated in the detail. The slot should be ¼ in. wide. Some polishing heads have larger pulleys than others, making it necessary to dado or recess the underside of the top as indicated by the dotted lines in Fig. 1 to provide clearance for the pulley and belt. If required, this cut can be made at the time the groove is cut. Cutting the belt slot in the table support, Fig. 5, is easy; just bore a 2⅛-in. hole with an expansive bit and make two saw cuts inward from one edge of the piece to remove the waste. Then reinforce the opening with two blocks attached to the back face with screws. Fasten

Figure 1 labels: WARDROBE DOOR-CHANNEL TRACK; MAPLE RULER FLUSH WITH TOP; 17½"; ¾"; DADO UNDERSIDE ⅜" DEEP FOR TOP OF POLISHING HEAD; 20⅝"; SAW SLOT; 2⅞"; 5⅝"; 6"; 3"; 2½"; ¾"; ⅞"; ³⁄₁₆"; 4½"; 6½"; **1** TOP

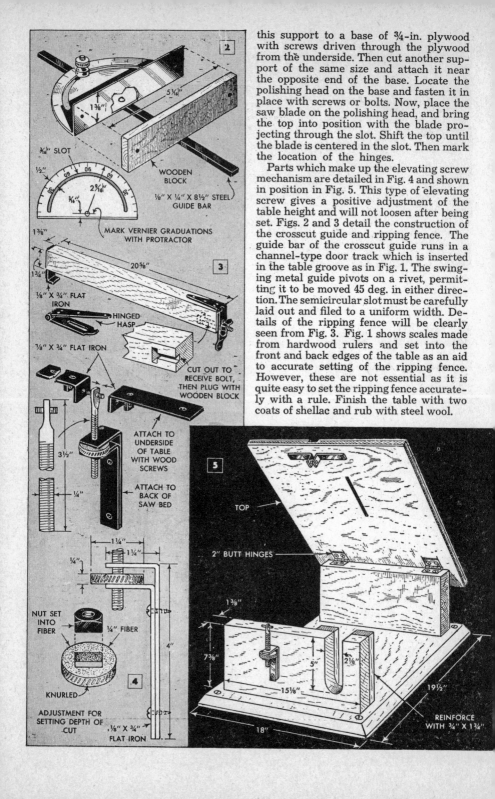

this support to a base of ¾-in. plywood with screws driven through the plywood from the underside. Then cut another support of the same size and attach it near the opposite end of the base. Locate the polishing head on the base and fasten it in place with screws or bolts. Now, place the saw blade on the polishing head, and bring the top into position with the blade projecting through the slot. Shift the top until the blade is centered in the slot. Then mark the location of the hinges.

Parts which make up the elevating screw mechanism are detailed in Fig. 4 and shown in position in Fig. 5. This type of elevating screw gives a positive adjustment of the table height and will not loosen after being set. Figs. 2 and 3 detail the construction of the crosscut guide and ripping fence. The guide bar of the crosscut guide runs in a channel-type door track which is inserted in the table groove as in Fig. 1. The swinging metal guide pivots on a rivet, permitting it to be moved 45 deg. in either direction. The semicircular slot must be carefully laid out and filed to a uniform width. Details of the ripping fence will be clearly seen from Fig. 3. Fig. 1 shows scales made from hardwood rulers and set into the front and back edges of the table as an aid to accurate setting of the ripping fence. However, these are not essential as it is quite easy to set the ripping fence accurately with a rule. Finish the table with two coats of shellac and rub with steel wool.

CLAMPS

C LAMPS commonly used in making glued joints include handscrews, C-clamps and bar clamps. The actual mechanics of working and applying these clamps is often obvious, yet there are certain tricks in operation that save time and help to produce better work.

Swinging a handscrew: Oldest of all clamps, the handscrew often is misused. Learn, first, to swing it—grasp the end of the spindle with the right hand, Fig. 1, and then rotate the right hand toward

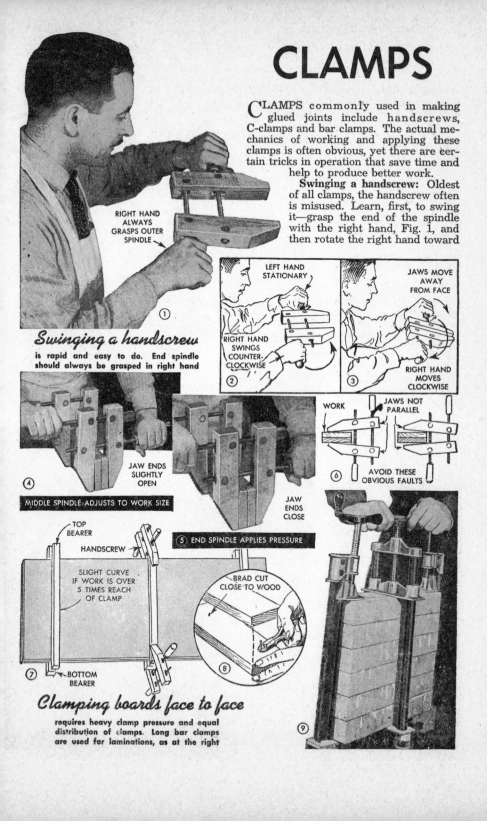

RIGHT HAND ALWAYS GRASPS OUTER SPINDLE

① *Swinging a handscrew*

is rapid and easy to do. End spindle should always be grasped in right hand

LEFT HAND STATIONARY

② RIGHT HAND SWINGS COUNTER-CLOCKWISE

③ JAWS MOVE AWAY FROM FACE — RIGHT HAND MOVES CLOCKWISE

④ JAW ENDS SLIGHTLY OPEN

MIDDLE SPINDLE ADJUSTS TO WORK SIZE

JAW ENDS CLOSE

⑤ END SPINDLE APPLIES PRESSURE

⑥ WORK — JAWS NOT PARALLEL — AVOID THESE OBVIOUS FAULTS

⑦ TOP BEARER — HANDSCREW — SLIGHT CURVE IF WORK IS OVER 5 TIMES REACH OF CLAMP — BOTTOM BEARER

⑧ BRAD CUT CLOSE TO WOOD

Clamping boards face to face

requires heavy clamp pressure and equal distribution of clamps. Long bar clamps are used for laminations, as at the right

⑨

or away from your face, Figs. 2 and 3, to open or close the jaws as required. Always grasp the end spindle in your right hand. If you have trouble remembering the direction of swing, simply think "open face," indicating a swing of the jaws toward your face to open them, as in Fig. 2. New clamp jaws are oiled. Get rid of any excess oil by clamping over a soft board or blotter before you proceed with actual work.

Face-to-face joints: The method of applying handscrews when gluing boards face to face is shown in Figs. 4 and 5. The same technique applies in any other use of handscrews. First, swing the handscrew to get the approximate jaw opening needed. Apply it to work, and turn both handles so that the jaws take the position shown in Fig. 4, with the tips slightly open. Use end handle to apply pressure, Fig. 5, bringing the jaws parallel. If the jaws do not come parallel, loosen middle spindle slightly, and then retighten it. Avoid the obvious faults shown in Fig. 6. The final position of the clamp jaws should be parallel for all average work. If the work is too wide to be clamped with handscrews alone, use bearers at top and bottom, Fig. 7. A few small brads driven into the wood and cut off close as in Fig. 8 will prevent creeping when clamp pressure is applied. Of course, clamps other than handscrews can be used for face-to-face joints. The use of single and double bar clamps for this work is shown in Fig. 9.

Edge-to-edge joints: Alternate the boards, one with the heart up and one with it down as in Fig. 10 when assembling work of this kind, in order to minimize warping. Match the grain as closely as possible. Place bar clamps on a level surface and assemble the work face down over the

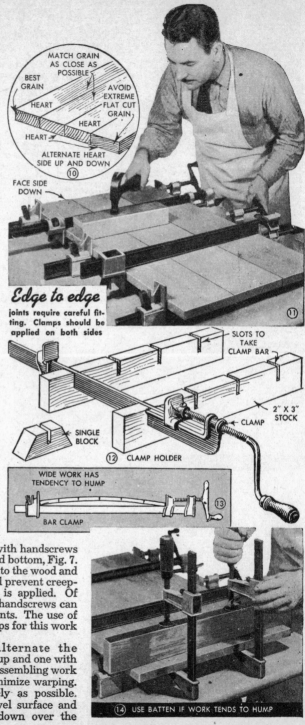

MATCH GRAIN AS CLOSE AS POSSIBLE

BEST GRAIN

HEART

AVOID EXTREME FLAT CUT GRAIN

HEART

HEART

ALTERNATE HEART SIDE UP AND DOWN

(10)

FACE SIDE DOWN

Edge to edge joints require careful fitting. Clamps should be applied on both sides

(11)

SLOTS TO TAKE CLAMP BAR

2" X 3" STOCK

CLAMP

SINGLE BLOCK

(12) CLAMP HOLDER

WIDE WORK HAS TENDENCY TO HUMP

BAR CLAMP

(13)

(14) USE BATTEN IF WORK TENDS TO HUMP

FAULTY CLAMPING CAUSES WORK TO BUCKLE

JOINT OPENS

⑯

TRUE CLAMPING LINE

GLUE BLOCK OR BATTEN

CORRECT CLAMPING ON TRUE CLAMPING LINE

⑰

BAR CLAMP

BLOCK GLUED ON OR BATTEN CLAMPED ON

TRUE LINE OF PRESSURE

⑱

⑲

EAR

ON FLAT, CURVED WORK LEAVE EARS FOR CLAMPING, OR, GLUE FIRST AND CUT LATER

CUT TO BE MADE AFTER ASSEMBLY ⑳

SAW AFTER ASSEMBLY

FRAME GLUED UP "IN THE SQUARE" ㉑

Clamping curved work

is not difficult and good results are always obtained if clamp parallels true pressure line

clamps. Some styles of clamps will stand alone; others will need holding blocks, as in Fig. 12, to maintain an upright position. Use paper at points where clamp bars cross glued joints to prevent sticking or staining. Tighten the clamps gradually, in rotation, leading off with the center clamp. The tendency of work is to hump, Fig. 13, and this should be eliminated by fitting clamps on both sides or by applying a batten as in Fig. 14. After medium pressure has been applied, go over the joints with a hammer and wood block as shown in Fig. 11, pounding all joints flat.

Clamping curved work: Curved work illustrates one basic rule of clamping: The pressure always must be directly across the joint. Note in Fig. 16 how violation of this rule would cause work to buckle. Correct clamping, Figs. 15 and 17, keeps the work in proper position. Figs. 18 and 19 show other examples. Blocks necessary to establish a clamping line can be glued or clamped on as desired. If glued on, they can be knocked off with a chisel when the glue joint has dried. The correct clamping line on flat work is established readily by leaving ears on the work as in Fig. 20, or by gluing up "in-the-square," Fig. 21.

Framing: Framing is the classic of clamping operations in woodworking. It applies to tables, cabinets, frames—any kind of work assembled from legs or stiles

and rails. Check work of this kind carefully for wind (twist), squareness and flatness as shown in the photos, Figs. 22, 23, 24 and 26. Use a batten, Fig. 25, if the work is not level. Adjust clamps as in Fig. 27, if work is not square, or, apply a clamp diagonally, Fig. 28. Correct any twist by shifting the clamps in the direction of the arrows, Fig. 29. If the work leans or twists in any direction, the ends of the clamps are always shifted in the same direction as

Framing, four tests for trueness

All frames should be tested for trueness immediately after initial clamping. Corrections can usually be made by shifting the clamps, as shown in diagrams

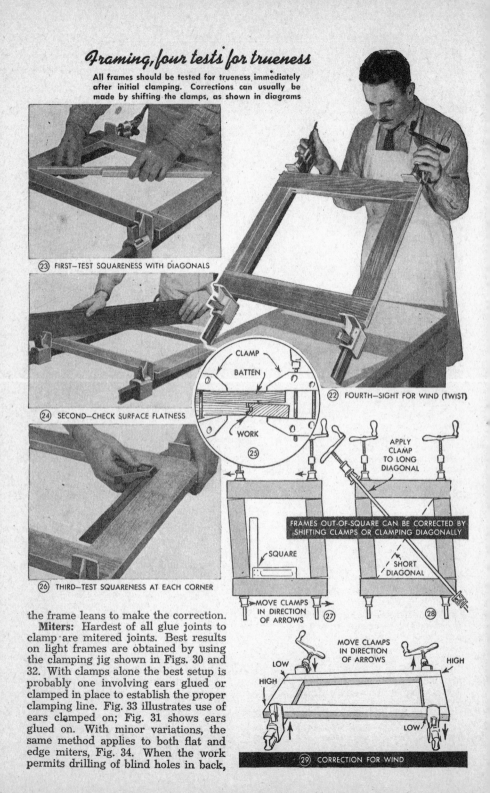

㉓ FIRST—TEST SQUARENESS WITH DIAGONALS

㉔ SECOND—CHECK SURFACE FLATNESS

㉖ THIRD—TEST SQUARENESS AT EACH CORNER

CLAMP

BATTEN

WORK

㉕

㉒ FOURTH—SIGHT FOR WIND (TWIST)

APPLY CLAMP TO LONG DIAGONAL

FRAMES OUT-OF-SQUARE CAN BE CORRECTED BY SHIFTING CLAMPS OR CLAMPING DIAGONALLY

SQUARE

SHORT DIAGONAL

MOVE CLAMPS IN DIRECTION OF ARROWS

㉗   ㉘

MOVE CLAMPS IN DIRECTION OF ARROWS

LOW   HIGH

HIGH

LOW

㉙ CORRECTION FOR WIND

the frame leans to make the correction.

Miters: Hardest of all glue joints to clamp are mitered joints. Best results on light frames are obtained by using the clamping jig shown in Figs. 30 and 32. With clamps alone the best setup is probably one involving ears glued or clamped in place to establish the proper clamping line. Fig. 33 illustrates use of ears clamped on; Fig. 31 shows ears glued on. With minor variations, the same method applies to both flat and edge miters, Fig. 34. When the work permits drilling of blind holes in back,

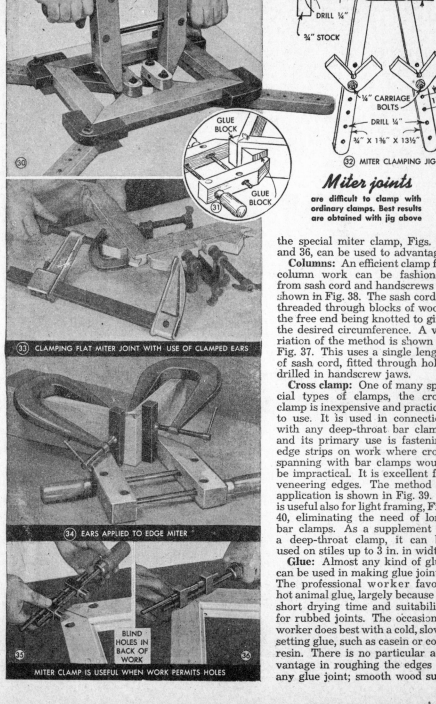

⌐3¼"⌐ 1 5/16"

DRILL ¼"

¾" STOCK

⌐3¼"⌐ 1⅜"

¼" CARRIAGE BOLTS

1¼"

DRILL ¼"

¾" X 1⅜" X 13½"

(32) MITER CLAMPING JIG

Miter joints

are difficult to clamp with ordinary clamps. Best results are obtained with jig above

(30)

GLUE BLOCK

(31)

GLUE BLOCK

(33) CLAMPING FLAT MITER JOINT WITH USE OF CLAMPED EARS

(34) EARS APPLIED TO EDGE MITER

(35)

(36)

BLIND HOLES IN BACK OF WORK

MITER CLAMP IS USEFUL WHEN WORK PERMITS HOLES

the special miter clamp, Figs. 35 and 36, can be used to advantage.

Columns: An efficient clamp for column work can be fashioned from sash cord and handscrews as shown in Fig. 38. The sash cord is threaded through blocks of wood, the free end being knotted to give the desired circumference. A variation of the method is shown in Fig. 37. This uses a single length of sash cord, fitted through holes drilled in handscrew jaws.

Cross clamp: One of many special types of clamps, the cross clamp is inexpensive and practical to use. It is used in connection with any deep-throat bar clamp, and its primary use is fastening edge strips on work where cross spanning with bar clamps would be impractical. It is excellent for veneering edges. The method of application is shown in Fig. 39. It is useful also for light framing, Fig. 40, eliminating the need of long bar clamps. As a supplement to a deep-throat clamp, it can be used on stiles up to 3 in. in width.

Glue: Almost any kind of glue can be used in making glue joints. The professional worker favors hot animal glue, largely because of short drying time and suitability for rubbed joints. The occasional worker does best with a cold, slow-setting glue, such as casein or cold resin. There is no particular advantage in roughing the edges of any glue joint; smooth wood surfaces hold just as well as rough, provided that the edges to be glued are flat and even throughout. End grain joints should be sized with a priming glue coat to stop suction. Oily woods, such as teak, rosewood, pitch pine, etc., should be sponged with a weak caustic solution (or any household cleaner) to cut the oil film. Joints in hardwood should stand in the clamps two or three hours longer than softwood; minimum drying time will depend on glue used and temperature of room, but in all cases a full 12 hours' drying time insures sound joints. Extensive use should be made of dry setups to check fitting and accuracy of all joints so that when the work is finally assembled and glued, the job can proceed smoothly without the annoying delays which would be necessitated by taking apart the joints and refitting them.

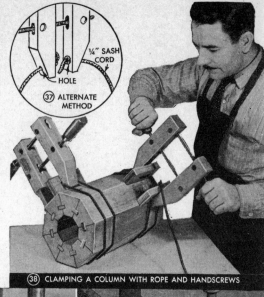

(37) ALTERNATE METHOD

1/4" SASH CORD

HOLE

(38) CLAMPING A COLUMN WITH ROPE AND HANDSCREWS

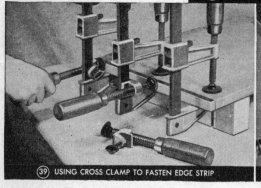

(39) USING CROSS CLAMP TO FASTEN EDGE STRIP

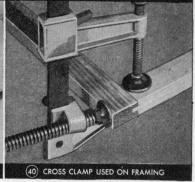

(40) CROSS CLAMP USED ON FRAMING

Bar Clamp Made Like Sawhorse

Designed by a woodworker for special work in assembling heavy doors, this saw-horse-clamp unit does double duty as a combined support and bar clamp when assembling and gluing other types of work. It is made in the same manner as an ordinary sawhorse, except that the bottom of the beam is notched, each notch having one straight and one slanting face to engage the ratchet ring attached to the sliding jaw. This permits moving the sliding jaw to any point along the beam to position it for clamping work of various widths. A hardwood block bolted to the top of the sawhorse beam is drilled to take an ordinary vise screw in a loose fit. The threaded vise-screw pad is then bolted to the inside face of the block. The end of the vise screw is

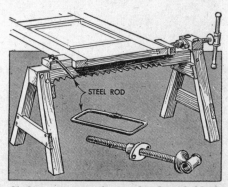

STEEL ROD

filed square so that a hardwood block placed between the end of the screw and the edge of the work will act as a jaw when tightening the clamp.

Wood Frame Substitutes for Clamps in Gluing

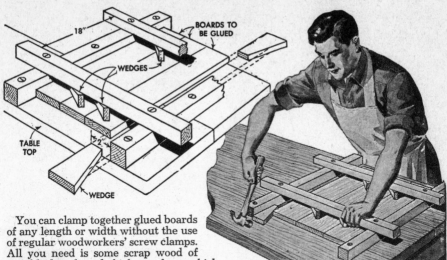

You can clamp together glued boards of any length or width without the use of regular woodworkers' screw clamps. All you need is some scrap wood of suitable length and thickness from which to improvise a frame, as shown in the detail. The frame can be screwed to an old table top or work bench—even to the floor or a wall, if the resulting screw holes are not objectionable. First measure the width of the work to be clamped. Add about 2 in. to the width, and screw two lengths of 2 by 4-in. stock or other wood this distance apart on the table, bench or other working surface. Of course, the pieces should run across the planks of the bench or table top so that these are not forced apart under pressure. Then screw crosspieces over the frame near the ends. Slide the work into the frame, insert a wedge at each end and set smaller wedges under the crosspieces over each glued joint to prevent the work from buckling. It is advisable also to lay paper between the work and the wedges to prevent the latter from adhering to the work when the glue dries. When all wedges are in position, tap each slightly with a hammer, as shown in the illustration, to force the joints together tightly, and leave the work until the glue is dry.

Inexpensive Gluing Clamps Made From Turnbuckles

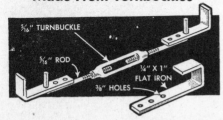

Gluing clamps for most woodworking projects can be made from turnbuckles, rod and flat iron. Force the eyebolts of the turnbuckles open to form the linkage for the hooks, as shown. The hooks are bent from flat iron and a series of holes is drilled in each one to permit attaching to the linkage. The capacity of the clamps is determined by the length of the rods.

Short Angle Improves C-Clamp

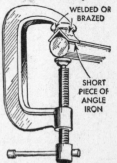

By welding or brazing a short length of angle iron to the anvil of a C-clamp you won't be troubled with it slipping off round work. Such a clamp will be found particularly handy in holding both rod and flat stock together for welding. A shallow V-groove filed in the swivel jaw of the clamp will allow it to ride the work also, and a block placed in the angle iron permits clamping flat work as before.

CAM-ACTION CLAMPS

If an occasional gluing job does not warrant investing in expensive bar clamps, excellent cam-action ones of hardwood can be made at very little cost. These clamps are adjustable and withstand considerable pressure. First, make the frame, slotting it for the cam assembly and fitting it with a stop block as in Fig. 2. Next, cut out the cam, Fig. 1, and drill it for a pivot bolt. After this, assemble the cam to the frame by inserting the pivot bolt through an anchor block, two bushings and a piece of flat iron. The latter clamps the assembly to the frame and the lower bushing facilitates moving the cam in the slot. Note that a series of holes for a locking pin is drilled near one edge of the cam. To use the clamp, set the work against the stop block, tighten the cam about ¼ in. from the edge of the work and then adjust the cam to exert pressure on the joint. Finally, lock the cam by slipping a locking pin (a screw eye will do) through one of the holes and against the edge of the frame.

1 CAM — 1" STOCK

1" SQS.

¼" HOLES, EQUALLY SPACED

1¹¹⁄₁₆" HOLE

GRAIN

2½" R.

1¹³⁄₁₆" R.

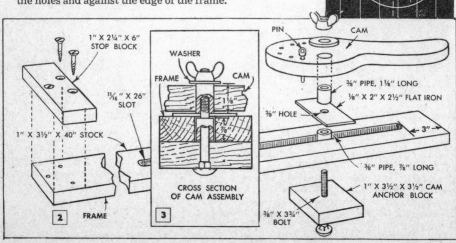

1" X 2¼" X 6" STOP BLOCK

WASHER

FRAME

CAM

PIN

CAM

¹¹⁄₁₆" X 26" SLOT

1⅛"

⅞"

⅜" PIPE, 1⅛" LONG

⅛" X 2" X 2½" FLAT IRON

⅜" HOLE

3"

1" X 3½" X 40" STOCK

⅜" PIPE, ⅞" LONG

CROSS SECTION OF CAM ASSEMBLY

1" X 3½" X 3½" CAM ANCHOR BLOCK

⅜" X 3¾" BOLT

2 FRAME

3

CLEANERS AND FINISHERS

WALL CLEANERS AND STARCH

Soap Jelly

Pour 1 cup of hot water over 2 cups of mild soap flakes and beat to a jelly with a rotary egg beater. Apply jelly to soiled surface with a damp sponge or cloth, cleaning a small area at a time. Rinse surface thoroughly with sponge or cloth wrung out of clear soft water.

Wall-Cleaning Solution

This is a good cleaner for enameled and painted walls. To make one gallon of it, dissolve ⅓ tablespoon of trisodium phosphate and ½ tablespoon of washing soda (sodium carbonate) in 1 gallon of hot water. Add to this solution 1 tablespoon of soap flakes and stir until thoroughly dissolved. When solution is lukewarm, apply it to the soiled wall with a sponge or a soft cloth wrung out of the solution, using a circular motion. Rinse wall immediately with a second sponge or cloth wrung out of clear lukewarm soft water.

Wallpaper Cleaner

Small quantity—1½ cups water, ½ cup salt, ½ oz. (2 tablespoons) aluminum sulfate or alum, 1 tablespoon kerosene or 1 tablespoon tetrachlorid, 2½ to 3 cups flour. Large quantity—1 gal. water, 2½ lb. salt, 4 oz. aluminum sulfate or alum, 4½ oz. kerosene or ½ cup carbon tetrachlorid, 9 to 9¾ lb. flour. Use a good grade of bread flour. Place water and salt in a kettle. Stir and heat to 180° F., or until bubbles appear on bottom of pan. Remove from stove and add kerosene and aluminum sulfate or alum. Add flour, stirring quickly to prevent lumps. Continue stirring until a smooth thick paste forms. Knead the dough until it is smooth and not sticky. It may be necessary to use a little less flour, since flours differ in starch content. Apply a small ball of dough to the soiled wallpaper with even strokes, working downward. Discard the dough when it becomes soiled.

Starch for Walls

· 1 cup dry laundry starch, cold water, 2 qt. boiling water, 1 qt. buttermilk. This starch will preserve the finish on oil-painted or enameled walls and nonrun wallpaper. Add enough cold water to starch to dissolve it. Combine boiling water with starch mixture, stirring constantly until starch becomes cooked, that is, until it becomes stiff. Cool and add enough cold water to make a thin liquid. Add buttermilk and strain through a cheesecloth. Apply freely to the wall with a calcimine brush. Do not try to cover a large area at one time. Brush on thoroughly in order that no brush marks will appear on the surface.

WAXES AND CLEANERS FOR WOODWORK

Wax Paste

½ lb. beeswax or ¼ lb. beeswax and ¼ lb. paraffin, ¼ pt. turpentine, ¼ pt. denatured alcohol. This is a soft paste suitable for waxing floors and furniture. Melt wax in pan over a slow fire, being careful not to spill it. Remove from fire and stir in turpentine and alcohol until mixture is a thick paste. Pour into covered jar. Paraffin wax can economically replace beeswax. Apply a small amount of wax with a soft cloth, rubbing thoroughly with the grain of the wood until there is no free wax remaining on the surface.

Thick Liquid Wax

One-fourth lb. beeswax, 1 lb. paraffin, 1¼ pt. turpentine, ¼ pt. raw linseed oil. This wax is used to clean, protect, and polish both finished and unfinished wood surfaces. Melt paraffin and beeswax in pan over a slow fire. Remove from stove and add linseed oil and turpentine, stirring mixture vigorously. Store in tightly covered jar. Put a small portion of the mixture on a soft cloth and rub it on the wood surface, polishing with the grain of the wood. Unfinished wood is darkened somewhat by the absorption of linseed oil.

Water-Wax Emulsion

One oz. soap flakes or soap cut into small pieces, 16 oz. (1 pt.) boiling soft or distilled water, 4 oz. carnauba wax finely ground, 16 oz. (1 pt.) soft or distilled cold water. In order to form a stable emulsion, correct weights of soap flakes and wax must be used. Dissolve soap flakes or soap in boiling water. Slowly add the carnauba wax, stirring constantly until thoroughly dissolved. When mixture has become a smooth emulsion, quickly add 16 ounces of cold soft water to cool it. Strain the emulsion through cheesecloth and store it in a cool place. Shake the wax solution before using it. With a soft cloth apply a small amount to the floor. Before the wax becomes dry, rub the floor lightly with a dry clean cloth or mop. When two coats of wax are used, thin the first coat with a little water before applying it.

Oxalic-Acid Stain Remover

This stain remover is for unfinished wood and enamel surfaces. To remove stains on unfinished wood, dissolve 1 teaspoon of oxalic-acid crystals (poison) in ½ cup hot water and let the solution cool. Apply to stain, let it remain on the wood for a few minutes, then wipe it off with a soft cloth. Repeat if the stain has not been removed. Rinse spot with ammonia solution consisting of 1 pt. 10 percent ammonium hydroxide dissolved in 1 gallon of water. To remove iron stains from enamel surfaces, use a dilute solution of 1 teaspoon of oxalic-acid crystals in 1 cup of hot water. Apply to stain and rinse immediately with ammonia solution. Then rinse with water.

All-Purpose Cleaner

The most popular type of all-purpose cleaner, which can be used with satisfaction for cleaning rugs, woodwork, floors, dishes, painted surfaces, linoleum, glass, porcelain, etc., consists of the following inexpensive solution:

I. Trisodium phosphate, 1 oz.; water, 1 gal. A large proportion of the liquid cleaners on the market are made to this type formula. A faint trace of a water soluble dye is sometimes added together with a cheap perfume, of the type used in soaps. Although these do not help the product, they disguise its simplicity.

II. The following cleaner is similar, and preferred for many purposes: Trisodium phosphate, 1 oz.; liquid soap, 2 to 6 oz.; water, 1 gal.

III. Another excellent all-purpose cleaner which is particularly efficient for polishing glass consists of: Sodium meta-silicate, 2 oz.; water, 1 gal. The silicate is dissolved in hot water.

Starch Solution Cleans Woodwork

Woodwork in your kitchen that has become stained from smoke and grease, can be cleaned by painting it with a solution of starch in water. After the solution has dried, it is rubbed off with a soft brush or clean cloth, which removes the stains. Treating the woodwork in this way does not harm the paint, and any finished surface treated with starch will remain in good condition for several years.

Kerosene Emulsion

One qt. hot water (120° to 130° F.), 1 teaspoon trisodium phosphate, 3 to 4 oz. beeswax, ⅔ cup kerosene. This cleaner is for painted, enameled, and varnished wood surfaces. Dissolve the trisodium phosphate in the hot water. Melt the wax in an aluminum utensil, remove from the stove, and add kerosene. While rapidly stirring the melted wax and kerosene solution, slowly add the hot water solution. With a soft cloth apply a small amount of the solution to the soiled woodwork. Rub dry, using a clean soft cloth. This solution is especially good for quick and frequent cleaning and for polishing greasy or sooty woodwork. If the emulsion has separated while standing, shake before using.

Oil Solutions for Cleaning

I. This is for ordinary dusting of non-waxed wood or metal surfaces. Put 1 tablespoon of paraffin, lemon, or boiled linseed oil into a quart jar, cover, and turn the jar in the hands until the oil is spread evenly over inner surface of jar. Put dust cloth in jar and leave overnight. The oil will be evenly distributed throughout the cloth.

II. For varnished, shellacked, oiled, or painted surfaces that are slightly soiled, mix together 4 tablespoons of boiled linseed oil, 1 tablespoon of turpentine, and 1 quart of hot water. Thoroughly wet a soft cloth in the mixture and wring out dry. Wipe furniture with treated cloth. Polish with a clean dry cloth.

III. For special cleaning of oiled floors not waxed, use ⅔ quart of boiled linseed oil with ¼ quart of turpentine. Apply to the floor with a soft cloth wrung dry out of the solution.

Be careful to have no flame in the room when preparing or using furniture or floor polishes that contain either linseed oil or turpentine, as both are very inflammable.

¶Painted bathroom walls often can be cleaned by filling the tub with very hot water and letting the room steam for about 5 min., after which the walls and ceiling can be wiped clean with a dry cloth.

SILVER, GLASS AND MARBLE CLEANERS AND POLISHERS

Electrolysis for Silver

One qt. boiling water, 1 teaspoon baking soda, 1 teaspoon salt, 1 sheet of aluminum (omit if aluminum kettle is used). This is a labor-saving method of cleaning silver. Add soda, salt, and sheet of clean aluminum to kettle of boiling water. If necessary, use several times the above amounts of water, soda, and salt in order to completely immerse the silver, which must be in contact with the sheet of aluminum. Keep water at boiling point throughout the cleaning process. Remove and wash the cleaned silver in hot soapy water, rinse, and polish with a soft dry cloth. A clean inexpensive aluminum kettle may be used in place of an enamel kettle and the sheet of aluminum. Since aluminum deteriorates somewhat in the cleaning solution, valuable utensils should not be used. Pour out the cleaning solution as soon as the silver is removed.

Silver or Nickel Polish

One cup hot water, ¼ teaspoon trisodium phosphate, 2 tablespoons mild soap flakes or homemade soap cut in small pieces, 1 lb. fine grade of whiting for liquid polish, or 2 lb. fine grade of whiting for paste polish. Dissolve the trisodium phosphate in hot water, add soap, and stir until dissolved. Add whiting to the soap solution, stirring until smooth and free from lumps. Store in glass jar with cover and label. With a soft cloth apply a small amount of polish to the silver and rub until the stain is removed. Wash the silver in hot soapy water, rinse, and dry thoroughly.

Whiting Paste for Metal Surfaces

Add enough water or ammonia solution to whiting to form a paste. Apply to tarnished silver, chromium, or nickel with a soft cloth and rub until the tarnish is removed. Let dry and polish. Wash the metal in hot soapy water, rinse, and dry.

Glass Polish

One cup hot water, ½ teaspoon trisodium phosphate, 2 tablespoons soap flakes or finely chipped soap, 1 lb. whiting. Dissolve trisodium phosphate in hot water, add soap flakes, and stir until dissolved. Remove from range, add whiting, and stir until mixture is perfectly smooth. Store in a wide-mouthed jar. Apply a small portion of polish on tissue paper or on a slightly damp cloth and rub on the glass surface. As soon as it dries, rub off with a clean dry cloth. When the paste becomes dry, add enough water to make a thick liquid.

Window Cleaning Fluid

Dissolve ½ tablespoon of trisodium phosphate in ½ cup of hot water. Stir in 4 tablespoons of whiting powder and then add enough water to make one quart of a smooth mixture. When this fluid is to be used, first remove surface soil from window with tissue or soft paper. Shake the fluid. With a soft cloth apply it to the glass and let dry. Then polish with a clean dry cloth. This fluid is especially good for cleaning sooty windows.

Cleaning Windows and Mirrors

Windows, mirrors and other glass surfaces may be thoroughly and easily cleaned with a compound made by mixing precipitated chalk, 7 oz., and tripoli, 2 oz., into a strong soap solution. The soap solution is made by dissolving castile or other equivalent grade of soap, 2 oz., in boiling water, 4 oz. After the soap has been completely dissolved, add the chalk and tripoli and stir until the mixture is smooth. This preparation is applied with a rag and the surplus removed after it has dried leaving a high luster.

Calcium Carbonate for Cleaning Glass

Sometimes, in framing a choice picture, it is desired to get the glass, particularly the side next to the picture, absolutely clean. It has been found that calcium carbonate will do the job to perfection. A little powder is applied to a dampened cloth, which is then rubbed over the glass. The moisture evaporates quickly leaving a fine coating of powder. Remove this by rubbing with a clean, dry cloth.

Solution to Clean Bottles

Bottles and other glassware are readily cleaned with a hot solution made by dissolving a small amount of the following mixture in boiling water. Sodium metasilicate, 1 oz., soda ash, 2 oz., and trisodium phosphate, 2½ oz. The ingredients are mixed together in a dry state to make the cleaning powder. The solution made by dissolving this powder in water may be used for a number of cleaning operations.

Water stains on glass pitchers, vases and

aquariums usually can be removed by rubbing them vigorously with a piece of freshly cut potato or a cloth which has been moistened with potato juice.

Removing Stains From Marble

Iron stains on marble can be removed by applying a solution of sodium citrate, followed by sodium hydrosulphite in dry form, and then covering with a paste of whiting and water. A poultice of whiting, soap solution and sodium carbonate will efface tobacco stains, while ordinary ink stains can often be deleted with a solution of whiting and sodium perborate, followed by a few applications of the sodium-citrate solution.

Marble and Porcelain Cleaner

Marble and porcelain are readily cleaned by applying the following preparation with a stiff brush: Diatomaceous earth 3 oz.; sodium sulphate, 5½ lb.; sulphuric acid, 9 oz. The acid is corrosive and should be handled with care. The finished product may be stored in glass bottles. After applying the cleaner it is washed away with water to prevent pitting of the ware.

HOW TO MAKE SOAP
Preparing the Fat

Sour and rancid fat, fat scraps, and tallow can be combined with new fat to make soap. All such materials must be clean and free from salt. To extract the fat from sour or rancid fat, meat scraps, and fryings, boil them in water. Use approximately equal quantities of fat and water and add 1 tablespoon of vinegar for each quart of water. Heat the mixture, stirring occasionally until it boils. Remove from stove, and add 1 quart of cold water to each gallon of hot liquid in order to settle impurities in the bottom of the dish. When the cooled fat forms solid cake, remove it from the water.

Mixing Ingredients

Enamel or iron utensils, not aluminum, should be used in soapmaking. If several times the amount of fat given below has collected, it is best to use a large iron kettle. The following ingredients are needed: 1 can lye (about 13 ounces), 2½ pints cold water, 6 pounds clean salt-free fat (equal amounts of lard and tallow are recommended). Place lye in kettle and carefully add the water, stirring slowly with a long-handled enamel or iron spoon. Allow solution to cool to room temperature (about 70° F.). In another kettle melt the fat and cool it until it is just warm to the hand. Pour the lye solution slowly in a thin stream into the melted fat. Stir mixture slowly and evenly while the lye is being added, and until the fat and the lye solution are evenly mixed.

Molding and Hardening

When the mixture is thick like honey, pour gently into glass or enamel pans or into firm pasteboard boxes lined with waxed paper. If the mold is greased with vaseline, the soap may be quickly removed. Cover mold with a heavy rug or blanket and leave it for a day or two in a place that is warm but not hot. Before the soap hardens, cut it into bars with twine or fine wire, and place it on shelves to dry for two or three weeks before using. Soap should not be allowed to freeze until after it has hardened for at least two weeks. Good homemade soap is free from excess alkali, which is harmful to skin and fabrics. It contains glycerin, which helps to keep the skin soft. For toilet soap, stir into the above mixture 2 to 4 ounces of glycerin after the lye solution and the fat have been combined.

Reclaiming Soap

Greasy layers in soap show that the fatty matter was not thoroughly combined with the lye because of inaccurate measurements or because the lye was stirred too quickly or unevenly into the grease. To reclaim soap with greasy layers, place it in a utensil with 2 quarts of water, melt with gentle heat, and stir occasionally. Boil the mixture slowly until it becomes thick and clear. Pour it into mold and cover for two days to keep warm before cutting into bars.

Liquid Soap

Sodium hydroxide, sticks, 2.14 oz.; potassium hydroxide, sticks, 2.14 oz.; cottonseed oil, refined, 21.40 fl. oz.; cocoatnut oil, refined, 5.30 fl. oz.; alcohol, 13.25 fl. oz.; distilled water, enough to make 1 gal. Dissolve the sodium and potassium hydroxides in a small amount of water and add the alcohol and then the oils. Heat gently on a water bath while stirring until the reaction starts, and remove the heat. Stir until the batch starts to cool and add enough warm water to make 1 gallon of soap solution.

Mechanics' Hand Soap

Rub 2 drams of corn starch to a paste with 3 ounces of glycerine. Heat this mixture slowly and until it assumes a jelly-like consistency. To the jelly add 8 ounces of powdered castile soap and 2 ounces of pumicestone with stirring and heating. If the mixture is too thick for use, add glycerine or water until a suitable consistency is obtained. The soap may be perfumed with 2 drams of artificial lemon oil or with other perfumes which are suitable for perfuming soaps.

Hand Cleaner, Powdered

Sodium carbonate, granular, 9 oz.; trisodium phosphate, 1 oz.; pumice, finely powdered, 2½ lb.; citral or other odor, 1 oz. The dry powders should be thoroughly mixed and the citral added. This is a very effective preparation for the removal of grease and grime.

Washing Powder

Many stubborn stains which are little affected by ordinary washing with soap and water are readily removed by adding a cleaner in powder form to the wash water. An inexpensive and easily made cleaning compound consists of the following: Sodium perborate, 3 oz.; borax, 4 oz.; trisodium phosphate, 5 oz. This powder is added in small quantities to the soapy water. A liquid cleaner which performs the same service is made as follows: Sodium perborate, 5 oz.; soda ash, 5 oz.; water glass, 2 fl. oz.; water, 1 gal. To this may be added sufficient soap chips to produce a good lather when the liquid is added to the wash water. The liquid cleaner will not retain its full strength for long, therefore it should be made up fresh as required for best results.

Washing-Soda Solution

Add 1 pound of washing soda to 1 quart of boiling water and stir occasionally until soda is dissolved. Pour into covered jar or bottle and label. Use 2 or more tablespoons of the solution to 1 gallon of water to soften moderately hard water or for cleaning.

WATER SOFTENERS

Ammonia Solution

Dissolve 1 pint of 10-percent ammonium hydroxide in 1 gallon of water, or 6 ounces of 28-percent concentrated ammonium hydroxide in 1 gallon of water. Usually the concentrated 28-percent solution is less expensive to buy than the 10-percent solution. The diluted strength is the same for both. Store in a glass jar or bottle with a tightly fitting glass or rubber stopper. The amount needed to soften water depends on the hardness of the water.

Trisodium-Phosphate Solution

For moderately hard water use ½ to 1 tablespoon of trisodium phosphate in 1 gallon of hot water. For very hard water use 1 to 2 tablespoons in 1 gallon of hot water. Dissolve the trisodium phosphate thoroughly in the water. Enough soap may be added to make a permanent suds.

Miscellaneous Cleaners

Rug Cleaning Preparation

Diglycol oleate, 3 pints; butyl cellosolve, 5 fl. oz.; ethylene dichloride, 12 fl. oz.; alcohol (denatured), 1 pint; oleic acid, 12 fl. oz.; ammonia (strong 28%), 12 fl. oz.; water, 3¼ pints. Mix together the diglycol oleate, butyl cellosolve, ethylene dichloride, alcohol and oleic acid. Add the ammonia to the water and pour this solution into the first mix. The mixture should be stirred thoroughly for several minutes. If a thinner product is wanted water may be added while stirring. The product is used like any other rug cleaning preparation.

Carpet Cleaner

Carpets and rugs may be cleaned by scrubbing them with a brush using pure castile soap suds. The rug should be scrubbed and allowed to dry on the floor to prevent deformation of the stiff sizing. No more water should be used than is necessary. If the color of the rug is fast, 2 lbs. of sodium carbonate, 1 lb. of fullers earth and 4 oz. of turpentine can be mixed with sufficient soft soap to make a paste. This compound will give good results if the color of the rug is fast and when grease and oil spots are to be removed.

Cleaning Willow Furniture

I. To clean your willow and sea-grass furniture, wash it with white soap and water, scrubbing it well with a stiff brush, I usually set the furniture out on the lawn and, after scrubbing it, wash off the soapy water with the garden hose. This method is not injurious to the furniture and is a quick way to clean it.

—A. W. Scheib, Arlington, Mass.

II. Willow furniture may be cleaned by brushing it with a strong solution of salt and water, after which it is wiped with a soft, dry cloth. Also, the solution prevents the furniture from becoming yellow.

Paint Brush Cleaner

Kerosene, 1 gal.; oleic acid, ½ gal.; ammonia (28%), 1 pint; alcohol (denatured), 1 pint. Mix the kerosene and the oleic acid. In a separate container mix the alcohol and the ammonia. Stir the ammonia-alcohol mixture into the kerosene solution and continue to stir until the product is smooth. To use: The brushes are allowed to stand in the mixture over night after which they are washed out with warm water.

Toilet Bowl Cleaner

I. A cleaning and disinfecting agent for lavatory pans, sinks, etc., consists of a mixture of sodium bisulphate, 9 oz., with ferric sulphate, 1 oz. The ingredients are mixed in powder form. Application is made by the same methods as would be used for other cleaning powders.

II. The most satisfactory agent for cleaning toilet bowls is potassium acid sulphate. This crystalline chemical should be used straight for the purpose. It may be packed in friction top cans.

III. White sinks, bathtubs, washbowls and toilet bowls may be cleaned with a soft cloth, moistened with turpentine; use kerosene where there is rust.

Removing Copper Stains From Limestone and Cement

Stains which form on masonry, stone or concrete blocks where water from copper downspouts, gutters, bronze plaques or house numbers drip, can be removed by washing the stone with a solution of potassium cyanide. Potassium cyanide is a deadly poison and should, of course, he used with great care. It should not be allowed to get on the skin as it is likely to be absorbed through cuts or abrasions. The chemical solution is best applied with a swab fastened to the end of a stick. After the stain has been removed the surface should be washed thoroughly with water, to remove the last trace of the cyanide.

Cleaning Brass Fixtures

Brass rules used in a printing office, or brass fixtures of any kind, can be cleaned with acetic acid. It is the best cleaner obtainable. Acetic acid is simply strong vinegar and can be purchased at any local drug store. Its action against fly specks is hastened by the addition of salt. This substance is not harmful to the hands and can be used without injury. The brass should be wiped with a dry cloth after the acid has removed the tarnish. It is also excellent for washing grease or fly specks from glass articles, especially windows.

Cleaning Concrete Walls

Concrete walls stained by dirt and weather can be cleaned by being scrubbed with a stiff fiber brush and water. If stains are persistent, sometimes a solution of 1 part of hydrochloric acid in 3 to 10 parts of water is effective. The walls should be dampened before the solution is applied, and when it stops foaming they should be washed with copious applications of water. In many cities there are firms that specialize in cleaning buildings and are equipped to use live steam and sand blasting. Efflorescence is a whitish deposit that sometimes occurs on masonry. It may be removed by the acid treatment just described. If the surface of the concrete is colored for ornamentation, it is best not to leave the acid on the wall longer than 4 minutes because it may etch the concrete. A second application can be made if necessary. Efflorescence can be removed also with a solution of equal parts of paraffin and benzine rubbed into the surface of the dry concrete.

Stone and Cement Cleaner

For cleaning stone and cement, the following solution has been found effective: Acetate of soda, 9 oz.; powdered alum, 4 oz.; oxalic acid in crystalline form, 2 oz.; and water, 1 gal. Dissolve the chemicals in the water and scrub the surface with the solution, after which it is washed off with clean water.

Cleaning Terra Cotta

In cleaning terra cotta the bureau of standards has found that sodium hydrosulphite is effective and does not corrode the glaze. Fluo-silicic acid also cleans the material satisfactorily but attacks the glaze slightly. Trisodium phosphate is a good cleaner on standard finishes but unsatisfactory for glazed finishes. Soap powder cleans slowly and has a tendency to scour, thereby roughening the glazed surface, and hydrochloric acid, which is also a fair cleaner, has a slight corrosive effect on the glaze. Hydrofluoric acid should never be used on terra cotta.

Sweeping Compound

Sweeping compound for use on shop floors is made by mixing, 2 oz. of melted paraffin wax with ½ pint of yellow paraffin oil and adding 10 lbs. of clean dry sawdust, ½ lb. of coarse salt and 4 lbs. of fine sand. A pleasant odor is imparted to this compound by adding 2 oz. of eucalyptus oil.

Chimney Cleaning Compound

Chimneys which become clogged with soot until they no longer produce a draft may be easily cleaned by throwing a quarter pound or more of a cleaning compound into the stove or furnace, on top of a hot bed of coals. The compound should be thrown onto the fire with a shovel and the stove or furnace door quickly closed so that the full draft will be available when the mixture takes fire. A good compound for the purpose is made from ordinary table salt, 7 lbs., potassium nitrate, 4 lbs., flowers of sulphur, 7 lbs., copper sulphate, 7 lbs., and ammonium chloride, 8 lbs. The chemicals are thoroughly mixed together until a uniformly colored powder is produced. If more of the mixture is made than is required for one application, the excess should be stored in a tightly covered can. The mixture is inflammable and should be handled accordingly. When a chimney is overloaded with soot and catches fire it is frequently desirable to extinguish it to prevent damage to surrounding property. This can usually be accomplished by throwing two or three large handfuls of common salt onto the bed of coals in the stove or furnace and quickly closing the door.

Chimney Cleaner

A mixture consisting of 10 lbs. of sal ammoniac, and 3½ lbs. of sulphur thrown into a furnace or stove will burn out soot. Too large a quantity of this compound should not be used at one time. Before throwing it into the fire close all drafts and watch out for burning particles of carbon falling on the roof.

Rain Spots on Felt Hat Bleached With Peroxide Spray

The trick in cleaning a white felt hat lies in removing rain spots, which are not affected by naphtha. First, brush the hat thoroughly with the naphtha, and then hang it on a line, changing its position every 10 min. or so to dry it evenly. If any rain spots show after this treatment, they can be bleached by lightly spraying them with peroxide of hydrogen. Two or three sprayings are usually sufficient. Allow the hat to dry between each application.

White Shoe Cleaner

Soda ash, 1½ oz.; soap flakes, 6 oz.; titanium dioxide (white) 4½ lbs.; gum arabic (solution), 4 fl. oz.; water, 3 qts. Dissolve the soda ash and soap flakes in the water (hot). When partly cool, add the gum arabic solution and stir. The gum arabic solution is made by soaking 2 oz. of powdered gum arabic in 2 fluid oz. of water for fifteen minutes and then stirring or shaking until dissolved. When the solution is cool, stir in the titanium dioxide. Stirring should be vigorous. The finished cleaner is bottled while being stirred and the directions should indicate that the product is to be shaken before applying.

Cleaning Buckskin Shoes

Soiled shoes made with the flesh side of the leather exposed can be cleaned on a fine-wire buffing wheel. The shoe should be held lightly against the rotating wheel, taking care not to damage the leather. This should not be done excessively, of course, as the cleaning is accomplished by the rotating wheel removing the soiled leather fibers and raising new ones.

Cleaning Rubber Goods

Ordinary soap and water is usually not sufficient to take dirt off the surface of soft-rubber goods, for instance oily stains on tires; nor are abrasive cleaners much better. Crystals of trisodium phosphate sprinkled on a wet brush and scrubbed vigorously on the rubber act quickly as a cleansing agent. Plenty of water should be used, and the crystals must be carefully washed off the rubber after it is clean.

Cleaning Books

Dust and dirt may be removed from the edges and bindings of books by rubbing them with bread dough. The well-cooked but doughy bread inside the crust of fresh rolls is excellent for this purpose. In applying it, rub the soiled book with a ball of the dough. The dough may be used until it is saturated with dirt. Grease spots may be removed from the pages by applying benzine (inflammable) and removing it with a blotter.

Cleaning Burnt Pans

Boiling soda water in burnt pans is often advocated but, although this method seems successful in removing the burnt food, it makes the pans apt to burn again. A better method is to fill the pans with a saturated solution of salt and water, letting the solution stand overnight. Then put the pan on the flame and bring the water to a boil, which will cause the burnt particles to loosen so they can be easily removed.

Rifle and Gun Cleaner

A non-corrosive cleaner which is effective for cleaning rifles and guns is made by mixing: Sperm oil, 1 oz.; turpentine, 1 oz.; acetone, 1 oz.; kerosene, 2 oz.; lanolin (anhydrous), ½ oz.

Cleaning Guns

Guns may be cleaned with a mixture consisting of 2 parts of machine oil dissolved in 1 part of benzine. Rust may be removed from the inside of gun barrels by scouring with a piece of oakum attached to the rod and saturated with a compound made by mixing 4 oz. of paraffin oil in 1 ox. each of turpentine and benzine (inflammable). Swabbing with this rust remover should be repeated until the last trace of rust is removed. The barrel should next be washed with a swab saturated with a solution made by dissolving ½ oz. of caustic potash in a quart of water. After this treatment the barrel must be thoroughly rinsed with water and dried with cotton. To prevent rusting it should next be thoroughly oiled with any good grade of gun oil. In using the caustic potash solution, care should be taken to keep it away from other parts of the gun.

CLOCKCASE

REPRODUCED in miniature, this authentic replica of the quaint double-steeple clock makes a handsome desk accessory or wall-shelf ornament. If made proportionately larger, it is also an interesting piece for the fireplace mantel. The clock works are taken from an alarm clock and bolted to a sheet-metal mounting plate which is set against cleats glued to the inside surfaces of the case. The face of the clock is carefully drawn on white paper and cemented to the front of the mounting plate, the latter being drilled for the shaft. The front of the clockcase is covered with two glass panels. These are held between ⅛-in. frames glued to the sidepieces and the slanted top. Decorative pictures or paintings are applied to the glass except for the section directly in front of the clock face, as shown in the photo.

Note that the ⅜-in. base and the 3⁄16-in. shelf are grooved to receive tenons on the ends of the sidepieces. These grooves terminate 1⁄16 in. from the front edges of both the base and shelf so that the sidepieces are set back from the front edges. In addition, the groove must be located ¼ in. from the edge of the work to allow ⅛ in. overhang at the sides.

The steeples are 7⁄16 in. square and 1½ in. long, having the upper half tapered to a sharp point. This can be done by cutting and sanding to shape or by turning the steeples two at a time in the lathe. The steeples are glued to the front corners of the shelf and in ¼ x ¼-in. notches cut in the edges of the roof. The back of the case consists of two sections of ⅛-in. mahogany, plywood or hardboard. The upper section is fitted with pins along the lower edge which engage holes drilled in the shelf, and the peak is held against a stop block by means of a sheet-metal tab screwed to the roof panels. The bottom section may be mounted permanently with glue or hinged on the inside to provide a "secret" compartment for storage of valuables.

After assembly, the front edges of the case are rounded and smoothed with fine sandpaper. Then the case is finished with a dark stain or simply finished in the natural color with several applications of paste wax. Take special care in fitting the joints, as good joinery in this instance is particularly important to the appearance and craftsmanship of the finished product.

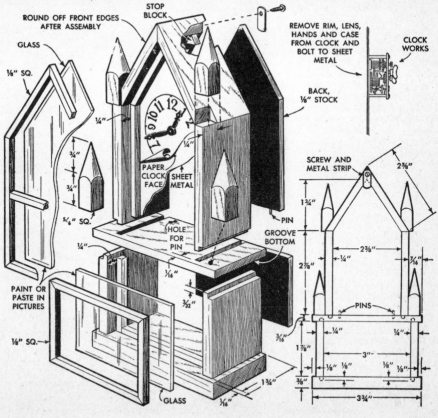

ROUND OFF FRONT EDGES AFTER ASSEMBLY

STOP BLOCK

REMOVE RIM, LENS, HANDS AND CASE FROM CLOCK AND BOLT TO SHEET METAL

CLOCK WORKS

GLASS

⅛" SQ.

¼"

¾"

¾"

⅝" SQ.

PAPER CLOCK FACE

SHEET METAL

¼"

BACK, ⅛" STOCK

PIN

GROOVE BOTTOM

HOLE FOR PIN

¼"

1/16"

3/32"

PAINT OR PASTE IN PICTURES

⅛" SQ.

GLASS

1/16"

1¾"

SCREW AND METAL STRIP

2⅜"

1¾"

2⅜"

¼"

7/16"

2⅞"

PINS

¼"

¼"

3/16"

1⅞"

3"

⅜"

⅛" ⅛"

⅛" ⅛"

3¾"

PERIOD CLOCKCASE

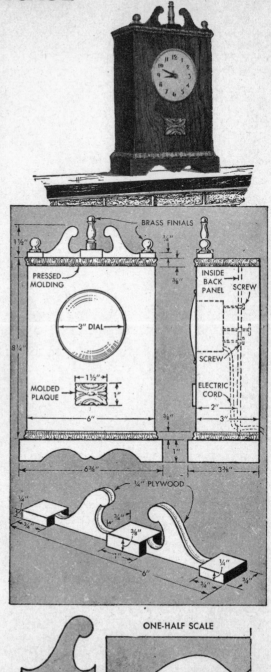

THIS SMALL clockcase is just the project for the craftsman who likes to work with fine veneers. The original case was made from flame-grained rosewood veneer glued to a core of ¼-in. pine with a backing veneer of mahogany. The case is proportioned for an electric movement having a 3-in. dial. First, cut the pine core stock ¾ in. oversize. Next, select the face veneers and trim roughly to the size of each piece of core stock. Also, cut the backing veneers to size. Then glue the veneers to both sides of the core. Scrolled parts of the broken-pediment top are of ¼-in. plywood which is faced on one side with a matching veneer. When the work is dry, cut the opening for the dial and run a ⅜-in. rabbet along each edge of the front piece of the case, the depth of the rabbet being equal to the thickness of the piece less the face veneer. Then join the sides to the front with a butt joint as in the lower left-hand detail, using glue and glue blocks. Finish the corner of the joint by sanding carefully. With this method of joining, the end grain is not exposed. The scrolled parts of the base are veneered with the grain running vertically to match the case and the pediment top. Use ¼-in. plywood as a core and join at the corners in the same manner as described above. Pressed moldings add decorative detail but plain, straight moldings can be used. Finish the wood in the natural color and add the finials which are the brass type used on table lamps. These are attached to the case in the positions shown with dowels which are turned into the threaded holes of the finials.

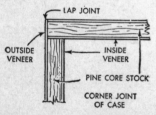

LAP JOINT

OUTSIDE VENEER

INSIDE VENEER

PINE CORE STOCK

CORNER JOINT OF CASE

CLOCK CASE-PLASTIC

WITH its red dial backed by a crystal ring, this colorful clock case is assembled from plastics, and makes a distinctive mantel piece. After jigsawing the figures in the dial, it is trued up on a disk sander, using a pivot pin as shown in the photos below, and cemented to the ring. The base of the case is a length of red plastic tube drilled to take two plastic rods as indicated, then cut in half and slotted to take the edge of the ring. The slot must be cut carefully to get a good fit. The clock is a small electric movement, which can be obtained from any clock dealer at a nominal cost. If specified when ordered, the hands that come with the clock will be of the proper length. If you already have a movement the hands can be shortened or lengthened easily with little trouble.

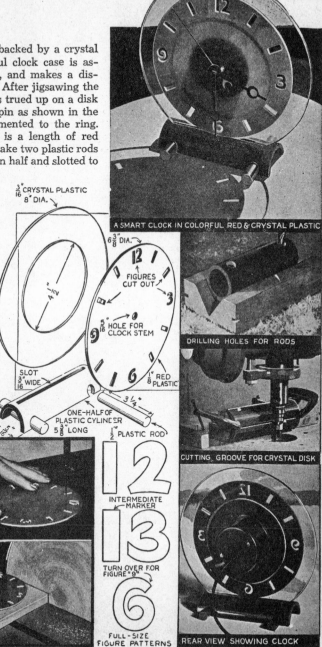

A SMART CLOCK IN COLORFUL RED & CRYSTAL PLASTIC

DRILLING HOLES FOR RODS

CUTTING GROOVE FOR CRYSTAL DISK

REAR VIEW SHOWING CLOCK

$\frac{3}{16}$" CRYSTAL PLASTIC 8" DIA.

4-1/2"

SLOT $\frac{3}{16}$" WIDE

$6\frac{3}{8}$" DIA.

12

FIGURES CUT OUT

3

9

$\frac{5}{16}$" HOLE FOR CLOCK STEM

6

1" RED PLASTIC

ONE-HALF OF PLASTIC CYLINDER $5\frac{3}{8}$" LONG

$1\frac{5}{16}$"

$3\frac{3}{4}$"

$\frac{1}{2}$" PLASTIC ROD

12

INTERMEDIATE MARKER

13

TURN OVER FOR FIGURE "9"

6

FULL-SIZE FIGURE PATTERNS

ORDER IN THE CLOSET

LIKE ALL DEEP, narrow closets having a clothespole stretched across the back, ours held comparatively few clothes and forced us to wade through a pile of suitcases, shoes and boxes. Moving the pole to the front of the closet was little help, as then we had to work our way through the clothes to reach the things stored in the back of the closet. We finally solved the problem to our complete satisfaction by installing a retractable clothespole along one side as in the lower photograph. Two L-shaped shelves were built at the top of the closet, the lower shelf supporting the clothespole. As a board wide enough to provide clearance for the clothes was not available, we used plywood for the lower shelf. The outer corner of this shelf is hung from the door casing with a length of flat steel, as in the details below. In addition to the top shelves, we installed a shoe shelf directly under the clothes. This is simply a board nailed to the top edge of the baseboard and supported at the front with a flat-steel angle brace screwed to the door casing. With the clothes now hanging on only one side of the closet, we had easy access to the rear, and as the clothes now could be pulled out of the closet for selection, we decided to include drawer space at the rear of the closet. This was done inexpensively by setting up a tier of used filing cabinets, which were painted and lined with wallpaper.

From This

to This

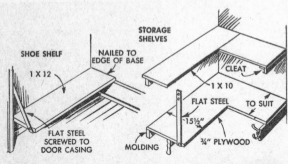

SHOE SHELF

STORAGE SHELVES

NAILED TO EDGE OF BASE

1 X 12

CLEAT

1 X 10

FLAT STEEL

TO SUIT

15½"

FLAT STEEL SCREWED TO DOOR CASING

MOLDING

¾" PLYWOOD

CLOTHES HAMPER

THIS hamper was designed with the simplest possible construction in mind and it is as easy to build as a box. Design features are a novel floral pattern, made by boring holes of varying size in the front and sides, and a recessed panel effect obtained by finishing the edges and corners with half-round molding, detail A. If an enamel finish is desired use birch plywood, ½ in. thick for the back and hinged top, and ⅛ or ¼ in. thick for the front and sides. Cut the back and bottom panels to size and join with screws and glue. Then make the frame, using ½ by ⅝-in. strips for the horizontal members and 1 by 1-in. strips for the corner uprights. Plane these latter members to a triangular shape as indicated in the sectional detail C, and assemble the frame members with nails and glue, or use screws. Next, cut the side and front panels to size and locate and bore the holes forming the floral design as shown on the squared pattern. Holes also are shown in the side panels and top, but these can be omitted if desired. Bore the large holes with an expansive bit. Then attach the panels to the frame using small brads and glue. True up all exposed edges by planing and sanding, then bevel the two front corners as in the sectional view C. Install the partition, using small triangular strips to hold it in place as in detail B. Sand the edges of the plywood top and hinge to the back panel. Finally attach the half-round moldings.

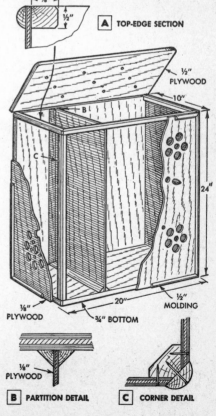

A TOP-EDGE SECTION

⅝" ½"

½" PLYWOOD

10"

24"

B

C

⅛" PLYWOOD

20"

¾" BOTTOM

½" MOLDING

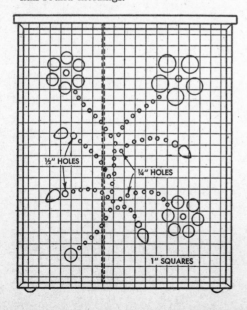

½" HOLES

¼" HOLES

1" SQUARES

⅛" PLYWOOD

B PARTITION DETAIL

C CORNER DETAIL

CLOTHESLINES

More Room on Indoor Clothesline Provided by Wooden Slats

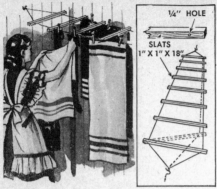

Where washing must be hung on an indoor clothesline in a limited amount of space, more clothes can be hung in the same area by using wooden slats to separate a double line. In this way, additional clothes may be hung over the slats and the two lines can be supported by one hook at each end. Holes should be drilled about 1 in. from the ends of the slats so the clothesline can be threaded through them. To balance the clothesline, adjust one of the end slats as indicated by the dotted lines. Clothes can be dried quickly during cold weather by using this compact clothesline suspended near a source of heat or in an unoccupied area of the house.

Retractable Clothesline for Low Basement Stored Against Ceiling Joists

This retractable clothesline is pushed up against the ceiling joists after the wash is taken down. Each end of the line is fastened to a length of pipe which slides in a wooden hanger. The latter is a piece of 2 x 4 drilled for the pipe and mounted on the side of a joist.

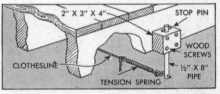

Springs in Basement Clothesline Help to Keep It Taut

To prevent a basement clothesline from sagging so that it strikes you on the head, tie one end of the line to a screen-door spring as indicated. As these springs are not strong enough to carry the weight

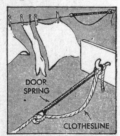

of a line of clothes, run the end of the line past the spring and tie it to the hook also, leaving enough slack so that when the spring stretches about one quarter of its length the slack is taken up and the pull comes on the line at the hook in the usual manner. With this arrangement, the springs will keep an empty line taut and not interfere when the line is in use.

Clothesline Prop Locked in Place Against Dislodgement by Wind

If the wind sometimes dislodges your clothesline prop, here is a simple way to prevent this trouble. About an inch or so from the upper end, drill a hole for the line and make a slot from the hole to the end

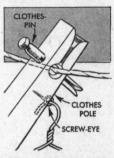

of the prop for insertion of the line. Then drill a smaller hole through the edge of the prop to break through the larger one so that a clothespin can be inserted to keep the line in place. When a prop is fixed in this way, it is handy for supporting a garment on a hanger, which can be hooked into a screw eye driven into the prop just below the hole for the line as indicated.

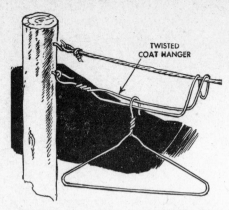

Fig. 1. A wire coat hanger, twisted and arranged as above, provides a line on which another hanger can be hung without danger of clothes falling to ground. Fig. 2. A multiple hanger like that below is easy to make and will help to conserve the closet space

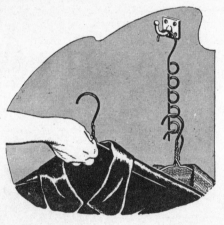

Fig. 3. You won't have to worry about wire hangers rusting and staining clothes if you wind cellulose tape around the wire as shown below. Fig. 4. The boot hangers shown below right are also made from coat hangers cut and bent to hold any kind of shoe

COAT HANGERS

HAS YOUR PATRONAGE of the dry cleaners resulted in an accumulation of more wire coat hangers than you think you can use? Are you just about ready to throw out these excess hangers? Hold on a minute! There are many places where wire coat hangers will come in handy.

Some of the hangers can even remain in the closet and earn their keep. If you want to make the most of your space in a small closet, take a single coat hanger and convert it into a multiple hanger, Fig. 2. Just straighten out the wire of one hanger, bend it into several loops as shown, and slip the hook of a coat hanger through each loop. Be sure to make the rack from a heavy-wire hanger so that it will withstand the excessive weight. If you don't have enough shelf space in the closet for hats, take a hanger and make it into a hat rack. Just shape the wire of the hanger to the crown, and your hat will be held against the wall as illustrated in Fig. 13.

You housewives have probably found hangers useful in drying clothes. Or do you frown on this practice because wire coat hangers rust and stain clothes? That rusting can be prevented by wrapping the wire with cellulose tape. Wrap the tape spirally around the hanger wire as in Fig. 3. On the other hand, do you find it difficult to keep the hanger on the clothesline when drying or airing clothing? There is a solution to

CELLULOSE TAPE

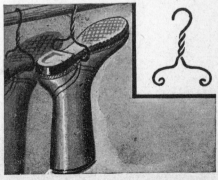

Fig. 5. A lawn mower is secured to the wall for storage by placing handles in a wire hanger as shown at left

this problem, too. You can keep garments from falling to the ground if the hangers are put on a rack made from a coat hanger like that in Fig. 1. The hanger is bent to fit over the line and to engage a screw hook driven into the clothes post.

Various types of racks can also be improvised from wire coat hangers. A temporary rack bent from a wire coat hanger is just the thing to hold freshly ironed clothes until they can be put away. Bend the wire as shown in Fig. 6 and hook it over the top of the door. An ordinary coat hanger also provides a handy rack for drying roll film. The hook part of the hanger is bent to fit over the top of the door and the arms are bent outward as in Fig. 7. When the film is hung at the ends of the arms, it is held several inches away from the door so that it is not likely to be damaged. If a towel rack is not located conveniently near a shower stall, a wire coat hanger will again make itself useful. Fig. 9 shows how a coat hanger can be used as a towel rack by inserting the hanger in the shower curtain as indicated. The hanger hook slips over the hoop supporting the curtain and slides easily with the curtain rings.

When storing or drying boots, converted clothes hangers like those illustrated in Fig. 4 can be used. The hanger is cut and bent as shown, the space between the eyes being governed by the width of the sole.

Do you have trouble keeping your lawn mower from rolling away when stored against a wall? If so, use a coat hanger to hold the mower against the wall, by twisting the ends of the hanger and bending the resulting loops down. These are then slipped over the mower handle and the hanger is hooked on a nail, as in Fig. 5.

A wire hanger can even be used to set up an improvised toaster in the event that your electric toaster gets out of order and has to be repaired. Just make a rack from a wire coat hanger by bending the ends to grip the sides of a hot plate and the hook to rest on the top (see Fig. 8). Then lay the pieces of bread on the wire rack and turn

Fig. 6. A rack like that shown above comes in handy to hold freshly ironed clothes until you can put them away

Fig. 7. Roll film can be dried on a rack like this without danger of damaging negatives

Fig. 8. A hot plate and a wire hanger bent in the proper way combine to form a temporary toaster, as at right

Fig. 9. A coat hanger is bent, inserted in the shower curtain and hooked on the hoop for the towel rack below

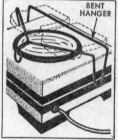

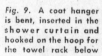

Fig. 10. Avoid singed fingers when lighting a gas oven or heater by using an extension handle like that above. The handle is easily made from a coat hanger

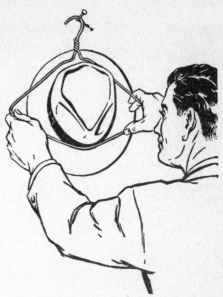

Fig. 13. The hat rack above is made from a wire coat hanger, which holds the hat securely against a closet wall, thus conserving shelf space for other articles

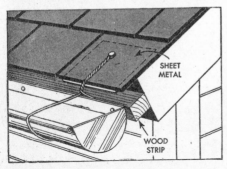

SHEET METAL

WOOD STRIP

Fig. 11. Much needless maintenance work can be eliminated by fastening rain gutters to the roof with wire coat hangers, as is done above. Fig. 12. If you have trouble with sagging drapery cranes, use wire coat hooks as supports, as in the drawing below

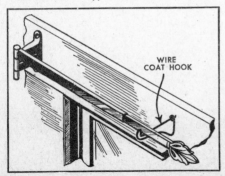

WIRE COAT HOOK

them over after they have browned on one side. Be sure, however, to burn the paint from the coat hanger before using it.

Because of its pliability and strength, the wire from which coat hangers are made can be reshaped into many other useful objects. One example is an extension handle for a match to avoid singeing your fingers when lighting the oven of a kitchen gas range. Form one end of the wire into a spiral holder to hold the match and bend the other end to form a handgrip. The spiral can be bent quickly by using a pair of pliers to wrap the wire around an ice pick. The extension handle, shown in Fig. 10, can also be used to light an oil-burning space heater.

If you are in need of a decoy to attract crows, make one out of a wire coat hanger like the one shown in Fig. 16. All you have to do is bend the wire frame to the profile of a crow and cover it with black cloth. Then press the pointed end of the wire into the top of a fence post or stump and wait for the crows.

Minnow fishermen will also be able to make use of a wire coat hanger by converting it into a dipper. The hanger is straightened and bent to form a hoop at one end, and a circular piece of plastic screen mesh is sewed to the wire hoop. The dipper, Fig. 14, should be small enough to fit in the tackle box.

In the field of home repairs, rain gutters can be secured to the roof with wire coat hangers, as shown in Fig. 11. To do this,

WIRE COAT HANGER

Fig. 14. Fishing for minnows is made easier with a net like that at left, which is made from wire coat hanger

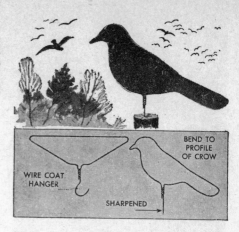

WIRE COAT HANGER

SHARPENED

BEND TO PROFILE OF CROW

Fig. 16. A wire hanger bent to the profile of a crow and covered with black cloth results in a quickly made decoy that will lure crows within shotgun range

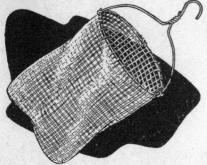

Fig. 15. The clothespin bag shown above, made of two coat hangers and an onion sack, is especially handy because it is always held open by the hoop

COAT HANGER

Fig. 17. Your ties will always have that newly pressed look if each one is kept on a tie stretcher like the one shown above which is made from a wire coat hanger

tack a square of galvanized sheet metal under the shingle and drive the hanger nail through this. Then nail the inside edge of the gutter to a wood strip that serves as a spacer. Finish the spacer with several coats of house paint to keep it from rotting.

Do you have trouble keeping track of fruit-jar covers from one canning season to the next? If so, make a practice of threading those covers on a coat hanger, as shown in Fig. 18. Cut the hanger near the twisted end and bend the severed ends into hooks.

Make a tie stretcher from a wire coat hanger and keep those neckties looking newly pressed all the time. Bend the stretcher into a shape like that shown in Fig. 17, and slip the tie over the end.

A couple of coat hangers and an onion sack can be combined into a handy clothespin bag. One hanger is straightened and made into a hoop, while the second hanger provides the hook bail for supporting the bag on the clothesline. Sew on an onion sack and you have a clothespin bag like the one shown in Fig. 15.

The hook part of a wire coat hanger can also be put to use as shown in Fig. 12. Sagging drapery cranes can be leveled by supporting them with these hooks turned into the window casing near the outer ends of the cranes. The hooks will be concealed.

Are you now convinced that those extra wire coat hangers are worth keeping? If so, you won't be sorry, for you may also invent many more ways to put discarded hangers to work.

Fig. 18. Keeping track of fruit-jar covers from one canning season to the next is no problem if the covers are threaded on a coat hanger as shown below

COFFEE TABLE

Diagonal slice from hardwood log produces beautiful grain effect to give this graceful coffee table a distinctive and exclusive touch. Legs are half-lapped and interlock

IF IT'S the unusual you crave in occasional furniture, this coffee table should really intrigue you. Its novel construction calls for a top sliced diagonally from a log. Cut in this manner, the top assumes the natural contour of the log and the grain is enhanced by the annual-growth rings which take on a beautiful pattern.

The original table top was cut from an 18-in. cherry log, 4 ft. long. The log should be fairly round, thoroughly seasoned and the bark should be removed. To mark the log for cutting, make a wooden frame from stock 1⅜ in. wide, measuring 18 by 29⅛ in., inside measurement. The frame is placed over the log as in Fig. 3 and is tacked temporarily in place. Then a pencil is run around both sides of the frame to mark the log and the space between the lines is chalked. Fig. 1 shows how the log can be supported at an angle with a ladder and braced for sawing. Work carefully with a crosscut saw and try to make both cuts parallel. The saw will produce a rough surface which must be planed flat on the side selected for the underside of the top. Then ³⁄₁₆-in. grooves are run on

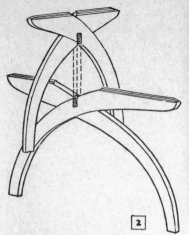

2

3

the underside for the leg tenons, locating them according to Fig. 4. Each groove can be cut on a bench saw by cutting a wooden strip to slide in one of the saw-table grooves and tacking it to the underside of the work parallel with the line of cut. A ¾-in. rim is marked around the top surface and the area inside the rim is routed ¼ in. deep. This can be done with a router bit in a drill press, or with a portable router. After sanding smooth, a sealer should be applied to both sides of the top to seal the end grain and to retard checking. Fig. 6 details the leg patterns. Although the point of half lap is indicated by dotted lines, it is best to determine this by placing one corresponding leg on top of the other, as in Fig. 5, and marking directly. The assembled pairs of legs are notched to fit together as in Fig. 2 and then the top is glued to the leg tenons.

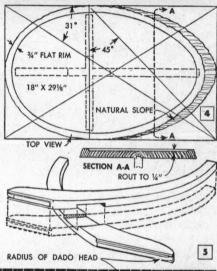

31°
45°
¾" FLAT RIM
18" X 29⅛"
NATURAL SLOPE
TOP VIEW
4

SECTION A-A
ROUT TO ¼"

RADIUS OF DADO HEAD
5

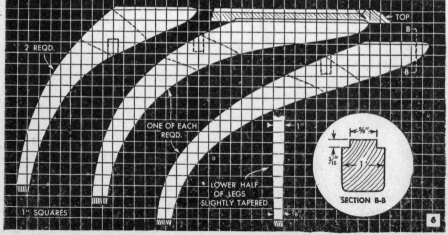

TOP
B
B
2 REQD.
ONE OF EACH REQD.
LOWER HALF OF LEGS SLIGHTLY TAPERED
1" SQUARES
1"
⅞"
SECTION B-B
⅝"
3⅛"
1"
6

COFFEE TABLE *in Mahogany*

SIMPLE modern styling, which features an offset top rail and a subdued combination of straight and curved lines, individualizes the design of this smart-looking coffee table. Although the table shown was made of mahogany, other woods can be used when it is desirable to match the finish of other furnishings in both color and graining. White mahogany (primavera) is a popular choice as it finishes light colored with an attractive ribbon grain. The top is built up to the required width by gluing together a number of narrow strips of ¾-in. stock. Use five ⅜-in. dowels equally spaced in each joint. After the glue is dry, sand the top smooth, trim it to the finish dimensions given on the opposite page and round the edges to a ½-in. radius.

The top rail is built up as a frame, the side and end members being mortised into rounded corner blocks. Note also that the corners of the top are rounded to the same radius as the blocks. The top corners of the rails and blocks are rounded to a ¼-in. radius as in section A-A of the assembly details. The completed rail is then attached to the top with screws and 12 triangular glue blocks spaced as shown. The legs are assembled as units, each consisting of two posts joined to a top and bottom rail with mortise-and-tenon joints. These units then are joined to top and bottom stretchers with mortise-and-tenon joints as in the assembly detail. Tenons on the top and bottom rails of the leg units are ¾ in. long and must be shouldered at an angle to give the posts the proper slant. Width of the top shoulder is given in the lower detail.

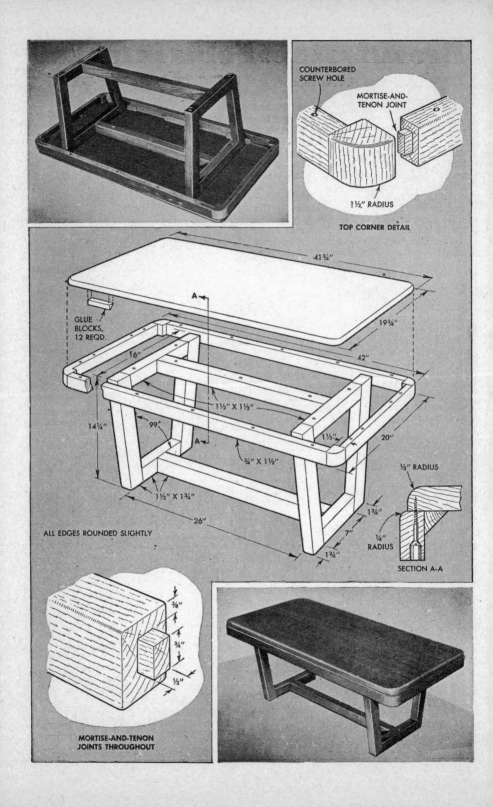

COUNTERBORED
SCREW HOLE

MORTISE-AND-
TENON JOINT

1½" RADIUS

TOP CORNER DETAIL

41¾"

GLUE
BLOCKS,
12 REQD.

16"

19¾"

42"

1½" X 1½"

99°

14¼"

1½"

20"

A

A

¾" X 1½"

½" RADIUS

1½" X 1¾"

¼"
RADIUS

26"

1¾"

ALL EDGES ROUNDED SLIGHTLY

7"

1¾"

SECTION A-A

⅜"

¾"

½"

**MORTISE-AND-TENON
JOINTS THROUGHOUT**

COLD CHISELS

CUTTING bar stock, shearing heavy metal, roughing down large pieces of metal, cutting oil grooves and keyways, and many other operations can be done quickly and accurately with cold chisels, if a few simple rules are observed in using them. Cold chisels are bars of steel, tempered and sharpened at one end, and of such size that they can be driven with a hammer for removing or cutting metal. The flat chisel, double and

To remove a large section of metal, first chip a number of grooves with a cape chisel, then remove metal between grooves with a flat chisel

Heavy sheet metal is sheared by clamping it in a vise so line to be cut is flush with the jaws, and using a flat chisel held at an angle to the work

single-facet cape chisels, round-nose and diamond-point chisels illustrated in Fig. 2 are the five main types. While there are variations of each of these designed for special purposes, these five styles usually are sufficient for most jobs.

Whether it is divided between one or two facets, the cutting angle should be kept about 65° or 70° for average work, as shown in Fig. 2. The edge of the flat chisel should not be more than ¾ in. wide because on iron and steel this will take all the driving power that can be applied with the usual shop hammer. When a heavy chip is to be removed, such as in cutting a keyway, a cape chisel is used. Round-nose chisels can be used for cutting oil grooves, filleting corners, etc. The diamond-point chisel is useful in trimming out sharp corners. To chip, or remove surplus metal from a broad, flat piece, chip grooves in the work with a cape chisel and remove the material between the grooves with a flat chisel, as shown in Fig. 1. The grooves should be spaced slightly closer together than the width of the flat chisel. The work is placed in the vise at about elbow height, and in such a manner that the blows are struck at right angles to the jaws to prevent the work from slipping. The chisel is

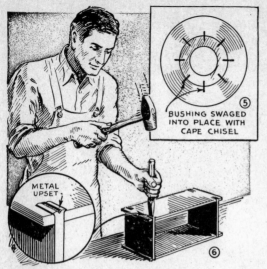

BUSHING SWAGED INTO PLACE WITH CAPE CHISEL (5)

METAL UPSET

6

fastening together small assembled parts where the pieces fit closely and need only a little upsetting of the metal to keep them from slipping apart. With a little care, hand knurling on small cylindrical pieces can be done. Place the work in a V-block and use a sharp flat chisel, making grooves around the work parallel to its length.

In order to do good work, chisels must be kept sharp. Some of the newer chisels on the market are made of alloys which are tough enough to stand hard use but still are soft enough to be filed sharp. Better results are obtained, however, by grinding chisels to sharpen them.

held firmly enough to guide it, but still loosely enough to prevent the shock of the hammer blow from imparting a sting to the hand through the chisel. As illustrated in Fig. 3, chisels should be held so that the lower facet or surface lies flat on the work. Too steep an angle will tear and gouge the metal. It helps to keep the eyes focused on the cut rather than the head of the chisel. When working with metals other than cast iron, chisels should be lubricated every few blows. Any good grade of cutting oil will be found satisfactory.

Heavy sheet metal can be trimmed or sheared to shape quickly as shown in Fig. 4. The line along which the cut is to be made is placed flush with the jaws of the vise. A flat chisel is used, the edge being held at an angle to the work to produce a shearing action. Holes in sheet metal can also be cut with cold chisels. The metal stock is placed on a flat surface and a narrow chisel is applied so that the cut conforms closely to the guide line. When trimming off large projections, such as bolt or rivet heads, a cape chisel is used. Always make the first cut down from the center, and then chip off the rest. This method will remove them easily and avoid damaging the surface of the work.

In cutting oil grooves or keyways, chip both ways toward the center of the desired keyway or groove to prevent the ends from breaking out. Swaging, as illustrated in Figs. 5 and 6, is best done with a flat or cape chisel. This procedure is useful for

Flat-Iron Handle Holds Chisel

Attached by a U-bolt, this handle for a cold chisel will prevent a worker's fingers from being injured if the hammer glances from the chisel. The handle is a length of light flat iron looped at one end for a grip and bent to a right angle at the other. This is slipped into the U-bolt and held by a crosspiece that is tightened against it by nuts. By loosening these, the bolt may be adjusted to hold the handle at any position.

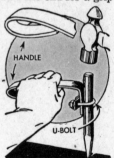

HANDLE

U-BOLT

LICK COLD-WEATHER STARTING PROBLEMS

DO YOU step into your car on a cold morning with a doubt in your mind that the motor will start? It will if it is in good mechanical condition. And good mechanical condition does not necessarily refer to a new car. Unless your car has already passed the 50,000-mile mark, the chances are that a few simple checks of the fuel and ignition systems, to bring them to peak condition, will enable you to start the "old bus" on the coldest mornings.

Probably the most frequent cause of hard starting in winter is a weak or defective battery. As winter approaches, the load on the car battery increases. Also, as temperature lowers, the efficiency of the battery decreases. As the weather grows colder, careful drivers keep a check on the battery charge with a hydrometer, Fig. 8, and if periodic checks show that the load is steadily decreasing the hydrometer readings below 1.250, the charging rate is increased sufficiently to maintain the full-charge reading,

1.250 or slightly higher. Many motorists supplement normal generator charging with a trickle charger connected to the battery overnight. If the battery is more than a year old, it's a good precaution to take a voltmeter reading of each cell at least twice a year. If a defective cell is detected by this test, the battery should be replaced.

Defective or weak-battery symptoms also can be caused by a loose ground connection or badly corroded cable connections. Often it is necessary to make a careful check to be sure that one defect is not mistaken for another. Keeping all battery and ground connections clean and tight will avoid any trouble from this source.

Cars kept in unheated garages frequently give trouble in starting due to wet spark plugs. When the temperature rises after a cold snap the engine "sweats," due to moisture condensation. Moisture coats the plugs and cables and the high-tension current jumps from the

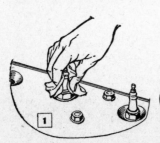

1. Wipe moisture from spark plugs and cables with a soft, dry cloth

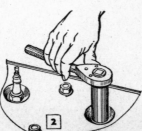

2. Use a deep-wall socket when tightening spark plugs to avoid breaks

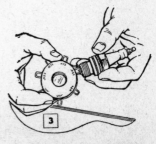

3. Check the electrode gap with a wire gauge made for the purpose

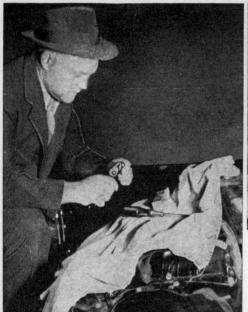

Overlubricating distributor may force grease into breaker mechanism and foul the points

plug terminal to the cylinder head, "shorting out" the plug. When this is the cause of failure to start, remove the cables and wipe the plugs and the cables with a dry cloth as in Fig. 1.

Exact gap spacing of the spark-plug electrodes, Fig. 3, is especially important in cold-weather operation of the car. Commonly recommended gap settings range from .025 to .029 in., but there are variations up to .040 in. Wide gaps and irregular gap settings in the same engine are a common cause of hard starting in cold weather. Some manufacturers recommend two settings, one for warm weather and another for cold-weather driving. In adjusting the gap always bend the side electrode and when removing plugs use a special spark-plug wrench or a deep-walled socket as in Fig. 2, to avoid cracking the porcelain. Make it a practice to clean the electrodes with fine sandpaper each time the plugs are removed. As plugs are replaced, always check the gaskets. Any that are scored should be renewed.

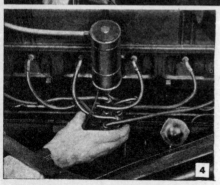

Above, lift the distributor carefully to avoid damaging the gasket. Below, clean the inside of the cap thoroughly with a dry cloth. Examine cap inside and out for cracks. Also check condition of rain guards

Making sure that the battery, battery cables and the spark plugs are in good condition eliminates a number of the common causes of wintertime starting troubles. This leaves the distributor still to be examined. Remove the cap, Fig. 4, and wipe the inside with a clean cloth, Fig. 5. Examine the cap carefully for cracks and indications of arcing. Unless the distributor is kept in good order by frequent cleaning and inspection, there is a tendency in some types of distributors for a dirt track to form inside the cap where the rotor contact travels. Here, fine dust, moisture and oil combine to form a heavy, sticky coating which in time will cause arcing, burn-

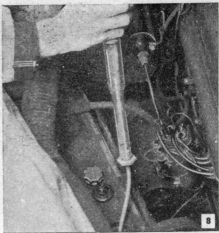

Remove rotor by pulling it off the driving shaft. When replacing be sure that it is properly positioned

Hydrometer readings of 1.250 or above normally indicate full battery charge. Check cells with voltmeter

ing and even cracking of the cap. Examine the top of the cap particularly for cracks. Be sure the spark-plug cables and the center cable from the coil make good electrical contact inside the socket terminals. Also be sure the rain guards over the cables fit tightly and have no cracks or wide breaks. Condition of the guards is especially important to good winter performance as they prevent moisture or a water splash from entering the distributor and suddenly "drowning" the ignition system.

Next, lift the rotor, Fig. 7, and examine the breaker mechanism. If the points are burned and deeply pitted so that they make only a partial contact, the parts should be renewed; also the condenser, which is a likely source of this trouble. On the other hand, if the parts seem to be in reasonably good condition, the points can be dressed to a true contact with a breaker-point file. The specified breaker-point gap ranges from .018 to .022 in. Check with a thickness gauge and set the gap according to the manufacturer's instructions. After setting the gap be sure the eccentric screw is tightened to hold the adjustment. Avoid overlubrication of the distributor shaft. Give the grease cup a turn or two after each 1000 miles, Fig. 6.

Automatic chokes generally have a winter and summer setting, which makes it possible to vary the richness of the starting mixture of fuel, and some are fitted with a fast-idle mechanism that simplifies starting a cold engine and gives better control during the warm-up period. The choke is operated automatically by a thermostatic control so located that it is actuated by changes in manifold temperature. Where the choke-control system includes a fast-

idle control, the thermostat actuates not only the choke valve but also a vacuum valve or piston which measures the idling fuel mixture. As soon as the engine reaches normal operating temperature, the choke becomes inoperative, but as the engine cools after operation, all parts of the choke mechanism return to the starting position. By carefully following the manufacturer's directions for setting, anyone can adjust the automatic choke. On older cars equipped with manually operated chokes, correct operation depends on the skill of the driver. Overchoking will flood the engine and make it difficult if not impossible to start. Flooding also will dilute the crankcase oil with unburned fuel, which passes the pistons. Running with the engine partially choked also can result in rapid wear of cylinder walls and piston rings as the raw fuel washes away oil which normally reaches the upper part of the cylinders. Ordinarily, the trick in operating the manual choke is to synchronize operation of the choke with that of the starter so that a rich fuel mixture is drawn into each of the cylinders on the first intake stroke. After the engine starts, the choke is closed by stages until the engine has reached operating temperature.

Poor compression due to leaky valves or worn rings causes hard starting any time. Such an engine needs both a valve and ring job to put it in proper condition for winter service. If poor compression is the cause of hard starting, an instrument check of the engine will show what parts are at fault. Sometimes a defective head gasket or possibly spark-plug gaskets are the cause of poor compression. These parts are quite commonly at fault in older cars.

COLLET ATTACHMENT
FOR THE
METAL
LATHE

Photo courtesy South Bend Lathe Works

A N INTERESTING turning project, this collet attachment for a 10-in. lathe permits rapid chucking of finished bar stock with precise accuracy. The three parts of the draw-in attachment, which are shown in Fig. 3, are readily machined on the lathe, but due to the difficulty of hardening and spring-tempering tool-steel collets it is better to purchase them ready-made. However, in the event you wish to machine a collet of mild steel or hard brass for occasional use, dimensions are given in Fig. 4.

Have at least one finished collet on hand when beginning work on the attachment, as the collet will serve as a gauge when taper-boring the closer to the correct angle, and the collet threads can be used to check the threaded end of the draw-in sleeve. In addition, the collet is necessary to determine the exact length of the sleeve in order to assure proper closing action when clamping the work in the collet. Note the cutaway detail, Fig. 6.

Start machining the collet closer, Fig. 1, by turning the No. 3 Morse taper to fit the headstock spindle. As this may require considerable fitting, the tool-steel round used for this part should be a little longer than ordinarily necessary. After fitting the closer, slip it in the headstock spindle and drive the work with the spindle while turning and facing the large flange on the outer end. Then counterbore the center hole and turn the inside bevel to match the taper on

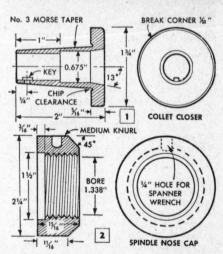

The drawing below shows how the finished parts of the collet attachment look and how they fit together. Note that the spindle nose cap is turned on the spindle before closer and collet are inserted

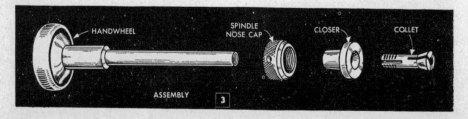

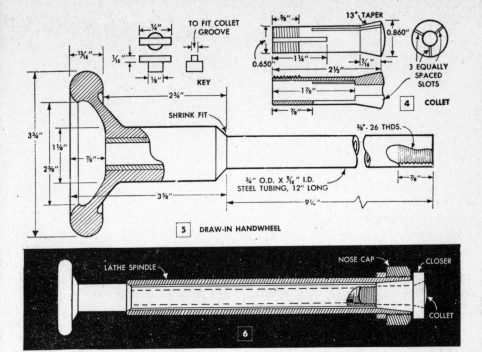

TO FIT COLLET GROOVE

KEY

13° TAPER

0.860"

3 EQUALLY SPACED SLOTS

4 COLLET

SHRINK FIT

⅝"- 26 THDS.

¾" O.D. X ⁵⁄₁₆" I.D. STEEL TUBING, 12" LONG

5 DRAW-IN HANDWHEEL

LATHE SPINDLE

NOSE CAP

CLOSER

COLLET

6

the collet head. Make the key, as in Fig. 5, and rivet it inside the tapered shank of the collet closer.

Chuck the draw-in sleeve to run dead true and cut the ⅝-26 internal threads. Run the threads with several light cuts and when nearing the finish dimension, check with the collet to determine the degree of interference between the two parts. They should engage lightly as otherwise the collet may turn in the closer when the handwheel is tightened. To locate the exact distance from the threaded end of the tube to the handwheel hub, insert the closer in the headstock spindle and slip the draw-in tube through the hollow spindle. Insert a collet in the closer, turning it into the tube, and

press the collet firmly against the closer. Mark the tube at the point where it projects from the opposite end of the headstock spindle.

Turn the handwheel and hub from a single piece of cold-rolled steel to the dimensions given in Fig. 5 and drill and ream the center hole for a shrink fit on the draw-in tube. The spindle nose cap, Fig. 2, not only protects the threaded end of the spindle while the lathe is in use, but also removes the collet closer from the spindle when it is backed off the threads. The cap is turned from a cold-rolled-steel bar and knurled for the handgrip. Then it is bored and threaded to fit the spindle. Drill a ¼-in hole in the cap for a spanner wrench. ★ ★ ★

One-Piece Depth Stop for Collet Chuck Quickly Locates Short Work

Fast, accurate facing and shouldering operations on duplicate short pieces held in a collet chuck are accomplished with this one-piece depth stop. To determine the size of the stop, measure the length and inside diameters of the collet. Then machine and shoulder a piece of tool steel to a close, sliding fit in the large inside diameter of the collet. Machine a clearance recess in the small end of the stop. Drill, counterbore, tap and slot the large end as shown in the details. Tap with an N. C. (National Coarse) thread to take a socket

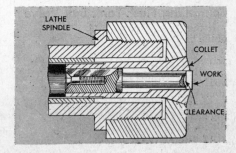

LATHE SPINDLE

COLLET

WORK

CLEARANCE

setscrew with a countersunk head of the type detailed. As the final operation, slip the stop into the collet and press it forward until the recessed end projects beyond the

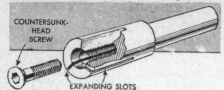

COUNTERSUNK-HEAD SCREW

EXPANDING SLOTS

collet. Tighten the locking screw in the stop to hold it firmly in position. Assemble the collet chuck in the lathe spindle and run a light, facing cut across the recessed end of the stop. This cut should leave a narrow, flat rim around the recess against which the work locates. To use the stop, simply locate it in the collet, tighten the locking screw and then locate the carriage stop and the tool for the desired cut.

Simple Collet Vise to Hold Small Round Work

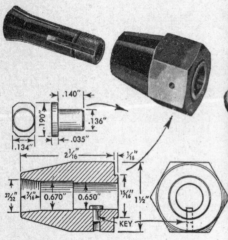

.140"
.190"
.136"
.134"
.035"
$2\frac{1}{16}$"
$\frac{1}{16}$"
$2\frac{7}{32}$"
$\frac{7}{16}$"
0.670"
0.650"
$1\frac{5}{16}$"
$1\frac{1}{2}$"
KEY

This little tool provides a convenient method of holding cylindrical parts in a vise mounted on a bench or machine tool. It uses standard draw-in collets of the type employed on lathes and consists of three parts, the body, a small key and a hexagon nut.

The body is made from tool steel to the dimensions shown. Those given are for standard collets as used on a popular lathe, but may be varied to suit. The lower portion of the body is of hexagon shape, which is convenient when the tool is to be used for holding parts on which a hexagon head is to be milled. Indexing is accomplished by changing the position of the fixture in the vise jaws. When machining the bore, make the angle of the tapered portion to match the corresponding angle on the collet. The lower portion of the bore should be of a size in which the collet body will

fit without appreciable looseness. For ordinary work, it matters little whether or not there is play between the collet and bore; but there should be none present when the fixture is used for indexing.

The key that keeps the collet from turning in the body is made from a piece of drill rod or similar steel. It is a drive fit in the hole in the body. If a nut to fit the collet threads is not available, you can bore out a standard nut and retap it. An improvement not shown is to drill a hole through the nut and thread it to receive a short handle. Then, with the fixture held in a vise so that the handle can move through a portion of a turn, you can loosen and tighten the collet when handling a number of duplicate pieces. It is best to harden the parts for maximum resistance to wear.

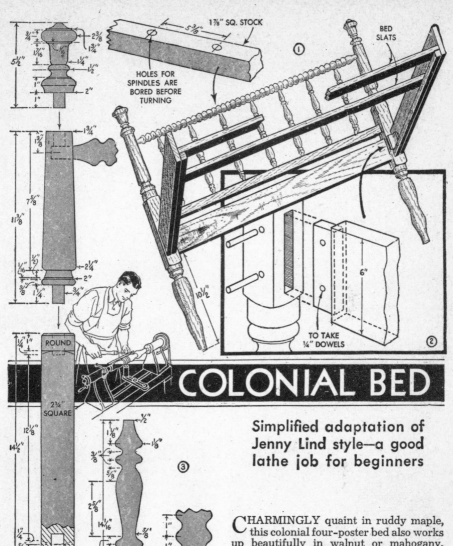

1⅞" SQ. STOCK

5⅜"

HOLES FOR SPINDLES ARE BORED BEFORE TURNING

BED SLATS

①

②

6"

TO TAKE ¼" DOWELS

10½"

③

ROUND

2¼" SQUARE

ROUND

POST

SPINDLE

STRETCHER

VARIES WITH THE TYPE OF BED

COLONIAL BED

Simplified adaptation of Jenny Lind style—a good lathe job for beginners

CHARMINGLY quaint in ruddy maple, this colonial four-poster bed also works up beautifully in walnut or mahogany. Except for mortising and tenoning the rails, the whole job can be done in a lathe. Construction is practically the same whether the bed is a single, twin, three-quarters or full size, only the number of spindles varying with the width. Fig. 4 gives the width for standard springs of the four sizes. The type of spring used will determine whether bed slats are needed, as some springs are made to rest on top of the rails.

Each post is made up of four sections as detailed in Fig. 3. However, if the capacity of your lathe permits, the two center sections can be turned in a single length of 2¼-in. square stock and the top and bottom sections turned separately and doweled to it. Solid turning squares are best for the posts, but where these cannot be had, built-up stock will do, providing the pieces are properly jointed and a good resin-type glue is

While the chart at the right gives both inside and overall widths of five standard-size beds, it's best to measure the spring which you plan to use

used. It is best to bore the holes for the stretcher tenons while the work is square, especially so in the case of the stretcher itself, Fig. 1. In turning each post, as well as all other duplicate parts, try to match each one as closely as possible, using calipers frequently to check the work at respective points. A jig consisting of a wooden strip having brad points projecting from one side and spaced to correspond with the drawing, will serve as a master pattern to use in marking off duplicate turnings lengthwise. If the posts are made in four sections, care must be used in centering the holes in the ends of the square sections, so that adjoining parts will be in alignment. Fig. 2 details how the end rails are cross-pegged in mortises cut in the posts. The narrow rail above it is about 1½ in. wide, and is pegged in the same way. In the case of the two front posts, the holes for the pegs should be made blind so that the dowels will not show on the face of the post.

Both head and foot are exactly alike. In assembling each one, glue the spindles to the stretcher and narrow rail first, then glue this to the posts as a unit at the same time the end rail is fitted. There are various type bed-rail fasteners available, one of which is shown in Fig. 6. In fitting them, locate the socket part on the posts to bring the top of the spring about 18 in. above the floor. The spring should be at hand in determining this as it will make a difference if the spring sets inside the rails.

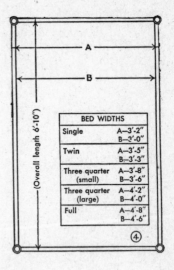

BED WIDTHS	
Single	A—3'-2" B—3'-0"
Twin	A—3'-5" B—3'-3"
Three quarter (small)	A—3'-8" B—3'-6"
Three quarter (large)	A—4'-2" B—4'-0"
Full	A—4'-8" B—4'-6"

(Overall length 6'-10")

The finish to apply depends upon the effect desired and the kind of wood used. Whether stained or left natural, walnut and mahogany require a paste filler to fill the pores of the wood, over which a thin sealer coat of shellac is applied, then lightly sanded and followed with several coats of high-grade varnish. Filling and wiping all turnings can be done conveniently while they are in the lathe. In fact, if a French polish of shellac and oil is desired, the turned work can be completely finished in the lathe. In following this method, you must be careful to see that tenons are kept free of shellac to assure good glue joints. If spraying equipment is available, a satin-sheen, lacquer finish can be applied. Here the work is filled as before and a coat or two of lacquer sanding sealer is applied as in Fig. 5. Because of the light body of a clear lacquer finish, it is important that the pores be filled perfectly flush. If upon close examination they are not completely filled, apply a second coat of filler. When the sealer coat is dry, it is sanded lightly with 7-0 paper, then dusted and sprayed with several coats of gloss lacquer, thinned 50 percent with lacquer thinner. Undercoats of gloss lacquer are preferred in building up a good body, as they contribute to a clearer finish. A fairly good imitation of a hand-rubbed finish is obtained by using a flat lacquer as a final top coat. This dries with a soft, satin luster, requiring no rubbing. "Orange peel" texture in the finish, which results when the gun is held too far from the work, or when the air pressure is too low, can be corrected to some extent by spraying the final top coat lightly with plain lacquer thinner. This has been found effective in leveling off the pebbled coat.

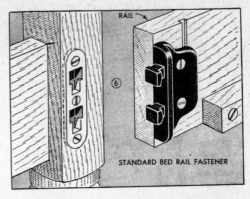

STANDARD BED RAIL FASTENER

Colonial Bookcase From Fruit Crates

NEARLY all the material used to build this colonial bookcase is obtained from discarded fruit crates. The standard apple crate is just the thing, as the ¾-in. ends of the crate are used for the sides of the bookcase and the thinner stock, which forms the sides and bottom of the crate, is carefully salvaged and used for shelves. Three crate ends are assembled end-to-end with strips spanning each joint lengthwise and attached on the inside with screws and glue. The strips also serve as shelf cleats. The as-

sembled sides are attached to a frame of 1 x 1-in. stock assembled as in the detail. Then the back and shelves are fitted and attached. The back is of ¼-in. plywood taken from a packing case and the scrolls for the top and shelves are of ¼-in. solid stock. The base is built up of two thicknesses of ¾-in. stock mitered at the corners. Finish the job with a coat of primer and two coats of quick-drying enamel.

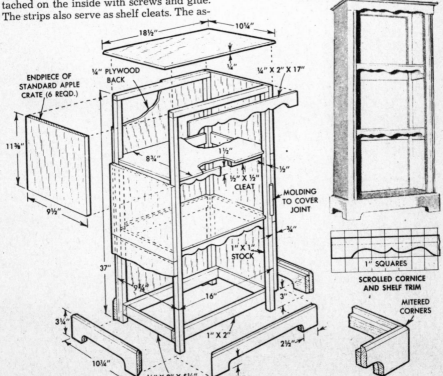

Colonial Chairs

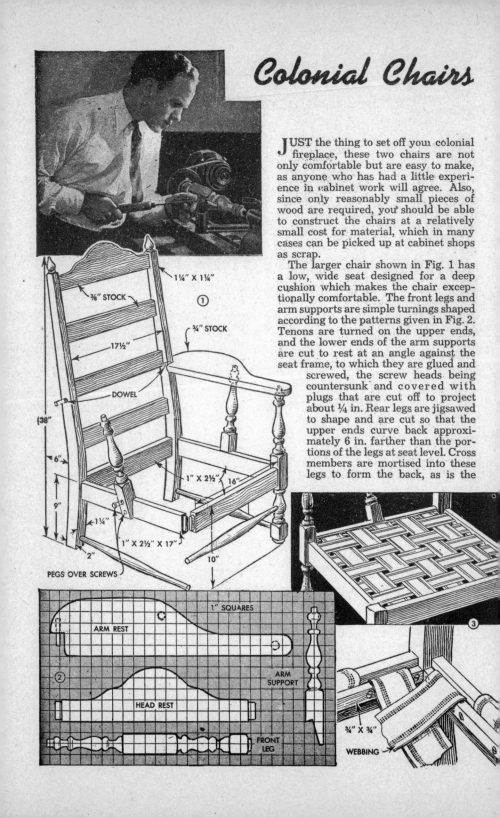

JUST the thing to set off your colonial fireplace, these two chairs are not only comfortable but are easy to make, as anyone who has had a little experience in cabinet work will agree. Also, since only reasonably small pieces of wood are required, you should be able to construct the chairs at a relatively small cost for material, which in many cases can be picked up at cabinet shops as scrap.

The larger chair shown in Fig. 1 has a low, wide seat designed for a deep cushion which makes the chair exceptionally comfortable. The front legs and arm supports are simple turnings shaped according to the patterns given in Fig. 2. Tenons are turned on the upper ends, and the lower ends of the arm supports are cut to rest at an angle against the seat frame, to which they are glued and screwed, the screw heads being countersunk and covered with plugs that are cut off to project about ¼ in. Rear legs are jigsawed to shape and are cut so that the upper ends curve back approximately 6 in. farther than the portions of the legs at seat level. Cross members are mortised into these legs to form the back, as is the

Figure 1 labels:
1¼" X 1¼"
⅜" STOCK
①
¾" STOCK
17½"
DOWEL
38"
6"
9"
1¼"
2"
PEGS OVER SCREWS
1" X 2½"
16"
1" X 2½" X 17"
10"

Figure 2 labels:
1" SQUARES
ARM REST
ARM SUPPORT
②
HEAD REST
FRONT LEG

Figure 3 labels:
③
¾" X ¾"
WEBBING

Complement Your Fireplace

head rest, which is cut to the size and shape indicated in Fig. 2. The seat frame is mortised and glued into the four legs. Care must be taken to make mortises and tenons fit tightly, otherwise the chair will be unsteady. Arm rests are jigsawed to the size and shape shown and are drilled to take the tenons on the arm supports and front legs. Notice that holes for the arm supports must be drilled at an angle. Rungs, of course, are simple, tapered turnings.

Installation of the upholstery webbing strips follows the usual procedure. One end of each strip is tacked to the inner surface of the seat frame, pulled tightly and tacked to the opposite side of the frame, the strips being interwoven as indicated in Fig. 3. When completed, wood cleats are screwed over the tacks to act as reinforcement and to help prevent strain from loosening the tacks. Cushions are used in the seat and on the back of the chair.

The sturdy chair pictured in Fig. 4 is of simpler construction. The seat is of solid wood cut as in Fig. 5 and reinforced across the underside with a hardwood spline glued into a groove. Front legs are turnings split at the upper ends to take wedges which spread the ends to bind the legs tightly in place when they are driven into holes in the seat. The rear legs are round and can be turned or shaped with a spoke shave. They are steamed and bent to shape so that the upper ends project back about

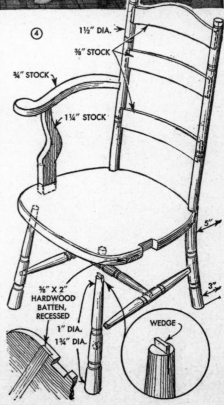

5 in. farther than the portions of the legs at seat level. The lower ends project back about 3 in. Cross members and head rest are mortised into the legs and are cut so that they curve back about 1 in. at the center. A bandsaw is ideal for shaping these pieces, although the work can be done with hand tools.

Rear legs and arm supports are mortised into the seat edges and glued and screwed, the screw heads being countersunk and covered with plugs. Arms and arm supports are jigsawed to the sizes and shapes given in Fig. 5 and are mortised and glued together. Rear ends of the arms are cut to the contour of the rear legs and joined with glue and screws. Seat and back cushions can be used in this chair also.

All parts of the chairs should be sanded smooth before assembly as this work is easier at this time. After the chairs have been completed they should again be sanded and then finished. They look best when finished in natural wood, but can be stained to match other furniture. Cushions should harmonize with other fabrics in the room.

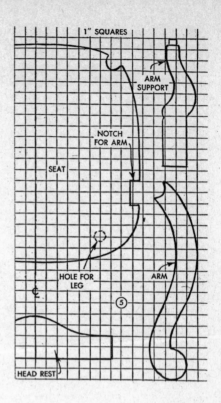

1" SQUARES

ARM SUPPORT

NOTCH FOR ARM

SEAT

HOLE FOR LEG

ARM

⑤

HEAD REST

COLONIAL

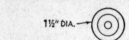

1½" DIA.

ROUNDED EDGES

DRAWER PULL 6 REQ'D

1"

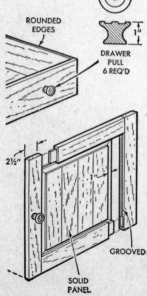

2½"

GROOVED

SOLID PANEL

CUPBOARD   Part One

To be traditionally authentic this quaint old piece should be reproduced in American black walnut, although it can be copied in maple or birch and finished to match other Early American pieces that you may have. A study of the pull-apart view on the opposite page will acquaint you with the way the whole job goes together. Start by gluing edgewise two or more ¾-in. pieces to build up wide panels for the top and ends of the lower unit. Except for the plywood panel covering the back of the cabinet, solid stock is used throughout, although the bottom could be of plywood, too, as the front edge of it is faced with a scrolled apron. The bottom is set 1¼ in. up from the lower edge of the ends and the turned legs are glued and screwed in the corners formed by the apron across the front. The bottom, however, is not assembled until the three drawer frames are made ready; then the whole unit is clamped together at one time. Note in the detail that the top frame is fitted to the ends in dovetail mortises, while the other two are simply doweled and glued in blind holes.

The ½-in. shelves of the upper unit can be doweled or set in grooves cut in the sides. The scrollwork around the face of the unit fits flush in the notched shelves and the back of the unit is paneled vertically with ½-in. pieces of varying widths. Drawers and doors are assembled as shown, the latter being held shut with spring-type friction catches.

COLONIAL CUPBOARD

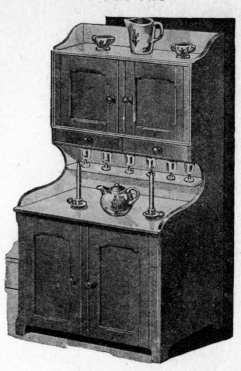

IF your taste in furniture leans toward the plain and simple lines of colonial days, here's a charming old cupboard that typifies the simplicity of early American craftsmanship. It's the type of furniture that challenges the skill of the craftsman who works with hand tools mainly and who takes special pride in producing an expert job of finishing.

Begin by building up two panels of solid stock for the sides of the cupboard. This is done by jointing four or five narrow boards, using either tongue-and-groove joints or plain butt joints doweled and glued. A saving in stock may be had by running only two of the boards the full length and using shorter lengths for the lower half. In arranging the pieces keep in mind that right and left-hand side members are required. You may find it more convenient to cut the rabbet for the plywood back if it is done before the boards are glued together. The scroll cuts likewise may be roughed out beforehand and later dressed down with a spokeshave or file, although they can be done afterward with a keyhole saw. Except for one shelf, which is set in a dado as shown in Fig. 2, the eight shelves simply are butted against the side members and glue-blocked. Note that the ½-in. shelves, Fig. 1, are cut out along the front edge, and that the desk shelf, Fig. 4, is notched at the front corners to project 1¼ in. and fit flush with the surface of the sides. The plywood back will add rigidity to the whole assembly, and it's a good idea when attaching it to do so while the framework is still clamped.

Next, the facing strips to which the lower doors are hinged are fitted to the front corners of the assembly. These are chamfered on the outer edge and are cut out at the bottom to form a part of the leg. Finally, the opening is divided equally with a beaded upright, which is fastened at the top to a nailing block and at the bottom by driving nails up through the lower shelf. The upper compartment is fitted the same way except that the pieces are set in flush with the sides and the shelves. A small molding like the one shown in the sectional detail A-A in Fig. 4 is mitered at the corners and glued and bradded to the facing edges of the opening. The two-drawer

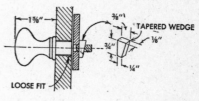

LOOSE FIT

TAPERED WEDGE

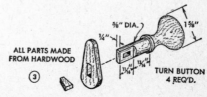

ALL PARTS MADE FROM HARDWOOD

TURN BUTTON 4 REQ'D.

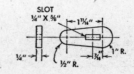

SLOT
¼" X ⅝"

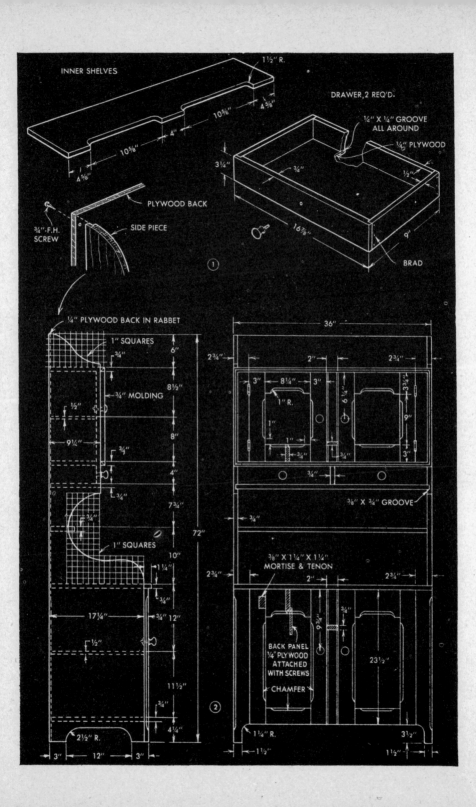

INNER SHELVES

1½" R.

10⅝"

4⅝"

4"

10⅝"

4⅝"

DRAWER, 2 REQ'D.

¼" X ¼" GROOVE ALL AROUND

⅛" PLYWOOD

PLYWOOD BACK

3¼"

¾"

½"

¾"-F.H. SCREW

SIDE PIECE

16⅞"

9"

BRAD

①

¼" PLYWOOD BACK IN RABBET

1" SQUARES

6"

¾"

8½"

¾" MOLDING

½"

8"

9¼"

¾"

4"

¾"

7¾"

1" SQUARES

¾"

10"

72"

1¼"

¾"

17¼"

¾" 12"

½"

11½"

¾"

4¼"

2½" R.

3"

12"

3"

②

36"

2¾"

2"

2¾"

3"

8¼"

3"

3¼"

1" R.

6¼"

9"

1"

¾"

¾"

3"

¾"

⅜" X ¾" GROOVE

¾"

2¾"

2"

2¾"

⅜" X 1¼" X 1¼" MORTISE & TENON

9¾"

¾"

BACK PANEL ¼" PLYWOOD ATTACHED WITH SCREWS

CHAMFER

23½"

1¼" R.

1½"

3½"

1½"

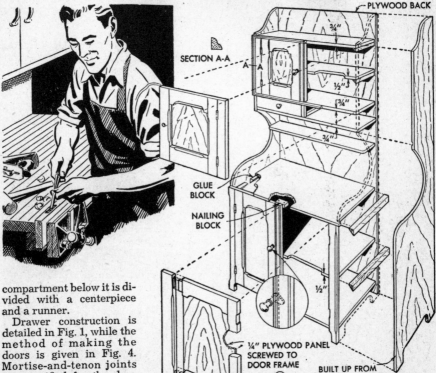

PLYWOOD BACK

SECTION A-A

A A

¾"

½"

¾"

¾"

GLUE
BLOCK

NAILING
BLOCK

½"

¼" PLYWOOD PANEL
SCREWED TO
DOOR FRAME
④

BUILT UP FROM
¾" SOLID STOCK

compartment below it is divided with a centerpiece and a runner.

Drawer construction is detailed in Fig. 1, while the method of making the doors is given in Fig. 4. Mortise-and-tenon joints are specified for the door frames but dowels may be used. Inner edges of the frames are chamfered to relieve plainness and plywood is screwed to the back of the frames. Fig. 3 shows how to make the wooden turnbuttons that are fitted to the doors. They should be installed to work freely and latch against the back of the beaded uprights. A natural or a varnish finish is applied to the exterior of the cupboard, but the interior may be painted a pastel shade of bluish-green.

THIS well-proportioned desk, which is one of the prized pieces in the Metropolitan Museum collection, was built about 1700. It is unique in that it is one of the few examples of early desks that were built on legs or a frame. The original desk, which was made of white pine, is painted dead black with dull brick-red trimming as in Fig. 3.

The frame should be made first as in Fig. 6. The rails are set flush with the faces of the square portions of the legs, as in Fig. 7, and a spacer piece, which also serves as a drawer guide, is placed inside. The drawer slides, instead of being framed as usual, are simply doweled to the front rail and screwed and glued to the spacers.

WRITING DESK

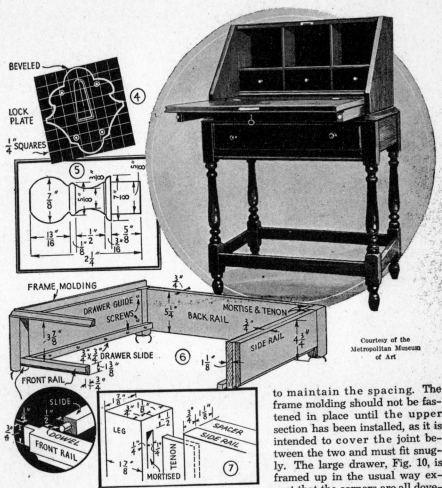

BEVELED

LOCK PLATE

④

¼" SQUARES

⑤

7/8"

3/100

5/100

5/100

7/100

13/16"

1/2"

5/8"

1/8"

2¼"

3/16"

FRAME MOLDING

DRAWER GUIDE SCREWS

MORTISE & TENON

¾"

5¼"

BACK RAIL

¾"

3⅜"

SIDE RAIL

4¾"

¾" X ¾" DRAWER SLIDE

⑥

1⅛"

FRONT RAIL

¼" ¾"

3⅜"

SLIDE

¼"

½"

¾"

DOWEL

FRONT RAIL

Courtesy of the
Metropolitan Museum
of Art

⑦

1½"

⅛"

¾" 1⅛"

¾"

¾" 1⅛"

SPACER

LEG

SIDE RAIL

¼"

¼"

¼"

TENON

1⅞"

MORTISED

In making the tenons for the rails the shoulder cuts are made first, then the cheek cuts. The molded lower edges of these pieces can be done on a circular saw, if you have a molding head, or on a universal plane. The legs are turned as in Fig. 1 before mortising. After the joints are cut and fitted, the frame should be set up, glued and clamped. As there is no top rail at the front, a piece of scrap wood should be tacked across the tops of the front legs to maintain the spacing. The frame molding should not be fastened in place until the upper section has been installed, as it is intended to cover the joint between the two and must fit snugly. The large drawer, Fig. 10, is framed up in the usual way except that the corners are all dovetailed, front and back. The upper section of the desk requires some wide stock which will probably have to be glued up.

The sides, top and writing bed should be cut to the finished size; then a ⅛-in. groove is cut on the inner faces of the side pieces to house the ends of the writing bed. The joints at the upper corners are dovetailed so that the dovetails are hidden on the sides. The dovetails should be laid out and cut on the ends of the top piece

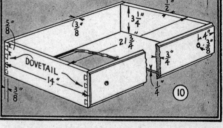

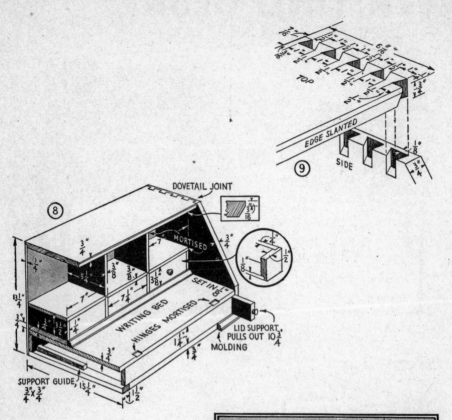

first, according to Fig. 9. A back saw is used to make the side cuts and a chisel for the bottom. If you place a piece of scrap wood under the piece and clamp both securely to your bench top, breaking out chips on the inner face when chiseling will be avoided. Be sure to mark the portions that are to be cut away as it is somewhat confusing and one can easily cut away the wrong portion. When cutting the square end of the dovetail which leaves a wall only ⅛ in. thick, it is advisable to support this wall by means of a cleat and hand screws.

The lid supports, pigeonholes, etc., are clearly shown in Fig. 8. To prevent the lid supports from pulling out too far, a hole

is drilled near the inner end in which a short piece of dowel rod is glued, to act as a stop. The front edge of the top piece is slanted so that it will receive the lid. When closed, the lip of the lid should be just slightly below the top. In the open position it will rest on the supports as shown in Fig. 2. Long clothespin type wood knobs, as in Fig. 5, are used on the large drawer. The hardware consists of hinges, desk lock and a ¹⁄₃₂-in. sheet brass escutcheon, Fig. 4.

COLONIAL MIRRORS

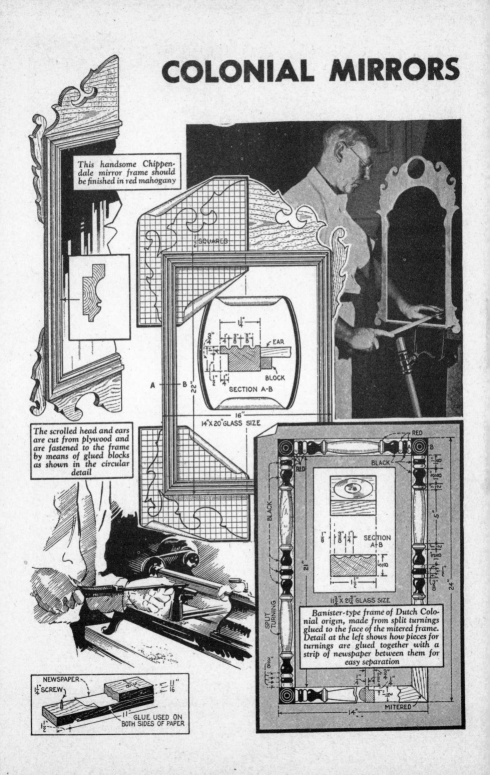

This handsome Chippendale mirror frame should be finished in red mahogany

The scrolled head and ears are cut from plywood and are fastened to the frame by means of glued blocks as shown in the circular detail

SQUARES

SECTION A-B
14" X 20" GLASS SIZE
EAR
BLOCK

RED
BLACK
SECTION A-B
11¾" X 21¾" GLASS SIZE
SPLIT TURNING
MITERED

Banister-type frame of Dutch Colonial origin, made from split turnings glued to the face of the mitered frame. Detail at the left shows how pieces for turnings are glued together with a strip of newspaper between them for easy separation

NEWSPAPER
1¼" SCREW
GLUE USED ON BOTH SIDES OF PAPER

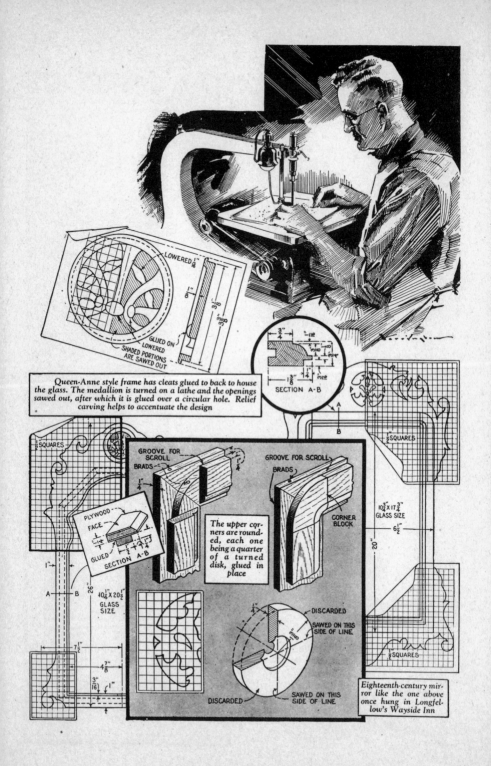

LOWERED 1/8"

1/8"

3/8"

3 3/100"

GLUED ON
LOWERED

SHADED PORTIONS
ARE SAWED OUT

3/4"
1/16"
13/16"
3/16"
1/4"

1 3/8"
1 1/4"

SECTION A-B

Queen-Anne style frame has cleats glued to back to house the glass. The medallion is turned on a lathe and the openings sawed out, after which it is glued over a circular hole. Relief carving helps to accentuate the design

1/2 SQUARES

GROOVE FOR
SCROLL
BRADS

1/4"

GROOVE FOR SCROLL
BRADS

CORNER
BLOCK

PLYWOOD
FACE

GLUED

SECTION A-B

The upper corners are rounded, each one being a quarter of a turned disk, glued in place

1/2 SQUARES

10 1/2" X 17 3/4"
GLASS SIZE

6 1/2"

20"

1"

A   B

26"

10 1/4" X 20 1/2"
GLASS
SIZE

7 1/2"

4 7/8"

3/16"   1"

DISCARDED

SAWED ON THIS
SIDE OF LINE.

DISCARDED

SAWED ON THIS
SIDE OF LINE

1/2 SQUARES

Eighteenth-century mirror like the one above once hung in Longfellow's Wayside Inn

COLOR PHOTOGRAPHY

UNTIL recently color processing transparencies and prints was one of those things no amateur even talked about doing for himself. But now he can process his own color work. More than that, he can set aside a few evenings and build this processing unit in his own workshop.

The completed unit is shown in Fig. 1, and the tank, which is the principal part of the assembly, is detailed in Fig. 8. It can be cut from a 28 by 34-in. piece of 24-ga. galvanized sheet steel. When cutting the metal allow ½ in. for lap joints at the corners. All joints are soldered and should be tested to be sure that they are leakproof.

Water inlet, as well as the main tank outlet, is made from 2 ft. of ⅜-in. copper tubing. A short piece of ½-in. copper tubing also is required for the wash tank outlet. Obtain a tire valve and cut off enough of the threaded end to expose the release pin so that the valve may be opened by pressing on the pin. To make the necessary bend in copper tubing, plug one end and partially fill with solder which then is melted with a torch. When the solder is cold the tubing can be bent without flattening. After shaping the tubing, melt out the solder, then solder the valve stem to the tubing as in Fig. 8-A. Two ¹⁄₁₆-in. holes, Fig. 8-A, drilled

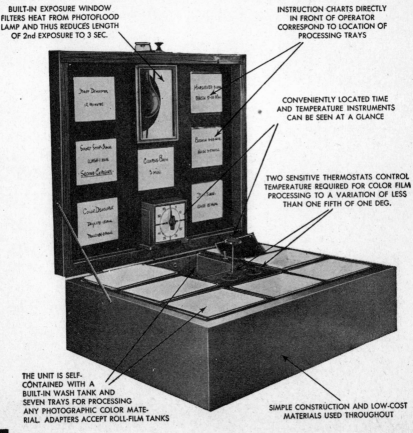

BUILT-IN EXPOSURE WINDOW FILTERS HEAT FROM PHOTOFLOOD LAMP AND THUS REDUCES LENGTH OF 2nd EXPOSURE TO 3 SEC.

INSTRUCTION CHARTS DIRECTLY IN FRONT OF OPERATOR CORRESPOND TO LOCATION OF PROCESSING TRAYS

CONVENIENTLY LOCATED TIME AND TEMPERATURE INSTRUMENTS CAN BE SEEN AT A GLANCE

TWO SENSITIVE THERMOSTATS CONTROL TEMPERATURE REQUIRED FOR COLOR FILM PROCESSING TO A VARIATION OF LESS THAN ONE FIFTH OF ONE DEG.

THE UNIT IS SELF-CONTAINED WITH A BUILT-IN WASH TANK AND SEVEN TRAYS FOR PROCESSING ANY PHOTOGRAPHIC COLOR MATERIAL. ADAPTERS ACCEPT ROLL-FILM TANKS

SIMPLE CONSTRUCTION AND LOW-COST MATERIALS USED THROUGHOUT

in the side of the inlet pipe where it passes through the wash tank, have a combined opening somewhat less than that of the inlet opening. When connected to a faucet part of the water passes through the valve into the larger tank where it is utilized for cooling purposes. Temperature is controlled by sensitive thermostats. The two holes in the tube keep the wash water in rapid circulation and constantly replenish it with fresh water.

Second exposure requires only a few seconds because light from photoflood lamp is heat-filtered by absorbing glass in window

Wash tank, Figs. 4 and 8, has a double wall, the space between the two walls being filled with insulating material. Where the water inlet tube passes through at the bottom of the walls, measure off and carefully prick-punch centers for the ⅜-in. holes. With the inlet tube loosely in place, solder the inner wall from the inside, the outer wall from the outside, Fig. 4. Solder the inlet tube in place last, making sure that it is exactly located, with the top of the valve stem 2⅞-in. above the tank bottom. Drill holes for the two tubes that serve as an outlet for the wash tank and an overflow for the main tank, using center distances indicated in the detail, Fig. 8, and solder them in place. Control-panel supports are ¾-in. angle pieces bent from strips of scrap 24 or 22-ga. galvanized sheet steel. Bend the ends over as shown and solder in place as indicated in Fig. 5.

Above, by use of adapters roll and cut-film processing tanks fit neatly into the unit. Below, soldering wash tank and insulation retainer in place.

Frame for the tank is detailed in Fig. 8 and consists of a wood frame to support the tank so that it can be effectively insulated against heat and cold. The frame sections are mitered and the corner pieces are rabbeted ¼ in. to provide a seat for the tank. In assembling, squareness is achieved by the method illustrated in Fig. 6. Corner pieces are braced as in detail B, Fig. 8. A waterproof wallboard bottom is tacked to the frame. Cover the bottom of the frame with a layer of fire-retardant insulation and then place the preheater element on top, as in Fig. 9, so that it will be in contact with the bottom of the tank when the latter is in position. The element is of the type used as an incubator heater, rated at 100 watts.

Control panel, Fig. 7, is the heart of the unit. Two thermostats are controlled with micrometer accuracy by a knob and dial on the control panel. One thermostat applies pressure to the stud projecting from the cold-water inlet valve. The other operates a snap-acting Micro switch in a self-contained "heat well," turning on 15 watts of electric heat to keep the

5 Construction of angle bars which support control panel and one tray. These can be seen in position in Fig. 14

6 In assembling the frame, clamp sections to corner brace to assure accuracy. Use nails and waterproof glue

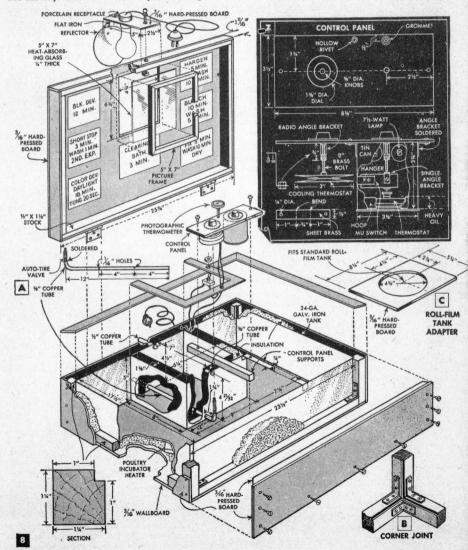

PORCELAIN RECEPTACLE
FLAT IRON REFLECTOR
5" X 7" HEAT-ABSORB-ING GLASS ¼" THICK
3/16" HARD-PRESSED BOARD
1 11/16"
5"   2½"

7

CONTROL PANEL
GROMMET
HOLLOW RIVET
1¾"
½"
3½"
¾" DIA. KNOBS
1¾" DIA. DIAL
2½"
8¾"

RADIO ANGLE BRACKET
7½-WATT LAMP
ANGLE BRACKET SOLDERED
¾"
2" BRASS BOLT
TIN CAN
HANGER
SINGLE-ANGLE BRACKET
3¾"
COOLING THERMOSTAT
3"
¼" DIA.
BEND
½"
1" ¾" 1"
SHEET BRASS
HOOP MU SWITCH
HEAVY OIL
THERMOSTAT
3¾"

HARDEN 5 MIN. WASH 10 MIN.
BLK. DEV. 12 MIN.
BLEACH 10 MIN. WASH 5 MIN.
4¾"
6¾"
SHORT STOP 3 MIN. WASH 1 MIN. 2ND. EXP.
CLEARING BATH. 3 MIN.
FIX 5 MIN. WASH 10 MIN. DRY
COLOR DEV. DAYLIGHT 16 MIN. TUNG. 20 SEC.
5" X 7" PICTURE FRAME

3/16" HARD-PRESSED BOARD

½" X 1½" STOCK

25⅝"

SOLDERED
AUTO-TIRE VALVE
¾" COPPER TUBE
1 1/16" HOLES
4"   4"
12"

PHOTOGRAPHIC THERMOMETER
CONTROL PANEL

FITS STANDARD ROLL-FILM TANK
8¼"   4½"   5¼"
4¾"
3/16" HARD-PRESSED BOARD

C
ROLL-FILM TANK ADAPTER

½" COPPER TUBE
7"
¾" COPPER TUBE
INSULATION
CONTROL PANEL SUPPORTS
¾"
24-GA. GALV. IRON TANK

4½"
6¾"
1¾"
5"
1¾"
4 23/32"
7¼"
17¼"
8"
23½"

POULTRY INCUBATOR HEATER

1"
1¼"
1"
3/16" WALLBOARD
1¼"
SECTION

3/16" HARD-PRESSED BOARD

B
CORNER JOINT

8

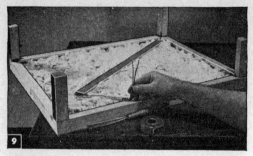

Preheating unit is laid directly on top of insulating material with which frame is packed. Protect leads with rubber tape

Before riveting sockets tightly, test with lamps. Afterward lamp bulbs are enameled flat black

temperature up to the required degree. The preheater also is wired into this circuit. After the preheater has brought the tank up to temperature, it is shut off by the snap or toggle switch and the heat well takes over. The latter dissipates its energy quickly, responds immediately to the thermostat and therefore is extremely sensitive. The heat well is a short tin can of $3\frac{3}{8}$-in. diameter. Either a Micro or Mu switch is stamped to indicate contacts for normally open or closed circuits. Connections should be made so that the switch is normally closed.

Radio angle brackets having double angles serve as supports for the brass thermostat control bolts. The latter, $\frac{3}{16}$ dia. and threaded to fit the thermostats, should be at least 2 in. long. Two brass nuts are required for each. Solder them on either side of one end of each angle bracket, using the bolt to keep the threads in line. Rivet the brackets to the control panel as in Fig. 10. Details of the assembly are shown in Fig. 7. Radio dial plates are likewise riveted to the face of the panel, Fig. 18.

Heaters are two $7\frac{1}{2}$-watt candelabra lamps. Sockets are mounted on either side of the right-hand angle bracket and are wired in parallel and coated with heat-resisting black paint to avoid light leakage, Fig. 17. A bracket bent from sheet brass supports the Mu switch inside the heat well, Figs. 7 and 11. It is sweat-soldered to the inside wall of the can as shown. Exact distance of the hanger from the bottom of the can is measured with the thermostat in place. The activating stud of the switch should be centered exactly over the pressure plate of the thermostat when the latter is at normal distension, or at a temperature of around 68 deg. F. It will be noticed that a single-angle bracket is bolted tightly over the back of the switch, so as to be under the activating stud. The bracket serves as a pressure plate for the end of the control bolt.

Thermostat and pressure plate are shown in Fig. 12. As the thermostat is of smaller diameter than the can, a wood embroidery hoop, Fig. 12, is split and cut down to make a spacer. Thermostat should not fit tightly. Extra sensitivity is accomplished by covering the thermostat to the top of the bellows with heavy lubricating oil

Soldering switch bracket inside heat well. Be sure it is properly located above the bottom

Section of embroidery hoop serves as a fitting for thermostat, which is covered with heavy oil

Switch and candelabra sockets are wired in series as in Fig. 15 and the preheater connection is made across socket contacts, or lugs

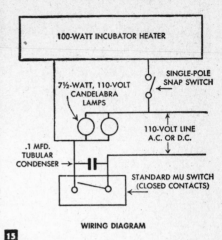

100-WATT INCUBATOR HEATER

7½-WATT, 110-VOLT
CANDELABRA
LAMPS

SINGLE-POLE
SNAP SWITCH

110-VOLT LINE
A.C. OR D.C.

.1 MFD.
TUBULAR
CONDENSER →

STANDARD MU SWITCH
(CLOSED CONTACTS)

WIRING DIAGRAM

Packing insulating material between walls of unit.
Insulation is covered with strips of hard-pressed board

after the control panel is finished. When wiring as in Fig. 15, a .1 mfd. tubular condenser is wired across the Mu switch to eliminate radio interference. Switch is wired in series with the two lamps, and the preheater leads, Fig. 13, are cut in on each side of the pair of lamps. A single-pole snap or toggle switch, Fig. 16, cuts the preheater circuit in and out, but is under thermostatic control at all times and cannot overheat. All connections should be soldered and taped. Completed assembly can be seen in Fig. 17. Heads of the 2-in. control bolts are cut off so that small radio knobs can be fitted as in Fig. 18. Cooling thermostat is screwed onto the lower end of the other control bolt, and the latter is screwed down until the thermostat comes directly over the valve stem of the cold-water inlet as you see in Fig. 19.

Paint the tank with an acid and alkali-proof plastic paint. Apply primer first, then two or three coats of the plastic paint. Do the painting with the tank on edge, Fig. 20. For covering over the outer frame use ³⁄₁₆-in. black hard-pressed board. Fit the tank inside the frame and attach the cover pieces with screws as in Fig. 8. Note that the sides are ³⁄₁₆ in. higher than the frame so that there will be space for finishing strips which retain the insulating material.

Figs. 8 and 14 show how the tank is insulated. Attach rubber feet to the bottom of the unit. The hinged cover, Fig. 8, is fitted with a window covered with a ¼-in.-thick sheet of heat-absorbing glass. This means that the film can be held closer to the light source than is ordinarily done. In processing, color films require a second exposure,

Fig. 2, and with this unit the exposure time is reduced to about 3 seconds by using a powerful photoflood lamp, mounted as in Fig. 21. As the lamp is directly back of the window, illumination will spread in a wide angle. However, when processing roll film, the second exposure will require that the strip be held at a distance sufficient for the entire length to be illuminated, or it will be necessary to move the strip so that the ends receive exposure equal to that at the center. The fixture is detailed in Fig. 8, and consists of a piece of hard-pressed board, a porcelain sign socket and an old photoflash reflector. A No. 2 photoflood lamp is used. As shown in Fig. 21, the fixture is held in place on the cover by an ordinary screw-type drawer knob which provides adjustment for locating the lamp.

Regular equipment consists of seven 4x6-in. porcelain enameled trays which fit on the tank. Processing is done from left to right and, to make it easier to keep proper sequence, instruction sheets are attached to the inside of the cover, Fig. 1. These occupy the same relative position as the trays and information on them pertains to the corresponding tray. On each card, letter or type the necessary data, such as description and time, for that step. Number them if you wish. Use a stiff cardboard and cover the face with Cellophane to prevent soiling. If you use more than one kind of color material have an alternate file of data cards for each. Use art corners to hold the cards in place on the cover. A set of roll-film tanks can be substituted for the trays by the use of adapters, detailed in Fig. 8-C and also in Fig. 3. To set up the unit for processing, connect the inlet tube to a water tap with a length of rubber hose. Attach another to

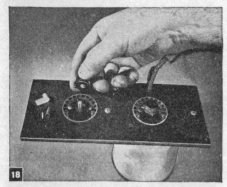

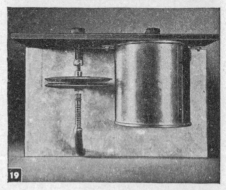

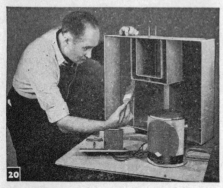

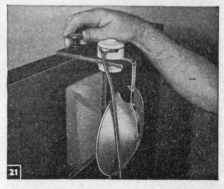

the outlet pipe and lead it to a drain. A third piece of hose is useful for filling the tanks for the first time. After the tanks have been filled, open the cold-water faucet just enough to circulate water rapidly in the wash tank. Insert dial thermometer through opening in the control panel and note temperature. If it reads above 68 deg. F., adjust the cooling thermostat, on the left side of the panel, by turning the knob to the right. Adjust to the desired 68 deg. Then loosen the locking screw of the knob and set it at the 68-deg. position on the dial plate. If the thermometer should read be-

low 68 deg. F. in the first test, switch on the preheater until water is warmed to that temperature. Turn off the preheater and adjust the heat-well knob. When you turn the knob to the right until there is an audible "click," it indicates that the switch is open. On turning the knob to the left there will be another click and the current will be on. Leave the knob in the "on" position until the thermometer registers exactly 68 deg. Now turn the knob to the right until you hear the click, then stop. This is the correct setting. Loosen the lock screw and position the knob.